W9-BIR-876

GENETICS OF MAN

GENETICS OF MAN

PAUL AMOS MOODY

Howard Professor of Natural History and Zoology
University of Vermont

W · W · NORTON & COMPANY · INC ·  NEW YORK

WITHDRAWN FROM
MOUNT SENARIO COLLEGE LIBRARY

LIBRARY
MOUNT SENARIO COLLEGE
LADYSMITH, WISCONSIN
MOUNT SENARIO COLLEGE LIBRARY

To the memory of my friend and predecessor
Henry Farnham Perkins, Ph.D.
Founder and Director of the
Eugenics Survey of Vermont

COPYRIGHT © 1967 BY W. W. NORTON & COMPANY, INC.

Library of Congress Catalog Card No. 67-10610

All Rights Reserved
Published simultaneously in Canada by
George J. McLeod Limited, Toronto

Printed in the United States of America
2 3 4 5 6 7 8 9 0

CONTENTS

Preface   vii

1. Why Study the Genetics of Man?   1

2. Essentials of Mendelian Thinking   9

3. Chromosomes, Mitosis, and Meiosis   24

4. Genes and Mutations   40

5. Mendelian Thinking Applied to Human Families   54

6. Studying Human Pedigrees   72

7. Mendelian Thinking Applied to Populations   88

8. Consanguinity or Inbreeding   111

9. Multiple Alleles: ABO Blood Groups   126

10. Multiple Alleles: Rh and Other Antigens   145

11. Polygenes: Multiple-Gene Inheritance   161

12. Sex Linkage   182

13. Mapping the X Chromosome   206

14. Autosomal Linkage and Chromosome Mapping   219

15. Sex Determination and Changes in Number of Sex Chromosomes   232

16. Chromosomal Aberrations of the Autosomes   246

17. Mutations: Rates and Effects   263

18. The Human Gene Pool and the Effects of Radiation   276

19. Multiple Births   288

20. The Twin Method in Human Genetics   297

21. The Twin Method: Quantitative Traits   310

22. The Eugenic Ideal and the Nature of Selection 324

23. Differential Fertility and Population Problems 336

24. Human Diversity and Its Origin 359

25. Genetic Counseling 380

Appendix A: Consanguinity 399

Appendix B: The von Dungern-Hirschfeld Hypothesis
of ABO Inheritance 401

Appendix C: The Chi-Square Test 403

Appendix D: Where to Look for Additional Information 406

Glossary 411

Index 429

PREFACE

The goal that I have had constantly before me in writing this book is to provide a meaningful understanding of the principles of human genetics without delving too far into the intricacies of mathematics and biochemistry, both of which are essential for research workers in the field. In music, there are subtleties and depths of enjoyment open only to listeners schooled in the piano or violin, yet a listener with no musical training can gain much by listening to Rubinstein or Heifetz. The music itself affords a rich contribution. In somewhat the same way, there are profundities in the science of human genetics that can only be plumbed by the thoroughly trained, yet an understanding and appreciation of the basic principles of genetics can be gained by any intelligent person who has the desire to do so. I have deliberately attempted to present a discussion of human genetics that will be comprehensible to readers with little or no formal background for the subject and that will enable them to understand how human geneticists think.

As I have hinted, to be a professional human geneticist one should be a mathematician or a biochemist, or preferably both. Yet it would be a pity if a knowledge of human genetics were confined to mathematicians and biochemists and denied to people in general, who are after all the ones most concerned with the implications of what the specialists are doing and discovering.

I have made no attempt to cover the vast field of medical genetics. At appropriate places in the text, the reader will find references to more encyclopedic treatments of the subject (see especially Appendix D). Although the illustrative examples are all of interest in themselves, they have been chosen primarily for clarity and pertinence in demonstrating how human geneticists solve their problems. In certain cases, analyses that are of historical interest are discussed with some care (e.g., Bernstein on blood group inheritance; Davenport on skin color inheritance), but when more recent investigations demonstrate methods of analysis with particular aptness, these investigations are discussed (e.g., Mann *et al.* on Xg^a blood group inheritance).

The mathematical analyses that are introduced employ the simplest algebra, and I have attempted to explain them so thoroughly that even the least mathematically-minded reader can follow the reasoning. Problems have been appended to certain chapters; these are the chapters for which problem solving provides a particularly appropriate means of checking one's understanding of the subject matter.

The meanings of technical terms are indicated when the terms are first introduced. In addition, a glossary is appended for ready reference. The definitions given in the glossary are for use in understanding the text and are not intended as substitutes for complete dictionary definitions.

It is a pleasure to acknowledge the assistance of the many persons who have made the book possible. First of all, I gladly express my gratitude to Dr. Frances Ann McKittrick whose skill as an artist has added so much to the value and attractiveness of the book. I am indebted to many authors and publishers for illustrations, and these are indicated in the captions of the figures. However, I wish to mention especially Dr. Victor A. McKusick (Figs. 5.1, 15.3 and 16.8), Dr. Raymond M. Mulcahy (Fig. 16.7), Mrs. John A. Harrell and Mrs. Robert H. Erdmann (Fig. 19.1), and Mrs. Paul A. Moody (Figs. 7.1 and 7.2), all of whom supplied previously unpublished photographs.

I am grateful to Dr. Sheldon C. Reed, who read the entire manuscript, and to Dr. Alexander S. Wiener, who read the discussion of Rh inheritance. Both made valuable suggestions but neither is accountable for any shortcomings the book may have.

I am indebted to the Literary Executor of the late Sir Ronald A. Fisher, F.R.S., Cambridge, to Dr. Frank Yates, F.R.S., Rothamsted, and to Messrs. Oliver & Boyd Ltd., Edinburgh, for permission to reprint a portion of Table No. IV from their book *Statistical Tables for Biological, Agricultural, and Medical Research.*

Finally, it is a pleasure to express my gratitude for the manifold assistance of the editorial staff of W. W. Norton & Company, and for the aid and skill of my typists: Mrs. Marjorie S. Murray and Mrs. Theodore T. Bachmann.

It is my hope that this book will be useful in courses designed for students who desire a general knowledge of the subject. At the same time I shall be gratified if some readers are stimulated by the unsolved problems to equip themselves with the needed mathematical and biochemical tools so that they, in turn, may be able to make constructive contributions to the science.

Burlington, Vermont
December 1966

Paul A. Moody

GENETICS OF MAN

1.

WHY STUDY
THE GENETICS OF MAN?

"The proper study of mankind is man." When the eighteenth-century poet Alexander Pope included this line in *An Essay on Man*, he was not thinking of human genetics. The study of human genetics did not exist in his day. More than a century was to elapse before the father of modern genetics, Gregor Mendel, performed his pioneer experiments with peas. *An Essay on Man* was over 150 years old before the scientific world realized the significance of Mendel's findings, and more than two centuries old before new techniques made possible the dramatic advance in the knowledge of human chromosomes that characterizes our own time.

When we say that the proper study of mankind is man, we are not implying that the study of other organisms is "improper." On the contrary, studies of other organisms have provided absolutely essential knowledge of principles applicable to man. It is natural, however, that to the majority of human beings other human beings are the most interesting organisms on earth. We find strong motivation for the study of any aspect of ourselves. One of the most interesting aspects is the manner in which we replace ourselves from generation to generation. The production of a baby is the most intricate and elaborate "manufacturing" process known to man. What are the controls that ensure the production of a perfect individual? We can learn something of them by studying instances in which a control failed to function. What determines the nature of the "product," his eye color, skin color, hair color, blood group, intelligence, and countless other traits? This book is an attempt to supply some of the answers, although frequently we shall encounter limits to our knowledge— limits that are challenges to further investigation.

The desire to understand ourselves is, then, the strongest reason for studying human genetics. This subject combines with many others to form the intellectual field that we call science. Science, in turn, combines with philosophy, religion, literature, and art to form the cultural or social inheritance, which is man's most distinctive attribute. No other organism on earth even approaches man in this respect. Hence a contribution to the knowledge of human genetics is a contribution to one facet of man's crowning achievement, his greatest distinction.

Some readers will consider this reason for studying human genetics a bit nebulous. "The author has his head in the clouds. Are there not more practical reasons?" Indeed there are. Let us consider first the application of human genetics to the theory and practice of medicine. When I was a young man, many of my medical colleagues looked on students of human genetics with thinly veiled amusement. What the latter were doing might be somewhat interesting in a dilettante sort of way, but it was of no real significance. Now many medical schools have their own departments of human genetics; even those that do not, treat human genetics with utmost seriousness. The revolution in thinking has come about partly because the diseases in which heredity was relatively unimportant have been largely conquered; as for example, the familiar childhood diseases. (Even here, however, heredity may play some role. If one twin contracts measles, why is the other twin more likely to do so if he is an identical twin than if he is a fraternal twin? See Chap. 20.) This successful conquest left the medical sciences free to concentrate on the degenerative diseases of advancing years, in which heredity frequently is an important factor. Furthermore, increasing knowledge led to realization of the importance of heredity in diseases and disorders in which its importance had gone unrecognized.

As we shall see in Chapter 25, knowledge of inheritance and of the patient's ancestors can be of assistance to the physician in determining diagnosis and in deciding on the most suitable treatment. The patient's blood does not clot normally. Is it hemophilia (pp. 195–198), or afibrinogenemia (pp. 117–118), or some other condition? A knowledge of the patient's family and ancestry may aid in answering the question. Again, if a physician knows that phenylketonuria (PKU) is in a woman's ancestry, he is forewarned to have her newborn infant tested immediately so that, if necessary, treatment may be started to save the child from idiocy (pp. 380–381).

Although most of us are not going to be physicians, we all profit from advances in medical science. However, most of us will be parents, if we are not already, and many genetic problems arise in connection with marriage and parenthood.

At one time I received the following inquiry: "A friend of mine is desirous of marrying his half-sister's daughter, would such a relationship be too close, relative to 'blood-lines,' for normal healthy children?" (See Fig. 25.1, p. 392, and accompanying text.)

A couple whose first child was an albino consulted a geneticist to ask whether a second child was also likely to be an albino.

If a mother has schizophrenia, are her children likely to be similarly afflicted?

We do not have all of the answers by any means, but as we progress through this book we shall find that some useful answers are possible to these and other vexing questions. As the science of human genetics advances, answers will become more precise.

Apparently from time immemorial some people have been concerned that we are not managing wisely matters of marriage and parenthood. Thus the Greek poet Theognis, viewing his contemporaries in the sixth century b.c., wrote: "We look for rams and asses and stallions of good stock, and one believes that good will come from good; yet a good man minds not to wed an evil daughter to an evil sire, if he but give her much wealth. Wealth confounds our stock. Marvel not that the stock of our folk is tarnished, for the good is mingling with the base" (Popenoe and Johnson, 1933*). More than 2500 years later Sir Francis Galton founded the eugenics movement, which survives today among people looking forward to possible genetic improvement of mankind and apprehensive of possible genetic deterioration (see Chap. 22).

For centuries, observers of the human scene have feared that the best-endowed segments of society were not producing their share of children, and they have speculated about the consequences. From Francis Bacon in the seventeenth century to Francis Galton in the nineteenth, we find concern over the fact that distinguished men were leaving relatively few descendants. Today, many people are less concerned with the make-up of the world's population than with its sheer size. One of the most pressing problems of our own time is control of population size. We use the term "population explosion" to express the speed with which the world is approaching overpopulation. The problem is so urgent that deliberate control of human reproduction is becoming more and more common and will surely become the rule in the not-distant future. Geneticists are nevertheless anxious to ensure that as quantity is brought under control, quality shall not suffer. We are concerned that the genes of people who contribute most to human life and culture shall not decline in relative abundance as generation follows generation. This matter will claim our attention again in Chapter 23.

As we learn more and more about human genetics, our hope increases that man may be able to exercise control over his own heredity. This control may have two aspects: prevention of deterioration and production

---

*Dates in parentheses following authors' names indicate references at the ends of the chapters.

of improvement.

We have hinted at the first aspect in our mention of the eugenics movement and of the problems arising from differences in fertility among different groups of people. Also involved are problems arising from increased exposure of our population to X-rays and other man-made radiations. Because such radiations are known to induce genetic changes (mutations) and many of these changes are harmful, geneticists are concerned that our descendents may inherit a "genetic load" of mutations that will give rise to a multitude of infirmities (see Chap. 18).

Turning to the second aspect, we find that geneticists are increasingly interested in the possibility of a form of biological engineering: the directing of heredity toward consciously desired goals (see Tatum, 1959). In the future, parents may be able to determine in advance whether they will produce a boy or a girl, whether the child will have blue eyes or brown, whether he will be musical or a mathematical genius, and so on. Many readers may feel that such conjecture verges on the realm of science fiction, but, in fact, possibilities of this nature are being considered by serious students of human genetics. Even now, methods are being perfected for separating male-producing sperm cells from female-producing sperm (Chap. 15). In the future, we may expect that a child of the desired sex can be produced at will, at least when artificial insemination is employed (see below).

Somewhat more distant is the possibility of altering man's units of heredity, the genes themselves. Yet experimental geneticists are already altering the genes of microbes in this way. A gene is an immensely long molecule of DNA (deoxyribonucleic acid; Chap. 3). We may compare it to the tape of a magnetic tape recorder of the type now popular. Like the magnetic tape, it contains a message—instructions for the life processes of the cell in which it resides. It is a remarkable fact that the DNA in a fertilized ovum must contain all the instructions for manufacturing a complete human being. In a similar manner, instructions for building a house may be recorded on a magnetic tape. Suppose that after the instructions are recorded we wish to make a change. Perhaps the original instructions were "paint the house white" and we wish the house to be red. We find the section of the tape bearing the words "paint the house white" and erase the words electrically. On that section of tape we then record the words "paint the house red." In a somewhat comparable manner, experimenters are now altering the genetic messages in the DNA molecules of microbes. It has been found that certain chemicals and enzymes will alter the message in very specific ways. Also, a section of DNA bearing one message can sometimes be substituted for a section of DNA bearing a different message. A crude analogy is afforded by snipping out the section of magnetic tape bearing the words "paint the house white" and splicing into its place a piece of tape containing the words "paint the house red."

The alteration of gene structure described above has been called genetic engineering (Tatum, 1965) or genetic surgery (Muller, 1965b). It is only a question of time until genetic engineering of human cells, including reproductive cells, will be possible. I fear, however, that the analogy to the simple procedures of manipulating magnetic tape may give the false impression that manipulating the DNA molecule is also simple. In fact, genetic surgery is complex and difficult almost past the imagination of all but specialists in the field. How much time will elapse before genetic surgery will become a significant means of improving human germ plasm? Participants in a symposium on the subject in 1963 spoke repeatedly of the twenty-first century (Sonneborn, 1965). Yet as we all know, unforeseen breakthroughs in science frequently make realities of possibilities thought to be remote. (See Sonneborn, 1965, for a stimulating discussion of present accomplishments, difficulties, and future possibilities in this fascinating field.)

Various geneticists have emphasized that while we are awaiting achievements in genetic engineering, we have available to us means of genetic improvement using germ plasm already present in mankind. Dr. H. J. Muller of the University of Wisconsin has called the method **parental selection** (Muller, 1965b).

A form of parental selection is used in dairying to improve milk production. Cows are selectively bred to bulls whose daughters were high-producers. By means of **artificial insemination,** using sperm cells that have been preserved in frozen state, a valuable bull may sire many more offspring than would be possible by any other method. Indeed, the bull need no longer be living at the time his sperm cells are used, since sperm may be kept frozen for long periods and reactivated as needed.

Human sperm cells can also be preserved in the frozen state. If kept at the temperature of liquid nitrogen, they apparently may be preserved for an unlimited time without deterioration (Muller, 1965b). Artificial insemination of wives is already practiced in some cases in which children are desired but the husband is sterile, or has a hereditary disease or disability that should not be passed on to children. Semen from a healthy, fertile male is introduced by instrumental means into the uterus of the woman. The donor is selected on the basis of health and general racial and physical similarity to the parents, but the selection is usually made by the physician rather than by the parents. In fact, to avoid emotional involvements, the identity of the donor of the semen is kept secret.

On the other hand, a fundamental principle of parental selection is that the parents *do* select the donor of the semen and that they do so because he possesses traits they wish their child to have. In a way, such selection would be similar to adoption, at least insofar as the male parent is concerned. It has been called **pre-adoption** by Sir Julian Huxley, prenatal adoption by Dr. Bentley Glass. Proponents of the method suggest that its use will not be confined to families in which the husband is sterile or possesses undesirable genes. They suggest that even when the husband is fertile, the parents may nevertheless decide that they wish a child to possess traits that the biological father cannot provide. They might, for example, wish their child to inherit from some eminent man of the past. If that man had contributed to a sperm bank during his lifetime, artificial insemination with his sperm would be possible. To avoid the emotional involvements to which we have alluded, Dr. Muller suggests that only semen from a man who has been dead for at least twenty years be used in the program. Moreover, the intervening years would not only help to confirm the judgment that the man did, indeed, possess qualities of eminence, but also might allow an evaluation of the quality of the children he had produced during his lifetime. This may be compared to the progeny test in the breeding of domestic animals, and it has relevance for, as everyone knows, some celebrated men fail to produce equally accomplished children. In the program we visualize, it would be important to select as sperm donors those eminent men whose superiority had a genetic basis and could be transmitted to offspring.

This is not the place to argue the pros and cons of parental selection. Eloquent espousal of the program will be found in Muller, 1961, 1963, 1965a, 1965b. We introduce the subject to indicate one of the possible applications of human genetics. In passing, we may note that we cannot now store ova in the frozen state as we do sperm cells. Human tissues can be grown outside the body in tissue culture, however. Perhaps ovarian tissue can eventually be grown in this way, so that we can produce ova as desired. When this day comes, banks of living ovarian tissue might be built up to supplement the sperm banks. In theory, a couple might then decide that they wished a child to inherit not from themselves, but from an eminent man *and* eminent woman of the past. A selected ovum would be fertilized by a selected sperm and then implanted into the uterus of the wife, where it would undergo normal development.

Many invertebrate animals reproduce by **parthenogenesis**—that is, an ovum is stimulated to develop without fertilization by a sperm. Experimenters have learned how to stimulate development of unfertilized ova in many species that are not naturally parthenogenetic. This is called artificial parthenogenesis, and it has been accomplished not only with invertebrate ova but also with the ova of mammals. Fatherless rabbits have been produced in this way. It could conceivably be done with human ova, but all offspring would be female (lacking a Y chromosome; Chap. 15). Thus, in theory, a race consisting entirely of women could be produced. I leave it to the reader to decide for himself whether or not this would be desirable!

Genetic engineering, parental selection, even the possibility of artificial parthenogenesis, illustrate ways in which man may become able to control his own genetic future. As the new methods become available, will man utilize them wisely? We, of course, hope so, but the question itself will serve to emphasize the point that although human genetics is a branch of biology it also touches on psychology, sociology, demography (study of populations), economics, ethics, religion, and, indeed, every facet of human life. These interrelationships will become even more apparent in our later discussions.

Before we can apply human genetics we must know more about the subject. Human genetics is the application to man of principles discovered largely by means of investigations on viruses, bacteria, plants, and lower animals. Investigations with these organisms offer an advantage in that experimentation is possible in ways prohibited when one is dealing with people. On the other hand, human populations offer advantages, too. Large numbers are available if desired, and verbal communication is an inestimable boon to investigation. For no other organism do we have such detailed knowledge of biochemistry, anatomy, physiology, and psychology, including anomalies and aberrations which frequently give clues to factors at work in normal development. Hence the investigations on man complement and supplement those on lower animals and plants of which they are the outgrowth.

We have called Gregor Mendel the father of modern genetics. Because the genetics of man is included in this term, we most appropriately begin our discussion with a brief review of his experiments. In this we wish to emphasize the thinking he employed in deducing from them those principles on which our science is founded. Then we shall apply those principles to human investigations to see how they can be utilized, and how modified, to fit studies in which the investigator cannot arrange the matings of his subjects.

Science and art are more akin than most people realize. Both have their beauties. There is esthetic appeal in a logical progression of thought or in a simple principle, which at a stroke reveals the explanation of diverse phenomena that had been mysterious. Although human genetics has its utilitarian aspects, it also has its full measure of beauty. I hope that this will become evident as we proceed, and that it will add to the enjoyment of the pages that follow.

REFERENCES

Muller, H. J., 1961. "Human evolution by voluntary choice of germ plasm," *Science,* 134:643–49.

Muller, H. J., 1963. "Genetic progress by voluntarily conducted germinal choice." In G. Wolstenholme, 1963. Pp. 247–62.

Muller, H. J., 1965a. "Better genes for tomorrow." In L. K. Y. Ng and S. Mudd (eds.). *The Population Crisis.* Bloomington: Indiana University Press. Pp. 223–47.

Muller, H. J., 1965b. "Means and aims in human genetic development." In T. M. Sonneborn, 1965. Pp. 100–122.

Popenoe, P., and R. H. Johnson, 1933. *Applied Eugenics,* rev. ed. New York: The Macmillan Company.

Sonneborn, T. M. (ed.), 1965. *The Control of Human Heredity and Evolution.* New York: The Macmillan Company.

Tatum, E. L., 1959. "A case history in biological research," *Science,* **129:**1711–14. (This is the lecture given when Dr. Tatum received the Nobel prize.)

Tatum, E. L., 1965. "Perspectives from physiological genetics." In T. M. Sonneborn, 1965. Pp. 20–34.

Wolstenholme, G. (ed.), 1963. *Man and His Future.* Ciba Foundation Volume. Boston: Little, Brown & Co. (Pages 274–98 contain a very lively informal discussion by leading scientists of questions raised in the present chapter.)

2.

ESSENTIALS OF
MENDELIAN THINKING

Variability provides the raw materials for genetics, the science of heredity. If all individuals were brown-eyed, we could learn nothing of the hereditary basis of eye color. However, because some people are blue-eyed and marry brown-eyed people, we can gain some knowledge of the genetics involved. (As we shall see in Chapter 11, this particular example has a more complicated genetic basis than people generally realize.) So it is with all genetic study: we constantly analyze the genetic bases of the *differences* between individuals. Some of these differences occur normally, such as differences in eye color, blood groups, or ability to taste PTC (phenylthiocarbamide). Other differences are abnormal, involving physical abnormalities and abnormalities in the processes of metabolism. For example, although most of us can break down the amino acid phenylalanine, derived from protein in our diet, to simpler compounds, for excretion, some people have a gene-determined inability to do this. They suffer from what is called phenylketonuria, which, if unchecked, leads to severe mental deficiency. Examples of this kind, involving gene control of enzyme systems, we shall find particularly instructive as we attempt to answer the question: How do genes work?

We might note in passing that the necessity of concentrating on differences imposes some limitations on genetics. There are definite limits to the variations that an individual can have and still survive. For example, we might wish to know the genetic basis for the formation of the liver, but as no human being could possibly exist without a liver, we are never likely to learn all the genetic complexities underlying liver formation. We can, however, analyze the genetic bases of differences in liver function that

9

are not severe enough to be lethal.

Our knowledge of genetics is based on investigations of plants and animals, which can be experimented on in a way impossible with human beings. Once hereditary differences are discovered, it is of great advantage to be able to arrange matings between the differing parents and to raise large numbers of offspring. It is no accident that the most fundamental principles operating in human genetics were first discovered in experiments with plants and animals. As a basis for our thinking, therefore, we should familiarize ourselves with the reasoning that arose from such experimentation.

The father of the modern science of genetics is Gregor Mendel, an Austrian monk whose classic experiments on garden peas are part of our common fund of knowledge. If these experiments are so familiar, why should we devote space to them here? Simply because many, if not most, of the people who know about them have never stopped to really think through the reasons that led Mendel to draw the conclusions he did. Every high school biology student knows the conclusions he reached. What we are interested in is: Why did he reach those conclusions? What was his thinking? How can this thinking be applied to human genetics?

Mendel's original paper was published in 1866. It has been translated into English and the translation published in many forms.

Mendel's Experiments

Mendel concentrated his attention on seven differences in peas. Some were tall; some were dwarf. Some had white flowers; some had colored ones. Some had seeds that were smooth when dry; some had wrinkled seeds. Because the experiments performed and the conclusions reached were similar in all cases, we shall concentrate on only one typical series of experiments.

One of the seven pairs of contrasting characteristics Mendel studied concerned the color of the cotyledons (rudimentary leaves) in the seed. These were yellow in the seeds produced by some plants and green in the seeds produced by other plants. Here he had a clear-cut difference with which to work. The yellow-seeded plants were pure-breeding and so were the green-seeded ones.

Mendel started his experiment by cross-pollinating these two varieties: placing pollen from the yellow-seeded variety on the stigmas of flowers of the green-seeded variety (the stamens of these flowers having been removed), and vice versa. In all cases, the seeds produced had yellow cotyledons. We might suspect that the green color and its genetic basis had simply been destroyed; this did not prove to be the case, as we shall see.

It has become customary to refer to such first-generation hybrids as the "first filial generation," or F_1 generation. Of the pair of contrasting traits being considered, the one that produced a visible effect in the F_1 generation Mendel called **dominant**. Conversely, he used the term **recessive** for the trait that did not produce a visible effect in this first generation. In genetics the term "dominant" lacks many of the connotations of the word in common speech. Dominant traits are not necessarily superior to or better than recessive ones. For example, one of the most severe types of mental defect in man (Huntington's chorea) is transmitted by a dominant gene.

Mendel next planted the hybrid seeds; 258 of them germinated. (In higher plants the seed is a miniature individual, enclosed in a seed coat and waiting suitable conditions to enlarge and develop. Hence the seed and the plant that develops from it both represent an F_1 individual in different stages of its life history.) These F_1 plants produced flowers, which were permitted to fertilize themselves (normal procedure in peas). The 258 plants produced a total of 8023 seeds. These seeds constituted a "second filial" or F_2 generation. Of these seeds, 6022 had yellow cotyledons and 2001 had green cotyledons. Thus the ratio of yellow to green was 3.01:1.

In his experiments with the other six pairs of contrasting traits, Mendel also found that approximately three fourths of the F_2 individuals showed the dominant trait, and one fourth showed the recessive trait. Here was a regularity to be explained. Mendel explained it as an indication that each pair of traits depended on a single pair of hereditary factors, which we call genes today. This brings us to the point of our discussion: *Why is obtaining uniformity in the F_1 generation, followed by a 3:1 ratio in the F_2 generation, regarded as evidence that inheritance depends on a single pair of genes?*

In answering the question, we assume at the outset that with regard to the traits under consideration, male and female parents contribute equally (through pollen grain and ovum). Although we may think that this point is too self-evident to stress, in the early history of biology equal contribution by the parents was not recognized. There are also situations in which the contributions of the parents are not equal (e.g., sex linkage, Chap. 12).

If inheritance from the two parents is equal, then a plant of the pure-breeding, yellow-seeded variety must have inherited "yellowness" from both of its parents. Both the ovum from which it developed and the pollen grain that fertilized that ovum must have contained a gene for yellowness. If the initial Y represents the gene "for" yellow, then a pure-breeding, yellow-seeded plant would have the genetic formula YY. The genetic formula is called a **genotype**. The visible trait, yellow color in this case, is called the **phenotype**.

A pure-breeding, green-seeded plant would have the genotype *yy* (*y* representing the gene for green color). *Y* and *y* constitute a gene pair, or, as we say, a pair of **alleles**. *Y* is the allele of *y* (its opposite number, so to speak) and vice versa. The occurrence of genes in allelic pairs is a fundamental assumption of Mendelian thinking.

Mendel crossed pure-breeding yellow peas with pure-breeding green ones to produce the F_1 offspring. In terms of our assumed genotypes we may represent this as: *YY* × *yy*. Let us suppose that in this cross the yellow parent contributed the pollen grains (as was true part of the time; which parent contributed pollen and which contributed ova made no difference in the outcome). We assume, following Mendel's thinking, that when pollen grains are produced the members of a pair of alleles separate, so that each pollen grain receives only one member of the pair (only one *Y* gene, in this case). This assumed separation of genes is sometimes called the **law of segregation, the first Mendelian law.** It asserts that in the cells of individuals, genes occur in pairs, and that when those individuals produce germ cells each germ cell receives only one member of the pair. This law applies equally to pollen grains (or sperm) and to ova.

Hence we may represent the cross as follows:

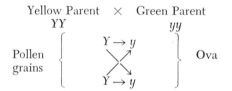

The arrows indicate all possible combinations of pollen grains and ova. We note that all combinations yield the genotype *Yy*. All these F_1 seeds had yellow cotyledons, yellow being dominant to green, or in genetic terms, *Y* being dominant to *y*. These F_1 individuals resembled the yellow parent in phenotype (being yellow) but not in genotype (*Yy* as opposed to *YY*). Both parents were **homozygous**: both members of that pair of alleles were the same. The yellow parent was homozygous for *Y* and the green parent for *y*. The F_1 individuals were **heterozygous,** having one *Y* and one *y*.

Succeeding events demonstrated that the genes *Y* and *y* were not altered or modified in any way by being combined in the cells of a heterozygote. We note especially that the gene *y*, although it produced no phenotypic effect in the heterozygote, retained all of its properties so that later, in a homozygous descendant (*yy*), the phenotype "green" was produced.

The flowers on the F_1 plants were permitted to fertilize themselves, each flower producing both ova and pollen. To facilitate comparison with animals and man, however, we shall represent a cross between two F_1 individuals, as if one parent produced all the pollen grains, the other all the ova. (This really does no violence to Mendel's experiments, for he would have obtained the same results if he had used a technique of artificial pollination, taking pollen from one F_1 flower and placing it on the stigma of another one.)

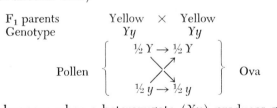

F_1 parents   Yellow × Yellow
Genotype Yy Yy

Pollen $\frac{1}{2}\,Y \rightarrow \frac{1}{2}\,Y$ Ova
                $\frac{1}{2}\,y \rightarrow \frac{1}{2}\,y$

What happens when a heterozygote (Yy) produces germ cells? As in the preceding generation, each germ cell (**gamete**) receives only one member of a pair of alleles, either Y or y. We assume that the chances are equal that a given gamete will receive Y or y. Hence, on the average, half the pollen grains will contain Y and half will contain y; in the same way, half the ova will contain Y and the other half will contain y. On the face of it, this seems an eminently reasonable assumption to make. Mendel, however, was not familiar with the cellular mechanism that seems to underlie this production of two kinds of germ cells in equal numbers, which will be discussed in the next chapter.

The Role of Chance or Probability   Now we are ready for the combinations of the two kinds of pollen grains with the two kinds of ova. Mendel assumed that this combining followed the laws of chance or probability. This means that a pollen grain containing Y is equally likely to fertilize an ovum containing Y or an ovum containing y (as these two types of ova occur in equal numbers). The same is true of a pollen grain containing y. Note that we specifically assume that there is no tendency to preferential pairing (e.g., no tendency for Y-bearing pollen grains to fertilize Y-bearing ova more frequently than do y-bearing ones).

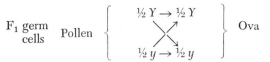

F_1 germ
cells   Pollen $\frac{1}{2}\,Y \rightarrow \frac{1}{2}\,Y$ Ova
                          $\frac{1}{2}\,y \rightarrow \frac{1}{2}\,y$

As in the diagram for the preceding generation, the arrows indicate all possible combinations, each of which is expected to occur one fourth of the time. As a result, the F_2 offspring are expected to occur as follows:

$\frac{1}{4}\,YY$ =   Yellow
$\frac{1}{4}\,Yy$ =   Yellow $\Big\}\ \frac{3}{4}$
$\frac{1}{4}\,Yy$ =   Yellow
$\frac{1}{4}\,yy$ =   Green $\frac{1}{4}$

It is most important to realize that these fractions depend on the operation of the laws of probability. A model using coins will help to emphasize the point. Such a model consists of two coins—a dime and a penny, perhaps—tossed at the same time. The dime may represent the pollen: at any given toss the chances are equal that the dime will come up "heads" or that it will come up "tails." Similarly, at any given fertilization the chances are equal that a Y-bearing pollen grain or that a y-bearing one will be transmitted.

The penny represents the ova. Again, the chances are equal for "heads" or "tails," just as the chances are equal that in any fertilization a Y-bearing or a y-bearing ovum will be involved. If we toss the two coins together and do it many times, we shall obtain an approximation of the following:

$\frac{1}{4}$ dime heads; penny heads $[= YY]$
$\frac{1}{4}$ dime heads; penny tails $[= Yy]$
$\frac{1}{4}$ dime tails; penny heads $[= yY]$
$\frac{1}{4}$ dime tails; penny tails $[= yy]$

If we regard "heads" as dominant, we find that three-fourths of the time there is at least one "head," one-fourth of the time no "heads" (both coins "tails"). Hence this gives us a model of the 3:1 ratio dependent on the laws of probability.

We can now see that obtaining a 3:1 F_2 ratio can be most simply explained by assuming that a single pair of genes is involved in the inheritance. It is further assumed (a) that the genes are paired in the cells of individuals, (b) that each germ cell (gamete) receives only one gene of the pair, (c) that heterozygotes produce in equal numbers gametes containing the dominant member of the pair and gametes containing the recessive member, and (d) that the laws of probability are followed when the two types of male gametes fertilize the two types of female gametes.

Someone may object that the fact that a 3:1 F_2 ratio "can be most simply explained" by assuming that a single pair of genes is involved does not *prove* that only one pair is involved. In point of fact there are more complex genetic situations (although they may perhaps not strictly constitute F_2 generations) that give rise to 3:1 ratios, but in each case the added complexity is revealed by further analysis. There is in science a **principle of parsimony** that advises against complicated explanations of phenomena for which simpler explanations will suffice. In the present instance the simplest explanation for obtaining a 3:1 ratio is that a single pair of genes is involved. Unless and until further evidence indicates that this simple explanation will not suffice, the principle of parsimony bids us accept the simple explanation as correct.

This is an appropriate place to point out that phenotypes are usually, if not always, the result of many genes working together. We speak, for example, of the gene "for" yellow. What we mean is that when this gene is absent, yellow color will not appear. However, the phenotype of the cotyledons was not determined solely by this gene. Mendel noted that the color of the yellow seeds might be pale yellow, bright yellow, or orange-hued. All had the gene Y. What caused the difference in shade? Two additional influences were doubtless also at work: (a) environmental factors and (b) other genes, which affected the phenotype determined by the "main gene." These other genes may have been of the type called **modifying genes**, perhaps genes that determined the quantity of yellow pigment present after the gene Y had determined that yellow pigment, in whatever quantity, should be present. When genetic analysis is thorough enough, the presence of modifying genes of this sort is almost always revealed.

We note that the 3:1 ratio we have been stressing is a *phenotypic* ratio. The *genotypic* F_2 ratio is 1/4 YY : 2/4 Yy : 1/4 yy. By further experiments, Mendel determined that the green F_2 plants bred true, but that not all the yellow plants did so. He found that one out of three of the yellow plants bred true but that two thirds of them behaved like their F_1 parents and gave 3:1 ratios in their turn (in an F_3 generation). These findings, agreeing with theoretical expectation, add further evidence that Mendel's explanation is correct—that single gene-pair inheritance is involved in the difference between yellow and green cotyledons in peas. The same conclusion applies to the other six differences he investigated.

Mendelian Inheritance in Animals

Dominance Present   Since Mendel's time, examples almost without number of single gene-pair inheritance have been investigated in many kinds of plants and animals. Figure 2.1 illustrates a well-known example from the animal kingdom, black versus white color in guinea pigs. As shown, if homozygous black guinea pigs are mated to white ones, the F_1 offspring are all black. Thus in guinea pigs the gene for black (B) is dominant, since these F_1 individuals are heterozygous.

When F_1 females are mated to F_1 males, the F_2 offspring display a phenotypic ratio of 3 blacks to 1 white. As with Mendel's peas, this is based on the laws of probability operating when two equally numerous kinds of sperm fertilize two equally numerous kinds of ova. The genotypic ratio in the F_2 generation is 1 BB : 2 Bb : 1 bb.

This is a good place to emphasize the fact that the most fundamental Mendelian ratio is 1:1, the ratio in which the two types of gametes are produced (½ B-containing : ½ b-containing). The 1:2:1 ratio is simply two of these 1:1 ratios multiplied together:

$$
\begin{array}{l}
1B \ + \ 1b \\
\underline{1B \ + \ 1b} \\
1BB \ + \ 1Bb \\
 \ 1Bb \ + \ 1bb \\
\hline
1BB \ + \ 2Bb \ + \ 1bb
\end{array}
$$

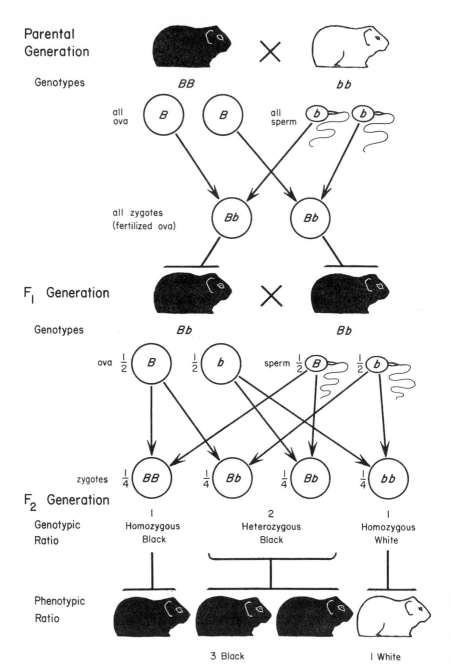

Parental Generation

Genotypes

all ova   all sperm

all zygotes (fertilized ova)

F₁ Generation

Genotypes

ova   sperm

zygotes

F₂ Generation

Genotypic Ratio

Homozygous Black

Heterozygous Black

Homozygous White

Phenotypic Ratio

3 Black   1 White

FIG. 2.1 Simple Mendelian inheritance of coat color (black vs. white) in guinea pigs.

At times this 1:1 gametic ratio may also be the phenotypic ratio. For example, when heterozygous black guinea pigs are mated to white ones (necessarily homozygous recessive), the two kinds of gametes produced by the heterozygous parent determine the two kinds of offspring and determine the ratio in which they shall occur (for the white parent contributes only *b*-containing gametes).

Such a cross is diagramed in Figure 2.2. It is sometimes called a **back cross**, because the heterozygous individual is genetically similar to an F_1 individual, and the white individual is genetically similar to one of the parents of such an F_1 individual. It is also known as a **test cross** because it is a means by which a geneticist can test whether an individual showing a dominant phenotype is homozygous or heterozygous. Suppose, for example, you wish to know whether a certain black guinea pig is homozygous or heterozygous. If you mate it to a white one and they produce one or more white offspring, you know at once that the black individual is heterozygous.

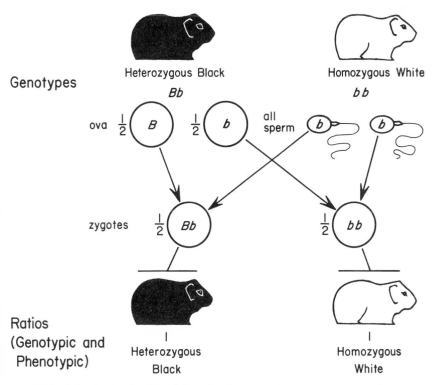

FIG. 2.2 A simple Mendelian back cross: heterozygote mated to homozygous recessive.

Dominance Absent   Returning to our 1:2:1 genotypic ratio we note that it also may be a phenotypic ratio. This occurs whenever the heterozygotes differ from both types of homozygotes, and this in turn occurs when dominance is lacking or incomplete. It so happened that Mendel worked with pairs of traits in which one trait did exhibit dominance over the other. Hence he did not observe a 1:2:1 phenotypic ratio. All of his examples were complicated by dominance, which converted 1:2:1 ratios into 3:1 ratios, as we have seen.

A well-known and easily visualized case in point is provided by Blue Andalusian fowls (Fig. 2.3). The "blue" birds are heterozygotes, produced in the first instance by mating a certain type of black fowl to "splashed white" ones. These latter birds are white, but some of the feathers are margined with black. If the black parents are represented as having the genotype BB and the splashed white parents as having the genotype bb, all the F_1 offspring will have the genotype Bb. These F_1 individuals are blue in color, and so afford an example of the situation mentioned above in which heterozygotes differ from both types of homozygotes.

Very probably this is a "dosage effect": two B genes together produce much black pigment, and so the BB individual appears black. One B gene by itself produces less black pigment spread thinly throughout the feathers. The blue color seen by the observer is the combined effect of this pigment and the refraction of light by the surface layer of the feathers. It is not, therefore, a matter of blue pigment versus black pigment. The optical effect "blue" occurs when there is less pigment than the amount that gives the optical effect "black." The genetically determined difference between BB and Bb individuals is doubtless mainly a quantitative one. We shall encounter many differences that are quantitative rather than qualitative (Chap. 11).

As shown in Figure 2.3, when Blue Andalusians are mated together they produce offspring in the ratio of 1 black : 2 blue : 1 splashed white, the genotypic and phenotypic ratios being the same.

Mendelian Ratios and the Number of Individuals

One aspect of Mendel's experiments is frequently overlooked although it has real significance for our thinking. Not all the F_1 plants produced yellow or green seeds in a 3:1 ratio. As we have seen, the *average* seed production of the 258 plants approximated the 3:1 ratio very closely, but individual plants varied widely. As extremes, Mendel recorded (a) one plant that had 32 yellow seeds and only 1 green seed, and (b) one plant

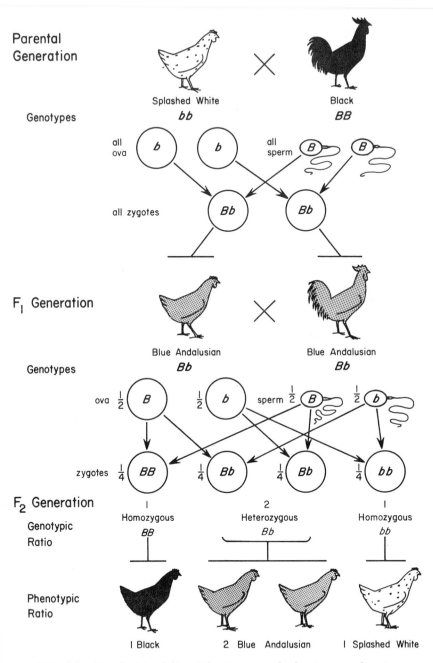

Parental Generation

Splashed White
bb

Black
BB

all ova   b   b   all sperm   B   B

all zygotes   Bb   Bb

F₁ Generation

Blue Andalusian
Bb

Blue Andalusian
Bb

ova $\frac{1}{2}$ B $\frac{1}{2}$ b   sperm $\frac{1}{2}$ B $\frac{1}{2}$ b

zygotes $\frac{1}{4}$ BB $\frac{1}{4}$ Bb $\frac{1}{4}$ Bb $\frac{1}{4}$ bb

F₂ Generation

Genotypic Ratio

1
Homozygous
BB

2
Heterozygous
Bb

1
Homozygous
bb

Phenotypic Ratio

1 Black   2 Blue Andalusian   1 Splashed White

FIG. 2.3 Simple Mendelian inheritance with dominance absent or incomplete: Blue Andalusian fowls.

that had 20 yellow seeds and 19 green seeds. In his paper he gave the seed counts for the first ten plants counted. The results were as follows:

Plant No.	Yellow Seeds	Green Seeds
1	25	11
2	32	7
3	14	5
4	70	27
5	24	13
6	20	6
7	32	13
8	44	9
9	50	14
10	44	18

Note how widely some of these departed from the 3:1 ratio. Yet plants having less than one fourth of the green seeds were compensated for by plants having more than one fourth of the green seeds, so that the average (based on 8023 seeds) closely approximated 3:1.

We emphasize this point because it is exactly what is expected when phenomena depend on the laws of probability. We have emphasized that these laws form the basis of all Mendelian thinking.

Because this is true, large numbers of offspring must be raised and studied if we are to attain close approximations to the theoretical ratios. Suppose, for example, that Mendel had raised only one F_1 plant and that the plant had been the one designated as No. 8 in the preceding table. It produced 53 seeds; 44 were yellow, 9 were green. This one plant by itself would never have suggested to Mendel that an underlying 3:1 ratio was present, for it gave an almost perfect 5:1 ratio. Only when large numbers were averaged was the true ratio revealed.

Large numbers can be attained easily with plants and lower animals, and notably with bacteria, molds, and other microorganisms. In recent years, many geneticists have turned to investigations on these latter, in part because of the tremendous numbers that can be produced with ease.

However, we are presently concerned with human genetics where, save for certain national population studies, numbers are always relatively small. We must draw what conclusions we can from small numbers; means of doing this are discussed in Chapter 5. At present, we wish to emphasize the point that when numbers are small, close approximations to the theoretical ratios are not to be expected.

A human characteristic that behaves as a Mendelian recessive is albinism (complete lack of pigment). We may represent its gene as a, the allele for normal pigment production as A. What will be expected when two normally pigmented but heterozygous individuals marry each other (the human equivalent of an $F_1 \times F_1$ mating)?

Parents   *Aa* × *Aa*

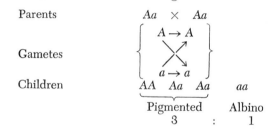

Gametes

Children   *AA   Aa   Aa*   *aa*

                  Pigmented   Albino

                     3   :   1

Thus three-fourths of the children can be expected to be pigmented, one-fourth to be albino.

Now suppose, as may well be the case, that this couple has only four children. What are the chances that three will be pigmented and one will be an albino? People who know just a little about Mendel's experiments would say that such an outcome is certain. Do not the Mendelian laws prescribe it? As we have seen, the Mendelian laws are special applications of the laws of probability. They prescribe that if, for example, a couple had 400 children (what a delight that would be to a human geneticist!) *about* 100 of them would be albinos, the rest pigmented.

But suppose we pursue our question a little further: What *are* the chances that a family (sibship) of four, born, to heterozygous parents, will consist of three pigmented children and one albino child?

The albino child may be any one of the four. The chance that any one child will be pigmented is ¾, the chance that he will be albino is ¼. What are the chances that the first child will be an albino and the other three pigmented? The chance that the first child will be an albino is ¼. The chance that the second child will be pigmented is ¾. The chance that the third child will be pigmented is ¾. The chance that the fourth child will be pigmented is ¾. Now each child is an "independent event"; whether or not the first child is an albino has no influence on whether or not the second child will be, and so on. The total probability of several independent events occurring together is the product of the probabilities that they will occur singly (thus the chance that three coins tossed together will all fall "heads" is $\frac{1}{2} \times \frac{1}{2} \times \frac{1}{2} = \frac{1}{8}$). In the present instance, then, we multiply the four probabilities: $\frac{1}{4} \times \frac{3}{4} \times \frac{3}{4} \times \frac{3}{4} = \frac{27}{256}$.

Thus the chance that the first child will be an albino and the following three pigmented is $\frac{27}{256}$.

However, it may equally well be the second child who is an albino (the first, third, and fourth pigmented). The chance of this is also $\frac{27}{256}$. In the same way, the chance that the albino child is the third one (first, second, and fourth being pigmented) is $\frac{27}{256}$. And the chance that the albino child is the fourth one (first, second, and third being pigmented) is $\frac{27}{256}$. The total chance that the family of four will consist of one albino child and three pigmented ones is $4 \times \frac{27}{256} = \frac{108}{256}$ or about ⅖. (A less laborious way of calculating such expectations is presented in Chapter 5, p. 62). Thus we see that less than half the time are families of four, born to heterozygous parents, expected to exhibit the 3:1 ratio exactly.

Now we readily understand the error in thinking made by a young couple of whom I once read. They had one child, an albino (thereby demonstrating that they were both heterozygous). They came to a genetic counselor with the question as to the chances that future children would also be albinos. He explained Mendelian principles to them as best he could, and they grasped the idea that they could expect one child in four to be an albino. Then they had the happy thought: "We have had our albino child; now we can go ahead and have three more children and be sure that they will all be normal!" They did not grasp the idea that each child is an independent event.

In concluding this part of the discussion, we may well mention that some people have argued that because small samples do not always show perfect fit to the ideal ratios, Mendelian principles of inheritance themselves are invalid. For example, Lysenko, deriding Mendelian genetics, wrote as follows (1946): "The Mendelians foist this 'pea law,' according to Michurin's happy expression, on the whole of living nature. But in reality it is basically wrong even for pea hybrids, including the factual material obtained by Mendel himself. The progenies of different hybrid plants varied even in Mendel's experiments much beyond the ratio 3:1. Thus, in the offspring of one plant there were 19 yellow and 20 green seeds, and of another plant—only a single green for 30 yellow ones."

Nevertheless, when the results were all pooled, the 3:1 ratio emerged. Not only do individual small samples varying from the 3:1 ratio not disprove Mendelian principles, but their occurrence can be predicted, statistically, in accordance with Mendelian principles. To return to our family of four children, if two fifths of such families are expected to consist of one albino and three normally pigmented children, then three fifths of such families are expected *not* to fit the 3:1 ratio exactly (i.e., to consist of four pigmented, or of two pigmented and two albino, or of one pigmented and three albino, or of four albino children).

In the next chapter we shall discuss the chromosomal basis of Mendelian genetics, a basis unknown to Mendel himself. Then in Chapter 5 we shall discuss ways in which Mendelian thinking can be applied to human genetics, where breeding experiments of the type employed by Mendel and his successors are not possible.

PROBLEMS

1. One of the traits studied by Mendel in peas was height of stem. He found that tallness was dominant to dwarfness. If you had homozygous tall peas and crossed them with dwarf peas what proportion of the F_1 offspring would be tall? What proportion would be dwarf? If you allowed the F_1 plants to self-fertilize and thus produced 1200 seeds, how many of these seeds would you expect to grow into tall F_2 plants? How many into dwarf F_2 plants? How many of the dwarf F_2 plants would you expect to be homozygous? How many of the tall F_2 plants would you expect to be homozygous?

2. In guinea pigs, short hair is dominant to long. A short-haired guinea pig was mated to a long-haired one. Five offspring were produced: three long-haired and two short-haired. Give the genotypes of the parents and of the offspring.

3. If homozygous short-haired male guinea pigs are mated to heterozygous short-haired females, what proportion of the offspring will be expected to be (a) homozygous short-haired, (b) homozygous long-haired, (c) heterozygous short-haired, (d) heterozygous long-haired?

4. Suppose that you experiment with a certain species of insect and discover that whereas most of the individuals are dark brown in color, an occasional individual is tan. When you mate dark brown individuals to tan ones, all of the F_1 offspring are dark brown. When these F_1 offspring are mated to each other, you obtain the following F_2 generation: 338 dark brown, 112 tan. What is the most probable explanation for these results? Assign symbols to the genes and give the genotypes of (a) the original parents, (b) the F_1 offspring, (c) the F_2 offspring.

5. How would your interpretation of the genetic situation in No. 4 have differed if the F_1 offspring had been light brown in color, and if the F_2 offspring had been as follows: 110 dark brown, 228 light brown, 112 tan?

6. A husband and wife both have normal skin pigmentation. Their first child is an albino. Give the genotypes of the parents and of the albino child. What is the chance that if they have a second child, he will be an albino? What is the chance that if they then have a third child he will be an albino?

7. An albino man marries a woman who has normal pigmentation. Their first child is an albino. Give the genotype of the mother.

REFERENCES

Lysenko, T. D. 1946. *Heredity and Its Variability.* New York: Columbia University Press.

Mendel, G. 1865. "Experiments in plant hybridization." (Original paper in *Verhandlungen naturforschender Verein in Brünn, Abhandlungen,* iv, [1865], which appeared in 1866. Two easily available sources for the English translation are Peters, J. A. [ed.] 1959. *Classic Papers in Genetics.* Englewood Cliffs, N. J.: Prentice-Hall, Inc. Pp. 1–20. Sinnott, E. W., L. C. Dunn, and T. Dobzhansky, 1958. *Principles of Genetics,* 5th ed. New York: McGraw-Hill Book Company, Inc. Pp. 419–43.)

CHROMOSOMES, MITOSIS,
AND MEIOSIS

Mendel's report on his research was published in 1866, and then completely ignored for about thirty years, only to be rediscovered in 1900 when several other geneticists, independently, came to conclusions that were substantially the same.

During this thirty years, great progress also was made in the study of the microscopic structure of cells and of the changes involved when cells divide and when gametes (germ cells) are formed. Early in the present century, two authors pointed out that in the process of gamete formation the **chromosomes**, deeply staining bodies in the nuclei of cells, behave in such a manner as to provide the mechanism for the type of inheritance Mendel had postulated (see Sutton, 1903).

As was noted in the preceding chapter, the Mendelian explanation of inheritance involves two assumptions: (1) units of heredity, which today are called genes, occur in pairs, and (2) in the formation of gametes the members of a pair of genes separate so that each gamete receives only one of the two. Sutton and Boveri both pointed out (1) that chromosomes occur in pairs, and (2) that in the formation of gametes the members of a pair separate so that each gamete receives only one member of the pair. (See Sturtevant, 1965, for historical background.) This striking parallel between the behavior of genes and chromosomes suggests that the chromosomes are indeed the bearers of the genes. Prior to the reports of Sutton and Boveri, the genes had been purely hypothetical units of heredity, postulated to explain the 3:1 ratio in F_2 generations. With their findings, the hypothetical unit became clothed with substance. Although this parallelism does not in itself prove that the chromosomes are bearers of the genes, the overwhelming amount of corroboratory evidence amassed in the last sixty years has firmly established the connection between gene and chromosome. (For an orderly survey of the evidence, see Snyder and David, 1957.)

Chromosomes

We have placed such great emphasis on the importance of chromosomes in Mendelian inheritance that it would now be well to inquire into their nature.

The Nature of Chromosomes   The investigation, although fascinating, is beset by great difficulty. In the first place, chromosomes are extremely small. The largest human chromosome is not over 10 *microns* in length (1/100 of a millimeter). Then, as the name implies, chromosomes stain deeply when prepared for study with the microscope—so deeply that internal details are difficult to discern. Their usual appearance is that of solid dark masses. Nevertheless, careful studies on a great variety of cells have permitted cytologists to discover much about chromosome structure, although many questions are still unanswered.

Chromosomes are seen most readily at the time that cells are dividing or undergoing meiosis (see below). When the cell is not engaged in these processes, chromosomes as such are usually not visible. Nevertheless, there is some evidence that each chromosome at this time is present as an exceedingly fine (attenuated) thread, less than 100 *angstrom units* in diameter (an angstrom unit is 1/10,000,000 of a millimeter). In Figure 3.1 A, such a thread is represented diagrammatically, although, of course, no line drawn with ink can be as fine as the thread we are talking about, nor is there space to make the thread as long as it should be in proportion to its diameter. In preparation for mitosis this thread duplicates itself, forming two threads, each called a **chromonema** (Fig. 3.1 B). Each chromonema will form a **chromatid,** and hence a separate chromosome, in one of the two daughter cells resulting from the cell division.

In very favorable material from plants and lower animals (not, so far, in human chromosomes), it is possible to see that these fine threads (chromonemata) undergo a series of coilings, first a minor coiling (Fig. 3.1 C) and then a major coiling—a coiling of the coil, so to speak (Fig. 3.1 D). In the figure, the coils are shown as loosely separated, so that we may see details; however, as the coiling proceeds, the coils become more and more tightly massed together. Eventually the dense appearance of Figure 3.1 E is attained. Perhaps additional material from the nucleolus enters into formation of these short, thick chromosomes.

At some stage in the process, the chromonemata separate (uncoil?) from each other so that each becomes a separate chromatid (Fig. 3.1 E). The figure shows the chromonemata coiled together as far as stage "D"; perhaps they should have been shown as separated by "C" of the figure. Detailed information on this point is extremely difficult to obtain. Eventually (Fig. 3.1 E) it is clearly discernible that the chromosome consists of two chromatids joined together at the **centromere** (see also Fig. 16.6).

Finer Structure of the Chromosome   At the present time there is a gap in our knowledge of the finer structure of the chromosomes. Using the light microscope and the electron microscope, we can see the details

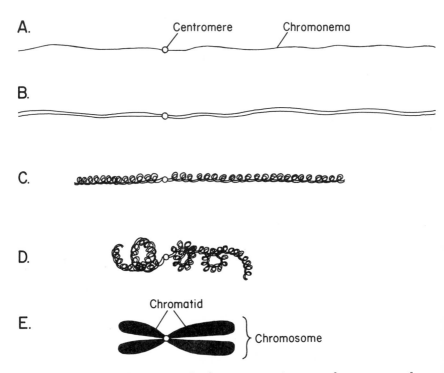

FIG. 3.1 Condensation of chromonema (in interphase stage of mitosis) to form paired chromatids comprising a chromosome as seen at metaphase. A) Chromonema before it has duplicated itself. B) The chromonema has duplicated itself, forming two chromonemata. C) Primary coiling of the duplicated chromonemata. D) Secondary coiling of the duplicated chromonemata. E) Chromosome as seen at metaphase. Prior to this stage, the coiled chromonemata have separated from each other and each chromonema has formed a chromatid.

described above, in favorable material. We also know something about the macromolecular structure of chromosomes, as we shall see presently. These details of molecular structure cannot be seen with microscopes although future electron microscopes may render them visible; rather, they are made known by a variety of physical and chemical methods, such as X-ray diffraction studies.

We have noted that coiling characterizes the chromonemata, the finest unit of chromosome structure we can see (Fig. 3.1). Of what are these chromonemata composed? Are they made up of bundles of still smaller fibrils (Ris, 1957)? Or are they composed of a single fibril strongly coiled or folded? Future research will undoubtedly answer these questions. At present, it is probably wisest to suspend judgment, although we may echo the comment of Sager and Ryan (1961): "It is tempting to assume that submicroscopic coiling occurs, too, and that the visible chromosome may be simply the condensed product of many ranks of coils, sufficient to bring the chromosome from a diameter of less than 100 Å [angstrom units] to that of a metaphase chromosome 1000 times thicker." When we emerge from this twilight zone of uncertainty into the region of molecular structure where, at present, knowledge is greater, we encounter a spiralled structure, the DNA molecule. Perhaps this spiralling is the basis of the visible coiling described above, but the answer lies in the future.

Mitosis

The series of changes in a chromosome shown in Figure 3.1 occur only when a cell is preparing to divide. The division of the cell body (cytoplasm) is preceded by a most precise distribution of the chromosomes in a process called **mitosis**.

Figure 3.2 A shows a cell prior to mitosis. The material of the chromosomes is in the attenuated, uncoiled state already described. The only visible indication that mitosis is about to occur is the fact that a tiny body outside the nucleus, the **centriole**, has divided, the two centrioles thus formed have started to move apart, and a spindle-shaped arrangement of fibers has formed between them. The centrioles continue to migrate until they reach the poles of the cell (Fig. 3.2 B and C), and the spindle becomes large. Although details of the mechanisms involved are still obscure despite much research, the spindle in some manner aids or guides the distribution of the chromosomes.

During the portion of mitosis known as the **prophase** (Fig. 3.2 B), each chromosome undergoes the series of changes shown in Figure 3.1. Hence by the end of the prophase each chromosome has come to consist

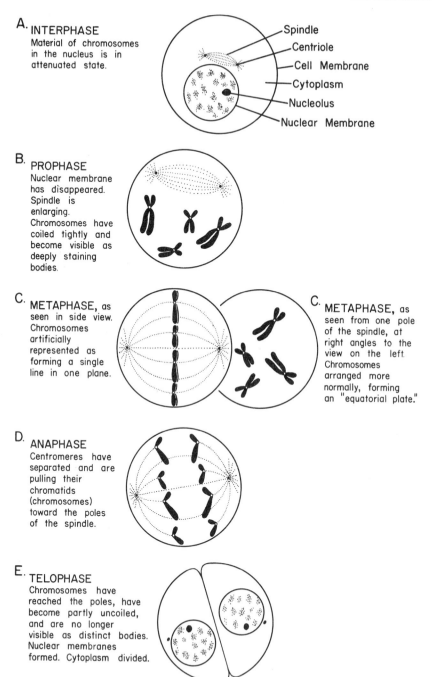

A. INTERPHASE
Material of chromosomes
in the nucleus is in
attenuated state.

Spindle
Centriole
Cell Membrane
Cytoplasm
Nucleolus
Nuclear Membrane

B. PROPHASE
Nuclear membrane
has disappeared.
Spindle is
enlarging.
Chromosomes have
coiled tightly and
become visible as
deeply staining
bodies.

C. METAPHASE, as
seen in side view.
Chromosomes
artificially
represented as
forming a single
line in one plane.

C. METAPHASE, as
seen from one pole
of the spindle, at
right angles to the
view on the left.
Chromosomes
arranged more
normally, forming
an "equatorial plate."

D. ANAPHASE
Centromeres have
separated and are
pulling their
chromatids
(chromosomes)
toward the poles
of the spindle.

E. TELOPHASE
Chromosomes have
reached the poles, have
become partly uncoiled,
and are no longer
visible as distinct bodies.
Nuclear membranes
formed. Cytoplasm divided.

FIG. 3.2   The genetically significant highlights of mitosis.

of two chromatids joined at the centromere. In Figure 3.2 there are four chromosomes, two long ones and two short ones; a human cell contains 46, but to include them all would make an unwieldy diagram.

The chromosomes line up at the equator of the spindle (Fig. 3.2 C). The cell is then said to be in **metaphase.** This arrangement of chromosomes is called an **equatorial,** or **metaphase, plate.** At this time the chromosomes are in the best position for counting and study (Chap. 16).

As we have noted, each chromosome consists of two chromatids united at the centromere. The centromere itself now divides (or if it had already divided, the halves now separate). This frees the sister chromatids from each other, and one moves toward one pole of the spindle, the other toward the other pole (Fig. 3.2 D). The cell is now said to be in **anaphase.** The motive force seems to be centered in the centromere, the remainder of the chromatid being dragged along rather passively. The nature of the forces that act on the centromere is still uncertain. The centromere is sometimes called the "spindle fiber attachment." Some investigators conclude that the attached fiber exerts a pull on the centromere, but the evidence is not conclusive either for or against this idea. At any rate the chromatids, each of which can now be called a chromosome in it own right, move toward their respective poles until they cluster about the latter.

About this time the cytoplasm of the cell starts to divide; in animal and human cells this is usually by formation of a furrow which grows deeper until the cell is cleaved in two (Fig. 3.2 E). At this stage, the **telophase,** a nuclear membrane is formed around each mass of chromosomes, and then the latter undergo a reversal of the process shown in Figure 3.1. The chromosomes elongate and uncoil until they regain the attenuated state they had exhibited before mitosis began. Each daughter cell has now become a cell in **interphase.**

During interphase, each chromonema (Fig. 3.1 A and B) duplicates itself in preparation for the next mitosis. This doubling of the amount of chromosomal material can be detected by chemical means even though the chromosomes themselves cannot be seen at this time.

What is the significance of mitosis? This rather elaborate process ensures that when a cell divides, each daughter cell will receive exactly the same amount and kind of chromosomal material received by the other one, and that the material received by both will be exactly the same in amount and kind as that possessed by the cell before division. Evidently the chromosomes are so important that nothing can be left to chance in their duplication and subsequent distribution. Evidence from plants and experimental animals indicates that the genes are arranged in a row (linear order) along the chromonema. Thus when a chromonema duplicates itself, all the genes throughout its length duplicate themselves. We may think of one as an original and the other as a carbon copy, but in this case the carbon copy is the equal of the original in every respect. Through mitosis one daughter cell receives the original, the other the carbon copy. As a result, both receive exactly the same genetic information.

Although the linear order of the genes cannot be seen, linearly arranged structures in chromosomes can be observed in favorable material. This is particularly true of the salivary gland cells of some of the flies (Order Diptera), *Drosophila* being the most thoroughly analyzed example (Fig. 3.3). In these cells the chromonemata remain uncoiled. They duplicate

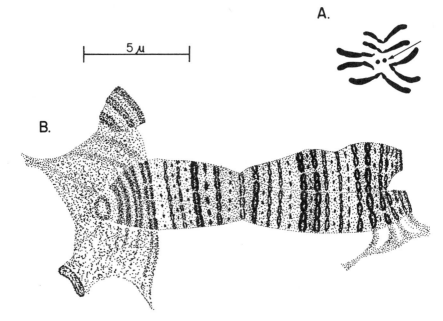

FIG. 3.3   Salivary gland chromosome No. IV of the fruit fly, *Drosophila*, compared with the same chromosome as seen at metaphase in a germ cell.   A) Metaphase plate of *Drosophila* chromosomes in a germ cell. The No. IV chromosome is indicated by the arrow.   B) The No. IV chromosome as seen in a cell of the salivary gland of larval *Drosophila*. Both drawings are on the same scale (5 microns = 5 thousandths of a millimeter). (Redrawn from Bridges, C. B., 1935. "Salivary chromosome maps," *Journal of Heredity*, **26**:60–64.)

themselves several or many times, forming a mass of threads referred to as a giant chromosome. Each thread is not uniform in diameter throughout its length but rather has irregularly spaced, nodule-like enlargements called **chromomeres.** The massing together of many chromomeres results in the banded appearance evident in the figure. Because the bands have a great variety of patterns, chromosomes and portions of chromosomes can be identified by experts almost as accurately as other experts can identify fingerprints. Hence genetic changes can frequently be seen to be associated with visible chromosomal changes. In many cases the location of a gene on or near a given band can be pinpointed with accuracy. Although this is not yet possible with human chromosomes, chromomeres can be discerned (Fig. 3.4) in favorable human material, giving hope that future research will enable us to connect the loci of genes with particular visible structures in the chromosomes.

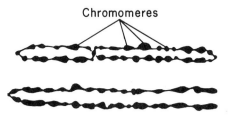

FIG. 3.4 Human chromosomes showing chromomeres. (Redrawn from Yerganian, G., 1957. "Cytologic maps of some isolated human pachytene chromosomes," *American Journal of Human Genetics*, 9:42–54.)

Meiosis

The role of chromosomes in Mendelian inheritance is most clearly revealed in the process by which gametes are produced from precursor cells, the process of **meiosis.**

As mentioned earlier, chromosomes occur in pairs in most of the cells of the body. The number of pairs per cell varies from species to species; in man, each cell normally has 23 pairs, a total of 46 chromosomes. One member of each pair came from the mother of the individual (and hence is called maternal) and the other member came from the father (paternal). In human beings, the ovum contains 23 chromosomes and the sperm contains 23; hence a fertilized ovum (formed by fusion of a sperm with an ovum) contains 46. Because the whole body of the offspring which develops from that fertilized ovum arises from the latter by repeated divisions and subdivisions (mitoses), all the cells of the body contain 46 chromosomes. (Although there may be some variation in number from cell to cell, this is the rule.)

As an embryo develops from a fertilized ovum, certain cells are set aside to form the reproductive cells of the individual. These are called **primordial germ cells.** Like the other cells (of skin, muscle, liver, etc.), they contain chromosomes in pairs. Because a diagram showing 23 pairs would be unwieldy, Figure 3.5 is drawn with two pairs only, as in the diagram of mitosis (Fig. 3.2). Figure 3.5 represents meiosis in a male (**spermatogenesis**); the primordial germ cells are called **spermatogonia**. The figure summarizes the history of a single one of these, although an embryo produces many of them.

Figure 3.5 shows the spermatogonium in two of its several stages. The first diagram represents it as a cell in interphase when the chromosomes are present as long, slender chromonemata (p. 25) that have not yet duplicated themselves. Actually each chromonema is longer and more twisted than the diagram indicates. A human spermatogonium at this stage would have 46 chromonemata so twisted and massed together that the individual ones would not be discernible. In the diagram, two long chromonemata and two short ones are shown. As in mitosis, each

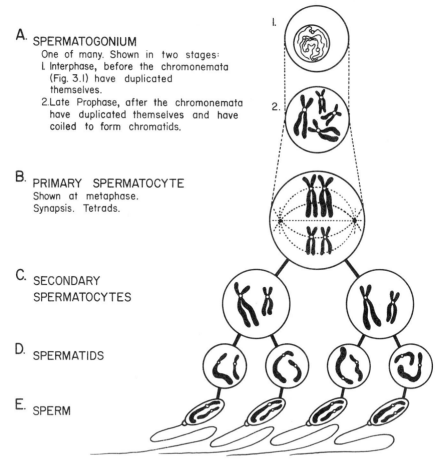

A. SPERMATOGONIUM
  One of many. Shown in two stages:
  l. Interphase, before the chromonemata
  (Fig. 3.1) have duplicated
  themselves.
  2. Late Prophase, after the chromonemata
  have duplicated themselves and have
  coiled to form chromatids.

B. PRIMARY SPERMATOCYTE
  Shown at metaphase.
  Synapsis. Tetrads.

C. SECONDARY
  SPERMATOCYTES

D. SPERMATIDS

E. SPERM

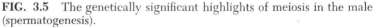

FIG. 3.5   The genetically significant highlights of meiosis in the male (spermatogenesis).

chromonema duplicates itself and then coils in complex fashion (Fig. 3.1). At the conclusion of this process the resulting chromosomes present the appearance shown in Figure 3.5 A,2. Each chromonema has become two chromatids held together by a centromere. The chromosomes then line up on the spindle, which has been forming meanwhile. By the time this happens, the cell is called a **primary spermatocyte** (rather than a spermatogonium).

In the primary spermatocyte stage, the chromosomes line up in homologous pairs, in what is called **synapsis** (Fig. 3.5 B). Thus the long chromosomes are shown side by side, and so are the short chromosomes. Because each synapsed pair of chromosomes consists of four chromatids, the pair is now called a **tetrad.**

Let us look closely at the primary spermatocyte, for it is a genetically important point in the history of germ cells. For clarity of diagraming, Figure 3.5 shows the chromatids of a tetrad well separated and lying smoothly parallel to each other. Actually the chromatids are tightly bunched together (Fig. 3.6 A). Frequently the chromatids are twisted about each other. At this time, portions of one chromatid may be exchanged with corresponding portions of another one in the same tetrad, in

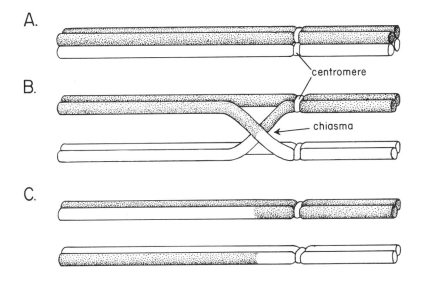

FIG. 3.6 Synapsis, crossing over, and chiasma formation. A) Tetrad consisting of four chromatids (two chromosomes) in synapsis. B) Chiasma formed as chromosomes separate following crossing over (represented by exchange of portions between two chromatids). C) Resulting chromosomes following crossing over and the disappearance of the chiasma.

a phenomenon known as **crossing over.** Since each chromatid contains many genes, such crossing over greatly increases the number and variety of combinations of genes. Soon the chromosomes composing a tetrad pull apart, and at this time an observer can see evidence that crossing over has occurred because of a tendency of crossed-over chromatids to cling together, forming temporary crosslike patterns called **chiasmata** (singular: **chiasma;** Fig. 3.6 B).

When the primary spermatocyte divides, the chromosomes composing a tetrad separate from each other, each daughter cell receiving one of each kind (Fig. 3.5 C). The resulting cells are called **secondary spermatocytes.** Because each chromosome is composed of two chromatids, each chromosome in a secondary spermatocyte is sometimes called a **dyad** (cf., tetrad).

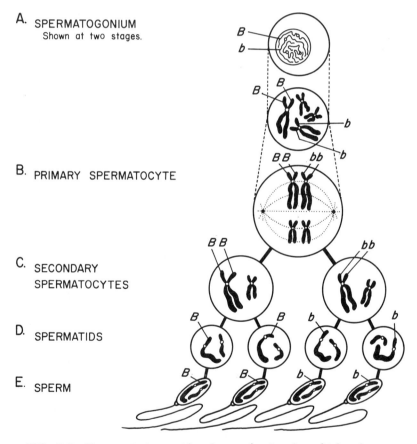

A. SPERMATOGONIUM
  Shown at two stages.

B. PRIMARY SPERMATOCYTE

C. SECONDARY
  SPERMATOCYTES

D. SPERMATIDS

E. SPERM

FIG. 3.7 How meiosis provides the mechanism by which a heterozygous male produces sperm of two kinds: half of them containing the dominant gene, half of them containing its recessive allele.

Thus far, the chromatids forming a chromosome have been held together by a centromere. Now the centromere divides, freeing the chromatids, each of which is now considered a separate chromosome. Each secondary spermatocyte divides, each of the two resulting cells receiving one of each kind of chromosome. These cells are called **spermatids** (Fig. 3.5 D).

As a last step, each spermatid undergoes a sort of metamorphosis, developing a flagellum (tail), which enables it to swim. It is now a mature **sperm** (Fig. 3.5 E).

In summary, we note that the spermatogonia contain chromosomes in pairs. The total number of chromosomes in such a cell (46 in man) is called the **diploid** number. Each sperm cell contains one of each pair of chromosomes present in the spermatogonium. The total number of chromosomes in a sperm cell is called the **haploid** number (23 in a man). Thus meiosis is an orderly process by which haploid gametes are produced from diploid primordial cells.

We can readily understand how this process provides the mechanism for Mendelian inheritance. Suppose, for example, that the spermatogenesis diagramed in Figure 3.5 occurs in a heterozygous black guinea pig, and that the genes concerned are borne by the long chromosomes, one of the latter containing *B*, one containing *b*. Figure 3.7 shows clearly how the behavior of the chromosomes results in the separation of *B* from *b*, and in the production of *B*-containing and *b*-containing gametes in equal numbers, as postulated by Mendelian theory.

Meiosis in the female (**oögenesis**) is in principle much like that in the male (Fig. 3.8). The primordial germ cells are called **oögonia**. Tetrads are formed as in the male, the stage in which they occur being called the **primary oöcyte**. When the primary oöcyte divides, the chromosomes separate just as they do in the male, but the division of the cell body (cytoplasm) is extremely unequal, one daughter cell being just large enough to enclose the chromosomes. This tiny cell is called the **first polar body**; although it may divide, nothing ever comes of it. This is merely a method of discarding chromosomes while retaining most of the cytoplasm in the other cell formed by the division, the **secondary oöcyte**.

Similarly, when the secondary oöcyte divides, the freed chromatids (now separate chromosomes) behave as they do in the male. The division of cytoplasm is again highly unequal, the **second polar body** receiving only enough to envelop the chromosomes. The second polar body, like the first one, disintegrates, leaving a single functional cell, the **ovum**. Note that the ovum contains the haploid number of chromosomes with a relatively large amount of cytoplasm. The importance of this large amount of cytoplasm is evident when we recall that, depending on the species, much of the nourishment for embryonic development must be provided by the ovum.

Figure 3.8 represents oögenesis in a heterozygous black female guinea pig. The fate of genes B and b may be followed as in the corresponding spermatogenesis (Fig. 3.7). In this case we have represented b as being discarded in the first polar body, the single ovum produced by that primary oöcyte containing the gene B. It is equally likely that the B gene will be discarded in the polar body; so other ova produced by other oöcytes will contain the gene b. Because the chances are equal that the B gene or the b gene will be retained in the ovum, a heterozygous female may be expected to produce during her reproductive life B-containing and

A. OÖGONIUM
 One of many. Shown in two stages:
 I. Interphase, before the chromonemata
 have duplicated themselves.
 2. Late Prophase, after the chromonemata
 have duplicated themselves and have
 coiled to form chromatids.

B. PRIMARY OÖCYTE
 Shown at metaphase.
 Synapsis. Tetrads.

C. SECONDARY OÖCYTE

D. OVUM

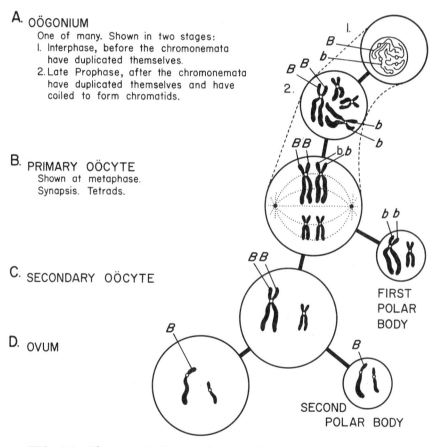

FIG. 3.8 The genetically significant highlights of meiosis in the female (oögenesis). The female is shown as heterozygous, Bb. The recessive gene, b, is shown discarded in the first polar body. Because the dominant gene, B, is equally likely to be so discarded, heterozygous females produce in equal numbers ova containing the dominant gene and ova containing the recessive gene.

b-containing ova in approximately equal numbers. Again, this accords with the postulates of Mendelian theory.

Independent Assortment

In the foregoing discussion of the genetical significance of meiosis, we have concentrated on one pair of genes in one pair of chromosomes. Frequently we wish to study the simultaneous distribution of two or more pairs of genes, in different pairs of chromosomes. In such cases we find that the manner in which the members of one pair of genes are distributed to gametes does not influence the manner in which the members of another pair are distributed. This principle of independent assortment is called the **second Mendelian law** (the first Mendelian law, the law of segregation, was discussed on p. 12).

We may illustrate the principle by considering the gametes produced by an individual who has the genotype *AaBb*. Following meiosis, half of his gametes will contain gene *A*, half of them will contain gene *a*.

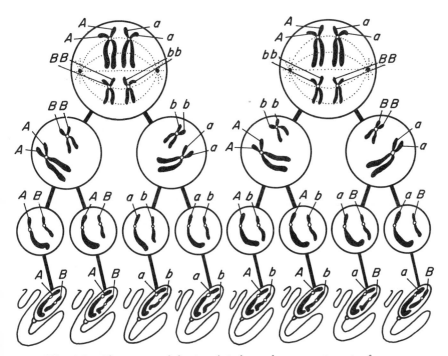

FIG. 3.9 Chromosomal basis of independent assortment of genes, starting with two primary spermatocytes in a doubly heterozygous individual: *AaBb*. Subsequent stages are those shown in Fig. 3.5.

Similarly, half will contain B, half will contain b. However, an A-containing gamete is equally likely to contain B or b, and an a-containing
gamete is equally likely to have B or b. Hence a person with the genotype
AaBb produces four kinds of gametes in equal numbers: AB, Ab, aB, ab.

It is important to realize that independent assortment depends on
independent distribution of chromosomes in meiosis. Chance determines
the arrangement of tetrads on the spindle prior to the first meiotic division.
Thus if the long chromosomes carry the genes A and a, respectively (Fig.
3.9) and the short chromosomes carry the genes B and b, two arrangements of the tetrads are possible, and equally likely. (1) A and B may be
on the left, with a and b on the right. (2) A and b may be on the left,
with a and B on the right. As shown in the figure, the outcome is the
production of the four kinds of gametes in equal numbers. A similar
mechanism underlies independent assortment in the female; a series of
ova produced by an AaBb female will include all four kinds with equal
frequencies.

Thus, we see that independent assortment characterizes genes located
on different chromosomes. The converse of independent assortment is
linkage, caused by the two genes (e.g., A and B) being on the same
chromosome (Chap. 14).

PROBLEMS

1. Before mitosis begins, a human skin cell contains 46 chromosomes. When
   that cell is at the metaphase stage of mitosis how many chromatids does it
   contain? How many centromeres? At the conclusion of mitosis how many
   chromosomes does each of the two daughter cells contain? How many
   centromeres?

2. When a human primary spermatocyte is at metaphase (a) how many
   chromatids does it contain? (b) how many centromeres? (c) how many
   tetrads?

3. How many chromatids does a human secondary spermatocyte contain? How
   many centromeres?

4. How many chromosomes does a human spermatid contain? How many does
   a sperm contain?

5. How many chromatids does a human primary oöcyte contain? How many
   does a secondary oöcyte contain? A first polar body? A second polar body?

6. If a woman has the genotype Aa, what proportion of her primary oöcytes
   will contain gene A? In each primary oöcyte *how many* A genes will be
   present? How many a genes? If a first polar body contains gene A, what
   does the corresponding secondary oöcyte contain? If an ovum contains
   gene A, what does the corresponding second polar body contain?

7. If a man has the genotype *Aa*, what proportion of his primary spermatocytes will contain gene *a*? What proportion of his secondary spermatocytes will contain *a*? What proportion of his spermatids? Of his sperms?

8. A man has the genotype *MmTt*. (a) What proportion of his primary spermatocytes will contain gene *M* and gene *T* (but not necessarily these only)? (b) What proportion of his spermatids will contain gene *M* and gene *t*? (c) What proportion of his sperms will contain gene *M* and gene *m*? (d) What proportion of the sperms that contain gene *M* will also contain gene *T*? Gene *t*?

9. During the lifetime of a woman having the genotype *MmTt* what proportion of the ova she produces will contain (a) *M* and *T*, (b) *m* and *T*, (c) *T* and *T*, (d) *T* and *t*?

10. During the lifetime of a woman having the genotype *MmTT* what proportion of the ova she produces will contain (a) *M* and *T*, (b) *m* and *T*, (c) *m* and *t*?

11. A man with the genotype *Mm* produces two kinds of sperms relative to these genes. A man with the genotype *MmTt* produces 4 kinds of sperms. How many kinds of sperms are produced by a man with the genotype *MmTtWw*? List the different kinds he produces.

REFERENCES

Ris, H., 1957. "Chromosome structure." In W. D. McElroy and B. Glass (eds.) *A Symposium on the Chemical Basis of Heredity*. Baltimore: The Johns Hopkins Press. Pp. 23–62.

Sager, R., and F. J. Ryan, 1961. *Cell Heredity*. New York: John Wiley & Sons, Inc.

Snyder, L. H., and P. R. David, 1957. *The Principles of Heredity*, 5th ed. Boston: D. C. Heath & Company.

Sturtevant, A. H., 1965. *A History of Genetics*. New York: Harper and Row.

Sutton, W. S., 1903. "The chromosomes in heredity," *Biological Bulletin*, 4: 231–51. Reprinted in J. A. Peters (ed.), 1961. *Classic Papers in Genetics*. Englewood Cliffs, N. J.: Prentice-Hall Inc. Pp. 27-41.

4.

GENES AND MUTATIONS

The Nature of Genes

In discussing this vast subject, we shall content ourselves with summarizing highlights of knowledge that will be valuable to us in our discussions of human genetics. More detailed discussions are legion (e.g., McElroy and Glass, 1957; Sager and Ryan, 1961; Strauss, 1960; Sutton, 1961) and contain additional information of great interest and importance.

Of what are chromosomes composed? From the genetic standpoint, the most important constituents are **nucleoproteins.** As the name suggests, these are complexes composed of proteins joined to nucleic acids. Ingenious experiments have demonstrated that the nucleic acid portion contains most of the genetic information. This fact does not rule out the possibility that the protein portion may also have genetic significance, but at the present time we know most about the genetic role of the nucleic acids.

Nucleic acids are of two kinds: **ribonucleic acid** or **RNA,** and **deoxyribonucleic acid** or **DNA.** RNA is found in both nucleus and cytoplasm of cells; DNA is more distinctively characteristic of the nucleus and is found in the chromosomes themselves. Both compounds are alike, consisting of long chains of molecules in which a sugar molecule alternates with a phosphate molecule. To each sugar molecule, a side group (organic base) is attached. The names reflect the difference in the sugar involved: in RNA the sugar is ribose; in DNA it is deoxyribose.

The units of structure composing a macromolecule of DNA are called **nucleotides.** A nucleotide consists of a molecule of sugar (deoxyribose),

40

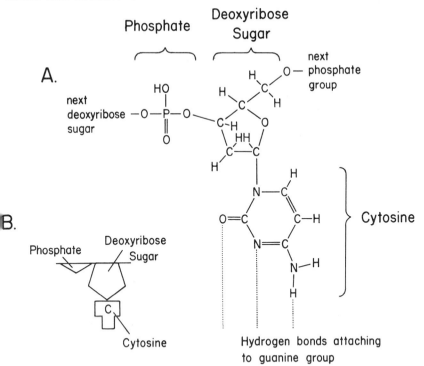

FIG. 4.1   Nucleotide incorporating cytosine as the organic base.   A)
Structural formula of the nucleotide.   B) Stereotyped diagram used
to represent this nucleotide in Figs. 4.2 and 4.4. The other three nucleotides in DNA differ only in the shape of the outline used to represent
the organic base.

a phosphoric acid radical, and an organic base. One such nucleotide is
diagramed in Figure 4.1.

The genetically significant portion of the nucleotide is the organic base.
Four kinds of these are found in DNA: two purines, **adenine** and **guanine**,
and two pyrimidines, **cytosine** (shown in Fig. 4.1) and **thymine.** Thus DNA
is composed of four kinds of nucleotides (distinguished by the four bases)
arranged in a long chain. If current thinking is correct, these nucleotides
are linked in all possible arrangements, and the arrangement constitutes
a code containing genetic information, much as the arrangement of letters
in this sentence conveys information to you. This code is diagramed in
Figure 4.2 A: deoxyribose (a pentose sugar) is represented by a pentagon
and phosphate by a triangle; adenine, guanine, cytosine, and thymine are
represented by stereotyped outlines bearing the initials A, G, C, and T,
respectively. The arrangement of these four as shown is purely arbitrary.

Careful analyses have indicated that the macromolecule of DNA is composed of two such nucleotide chains running parallel to each other and

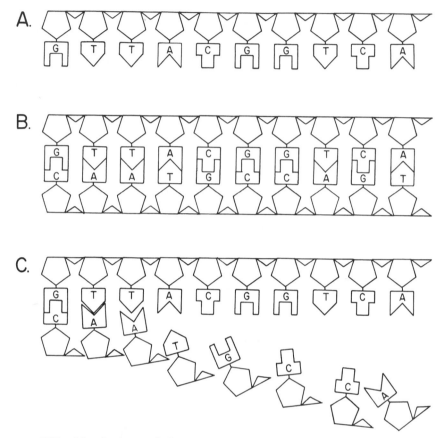

FIG. 4.2 Stereotyped diagram of a portion of the DNA molecule. A) Single strand composed of a chain of nucleotides (Fig. 4.1). B) Double strand composed of two chains of nucleotides joined by their complementary organic bases. C) A single strand duplicating itself by serving as a template or pattern on which nucleotides are assembled in a sequence complementary to the sequence of the template strand itself.

connected by the bases in such a way that adenine is always connected (by hydrogen bonding) to thymine, and guanine is always connected to cytosine. This is diagramed in Figure 4.2 B.

Furthermore, X-ray diffraction studies, which reveal the patterns in which atoms are arranged, suggest that this whole complex is twisted into the form of a helix. The famous Watson-Crick model of DNA structure is shown in Figure 4.3, in which the paired bases are represented as forming the rungs of a ladder.

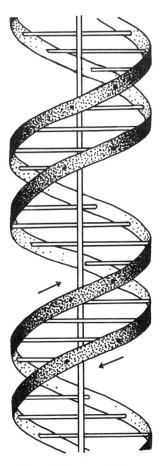

FIG. 4.3 The Watson-Crick model of DNA structure. The sides of the helical "ladder" are composed of sugar-phosphate chains (Fig. 4.2). Each "rung" is formed of two organic bases held together by hydrogen bonds (cf., Fig. 4.2, B). The vertical lines show the axis of the helix. (Redrawn from Watson, J. D., and F. H. C. Crick, 1953. "The structure of DNA," *Cold Spring Harbor Symposia on Quantitative Biology,* **18**:123–31.)

One of the most important functions of a gene is to duplicate itself exactly. We note that the pattern of parallel nucleotide chains is admirably adapted for exact duplication. If the two chains (Fig. 4.2 B) become separated, or single as in A of the figure, each becomes a template or pattern on which the other can be reconstructed from materials present in the nucleus. For example, in Figure 4.2 C we show the upper chain reconstructing a duplicate of the lower one from nucleotides represented as "loose" in the surrounding medium. The original lower chain would serve as a pattern for reconstruction of a new upper one in the same manner. In this way, two identical double chains would arise where only one had existed at first. Since gene, and chromosome, duplication is fundamental to all genetic phenomena, we see here a most important mechanism at work.

The Genetic Code

According to current thinking, it is the arrangement of the four bases, A, C, G, and T (coupled in pairs as indicated in Fig. 4.2), that conveys genetic information. They constitute a sort of four-letter alphabet, engaged in an ultramicroscopic game of anagrams. Take the four-letter word *same*, for example. If we rearrange the letters one way, we get *seam*, a word with an entirely different meaning. Or if we arrange the letters in another way, we have *mesa*, with a still different meaning.

A four-letter alphabet is a small one; is it adequate to the task it must perform? Before we can answer this question we must determine what that task is. It is primarily the control of the processes by which proteins are manufactured in the body. Proteins are all-important in living things. They form indispensible structural components of all cells of all tissues, and they serve as **enzymes,** those organic catalysts without which none of the complex processes of living (metabolism) would occur. Not only are digestion, excretion, respiration, movement, and all other such processes of the body controlled by enzymes, but, most important for genetics, growth and development are, too. In the last analysis, such things as whether a baby has blue eyes or brown eyes are dependent on enzyme systems operating during embryonic development. Consequently the most important, if not the only, function of a gene is to determine the nature of a protein.

What are proteins, and how does one differ from another? They are the most complex chemical substances known. They are composed of building blocks called **amino acids,** usually twenty, which are arranged in all sorts of combinations in long (polypeptide) chains. The nature of a protein, and hence the nature of its enzymatic activity, appears to be determined by the arrangement of these twenty amino acids.

If DNA controls the synthesis of proteins, its four-letter alphabet must be adequate to determine the arrangements of twenty amino acids. Dr. George Gamow, a physicist with wide interests, suggested in 1954 that each amino acid may be designated by a triplet of the four letters (bases). Thus the sequence adenine-adenine-guanine (AAG) in the DNA molecule might designate that the amino acid glutamic acid was to be added to a protein molecule in process of formation. The sequence given here refers to one of the two strands composing the DNA molecule. If at a certain place one strand is AAG, the other strand is necessarily TTC (thymine-thymine-cytosine), for reasons noted above. Although we shall know much more about this in the future, the arrangement of bases in one strand seems to be more important for coding purposes than is the arrangement in the other. At any rate we shall be speaking of only one of the two strands in the following discussion.

Why does the number three seem likely? If each of the four bases, A, C, G, T, represented an amino acid, only four amino acids would be provided for. Similarly, if each amino acid were represented by a pair of four bases, only $4 \times 4 = 16$ amino acids would be provided for. If each amino acid were represented by a triplet, however, more than enough three-letter words for designating twenty amino acids would be available ($4 \times 4 \times 4 = 64$). Perhaps some of the excess combinations form a means of "punctuation" or have functions still to be demonstrated.

Evidence accumulates that some amino acids are coded for by more than one triplet. Thus glutamic acid is represented by AAG, and also by AUG (the U stands for uracil, see below). Ideas in this area are new, tentative, and subject to change. Seemingly, this is a question of synonyms; just as in languages there are shades of difference in the meanings of synonyms, so perhaps there are also subtleties of difference in these seemingly synonymous triplets. Because each amino acid is represented by more than one code word, the genetic code is said to be degenerate.

Another source of confusion is introduced by the fact that the same code may designate more than one amino acid. Thus, CCG is the code for alanine and also for arginine. However, at the present time the actual sequence of letters in a triplet has not been determined in most cases. CCG may also be written GCC or CGC. Perhaps future research will reveal that one arrangement codes for alanine, another for arginine. In a further analogy with language, the context may be a factor in determining which of the two amino acids is designated at any given moment in protein synthesis. When we use the word "top," for example, the hearer judges our meaning by whether we are discussing mountains or children's toys.

Students of the subject disagree as to whether all three letters in the triplet are equally important. Perhaps in many cases two of the three provide the important information. Two code words for glutamic acid were mentioned above: AAG and AUG. Perhaps having one G and one A is important, but having A or U for the third letter is less important.

Uncertainties are to be expected in such an infant field of inquiry, but they will steadily be removed by the researches of investigators. No aspect of genetics is being pursued with more vigor than is the unravelling of the genetic code.

Table 4.1, compiled by Dr. Severo Ochoa of New York University School of Medicine, a leader in research on the genetic code, presents a tentative dictionary of the triplets designating the twenty common amino acids. These triplets may be called code words, or **codons**, to use a term introduced by Dr. F. H. C. Crick of Cambridge University, one of the pioneers in this field. Future research may be expected to establish the exact order of the letters in each triplet, and probably to add more synonyms.

TABLE 4.1   Tentative dictionary of genetic code triplets coding for the twenty common amino acids.

Amino acid	Code triplets
Alanine	CUG, CAG, CCG
Arginine	GUC, GAA, GCC
Asparagine	UAA, CUA, CAA
Aspartic acid	GUA, GCA
Cysteine	*GUU*
Glutamic acid	AUG, AAG
Glutamine	UAC, AAC
Glycine	GUG, GAG, GCG
Histidine	AUC, ACC
Isoleucine	UUA, AAU, CAU
Leucine	UUC, CCU, UGU, UAU
Lysine	AUA, AAA
Methionine	AGU
Phenylalanine	UUU, UCU
Proline	CUC, CAC, CCC
Serine	CUU, ACG, UCC
Threonine	UCA, ACA, CCA
Tryptophan	UGG
Tyrosine	*AUU*, ACU
Valine	UUG

At the time the chart was prepared, the arrangement of letters within a triplet had only been determined in the two italicized cases (cysteine and tyrosine). (From Ochoa, S. 1964, "The chemical basis of heredity—the genetic code," *Experientia*, **20**:57–68.)

This coding has been deciphered largely by research with bacteria and viruses. Only a small beginning has been made in determining the extent to which the code is the same for animals and for man, yet preliminary results indicate that the code may have an element of universality in the sense that the same word may code for the same amino acid in man as in virus. Dr. Nirenberg (1963) has commented: "It nevertheless seems probable that some differences may be found in the future. Since certain amino acids are coded by multiple words, it is not unlikely that one species may use one word and another species a different one."

The Roles of RNA   One feature of Table 4.1 requires explanation. This is the use of the initial U, standing for the organic base uracil. The words in the dictionary apply to RNA (p. 40) rather than to DNA itself. RNA has uracil present wherever thymine would be present in DNA. At times, a strand of DNA serves as a template for the formation of a strand of RNA (instead of another strand of DNA as in Fig. 4.2 C). When this happens, each A in the DNA strand causes a U (not a T) to be inserted into the RNA strand being formed.

To understand the role of RNA we must describe briefly the essentials of the complex process by which the DNA code is translated into a sequence of amino acids in a protein.

The DNA itself is found in the chromosomes in the nucleus. It is possible that each of our 46 chromosomes is one gigantic DNA molecule, although a molecule so large would usually be called a **macromolecule**. The proteins are synthesized outside the nucleus, in the cyptoplasm of the cell. What serves as the go-between, taking orders from the nuclear DNA, passing into the cytoplasm, and there superintending the carrying out of the orders? Evidence indicates that this function is performed by RNA of a type designated as **messenger RNA**. Messenger RNA is synthesized in the nucleus on a pattern or template formed by the DNA (Fig. 4.4).

The messenger RNA then leaves the nucleus, and becomes attached in the cytoplasm to the surface of a small body called a **ribosome.** In this position it, in turn, serves as a pattern or template for the arranging of a sequence of amino acids to form a protein. Each amino acid is brought into correct position by another form of RNA called **transfer RNA** (or soluble RNA). Each transfer RNA molecule may be compared to a tugboat with a barge in tow (the barge being the amino acid molecule). In some way, the transfer RNA molecule towing glutamic acid, for example, recognizes the triplet AAG in the messenger RNA molecule and brings its glutamic acid into position (Fig. 4.4). If, perhaps, the next triplet in the messenger RNA is UUU, a transfer RNA molecule attached to a phenylalanine molecule brings the latter into position so that it can attach to the glutamic acid. And so, step by step, long chains of amino acids are built up. The sequence of the amino acids in the chain is determined by the sequence of nucleotide triplets in the messenger RNA molecule attached to the surface of a ribosome. Hence, it is logical that the dictionary should be made in terms of the RNA words rather than of the DNA words, even though the latter determined the RNA words in the first place. (See Nirenberg, 1963, for a more detailed account of the process we have just summarized.)

The Nature of a Gene How much of a DNA molecule constitutes a gene? Is it three nucleotide pairs? Brilliant research on viruses by Dr. Seymour Benzer of Purdue University suggests that the smallest unit of a DNA molecule that can be exchanged in crossing over (a **recon**) may consist of no more than two nucleotide pairs, and that "the smallest element that,

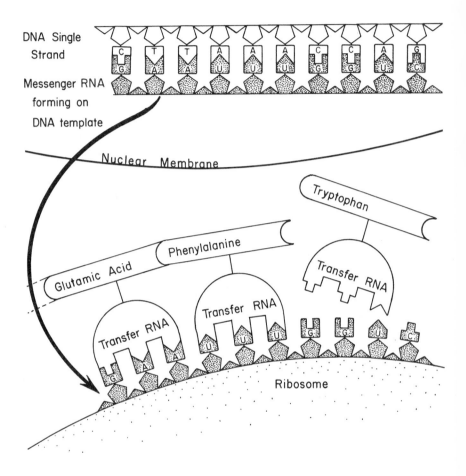

DNA Single
Strand

Messenger RNA
forming on
DNA template

Nuclear Membrane

Tryptophan

Phenylalanine

Glutamic Acid

Transfer RNA

Transfer RNA

Transfer RNA

Ribosome

FIG. 4.4 Highlights of the process by which the DNA code is translated into protein structure.

Upper portion: Synthesis of messenger RNA in the nucleus with DNA as the template. The strand of RNA detaches from the DNA, leaves the nucleus and becomes attached to one or more ribosomes in the cytoplasm.

Lower portion: The messenger RNA attached to a ribosome serves as a template for the assembling of a chain of amino acids. Each transfer RNA molecule "recognizes" the appropriate code word in the messenger RNA. The lining up of the transfer RNA molecules causes the attached amino acids to line up correspondingly. The amino acids become attached together to form a chain that will form part of a protein molecule. Having served its purpose, the transfer RNA becomes detached from the amino acids.

when altered, can give rise to a mutant form of the organism" (a **muton**) may consist of no more than five nucleotide pairs (Benzer, 1957). Is a muton a gene? Probably most investigators would say that it is only part of a gene, that the gene as a functional unit (**cistron**) involves much more than determining the nature of a single amino acid in a protein. In protein structure, amino acids join together to form peptides, which in turn join together to form the protein. Perhaps, as suggested by Strauss (1960), a gene is "that section of the DNA involved in the determination of the amino acid sequence of a single peptide." A gene so defined might involve several or many mutons. In this rapidly developing field, new research results and new interpretations will be current before this book can be published. For present purposes, greatest interest attaches to the fact that detectable genetic effects can arise from very slight changes in the DNA code.

Mutation

When a gene undergoes chemical change so that an altered phenotypic effect is produced, we say that a mutation has occurred. Such changes are called **gene mutations** to distinguish them from changes connected with visible alterations of chromosomes: **chromosomal aberrations** (pp. 246–262).

In terms of DNA structure, how can gene mutations arise? Rearrangement of the nucleotide pairs might have this effect. This would be equivalent in the anagram analogy to a rearrangement of the letters in the word "same" to form "mesa." Or, on the other hand, an actual change in a nucleotide pair might occur, analogous to the "a" in "mesa" being converted into, or exchanged for, another "s," thereby converting "mesa" to "mess."

For example, the sequence GUG (p. 46) might determine that a certain amino acid would be present in a protein (enzyme). If a change occurred in the third nucleotide pair, giving GUU, a different amino acid might be present, perhaps altering the enzymatic activity of the protein. If the enzyme were an important link in the chain of enzyme activity in a developing embryo, the result of this single change might be a considerable phenotypic effect.

If we had space for it, a wealth of illustrative material might be presented at this point. We shall content ourselves with a single example of a genetic change (mutation) that results in changing a single amino acid in a protein, with phenotypic effect. This example is particularly pertinent, for it concerns a human characteristic of considerable significance in itself, as we shall see later.

Red blood cells contain a protein called **hemoglobin**, important in the transportation of oxygen. Most of us have a normal hemoglobin, designated as **Hb A**, and our red blood cells remain circular in outline even when deprived of oxygen. The red blood cells of some people, however, change their outlines markedly when deprived of oxygen. This change of shape (Fig. 4.5) is called "sickling." Most people who have this "sickle trait" suffer few or no unfavorable effects from it, but occasionally sickling is accompanied by severe symptoms characterized as **sickle-cell anemia**. The life expectancy of people stricken with this anemia is low. Genetic

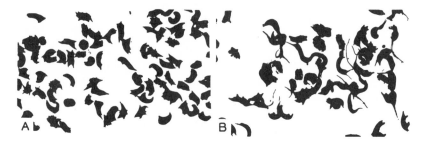

FIG. 4.5   Red blood cells exhibiting the phenomenon of sickling. A. Cells of a heterozygote showing the sickle trait. B. Cells of a homozygote (sickle-cell anemia patient). (Reprinted from *Human Heredity* by J. V. Neel and W. J. Schull by permission of The University of Chicago Press. Copyright 1954 by The University of Chicago.)

analyses have shown that sufferers from sickle-cell anemia are homozygous for a gene for which possessors of the simple sickle-cell trait are heterozygous (Neel, 1949, 1951). The genetic situation may be represented as follows:

$$Hb^A = \text{gene for production of normal hemoglobin}$$
$$Hb^S = \text{gene for production of sickling hemoglobin}$$

Genotype of normal individuals $= Hb^A\, Hb^A$
Genotype of individuals showing sickle trait $= Hb^A\, Hb^S$
Genotype of individuals having sickle-cell anemia $= Hb^S\, Hb^S$

The genetic designation implies that there are two types of hemoglobin, normal (**Hb A**) and abnormal (**Hb S**). Indeed, the two types have been identified. They differ in certain properties, including the electrical charge carried by the molecules. In an electrical field, dissolved normal **Hb A** will move toward the negative pole, whereas **Hb S** will move toward the positive pole (Pauling *et al.*, 1949). As shown in Figure 4.6 a, the hemoglobin of normal people is **Hb A** and moves toward the negative pole (to the left of the vertical arrow), whereas the hemoglobin of sufferers from sickle-cell anemia is **Hb S** and moves toward the positive pole (to the right of the vertical arrow). However, people who show the sickle-cell trait have both types of hemoglobin (Fig. 4.6 c). Evidently, then, both genes in an $Hb^A\, Hb^S$ individual produce their respective phenotypic effects. Thus we cannot say that one gene is dominant to the other. Such genes are said to be **codominant**.

Biochemists went to work to see whether they could find chemical differences between the two kinds of hemoglobin. Ingram (1956, 1958, 1963) digested the hemoglobin with trypsin, thereby separating the protein into its twenty-eight constituent peptides. He then analyzed (by electrophoresis and chromatography) the amino acid constitution of each of

(a) Normal   (b) Sickle-Cell Anemia   (c) Sickle-Cell Trait

FIG. 4.6 Movement of normal hemoglobin (**Hb A**) and of sickle-cell hemoglobin (**Hb S**) in an electrical field. (a) **Hb A** moves toward the negative pole (to the left of the vertical arrow). (b) **Hb S** moves toward the positive pole. (c) Heterozygotes, Hb^A Hb^S, possess both types of hemoglobin. (Redrawn from Pauling, L., H. A. Itano, S. J. Singer, and I. C. Wells, 1949. "Sickle cell anemia, a molecular disease," *Science,* **110**:543–48.)

these peptides. He found that twenty-seven of the peptides in **Hb A** and **Hb S** were exactly alike, but that in one peptide a difference appeared. What was the basis of this difference?

Intensive study of the peptide in which **Hb A** differed from **Hb S** showed that in one position in the chain of amino acids composing this peptide there is a substitution of amino acids in **Hb S**. In **Hb A**, the sequence of amino acids is: Valine-Histidine-Leucine-Threonine-Proline-*Glutamic acid*-Glutamic acid-Lysine. In **Hb S**, the sequence is: Valine-Histidine-Leucine-Threonine-Proline-*Valine*-Glutamic acid-Lysine. Thus in **Hb S** in position 6 of the eight-unit sequence, valine is substituted for the glutamic acid that occupies that position in normal hemoglobin. Here, then, we have a detectable genetic difference (and an important one) that depends on change of a single amino acid. As Ingram (1958) stated: "A change of one amino acid in nearly 300 is certainly a very small change indeed, and yet this slight alteration can be fatal to the unfortunate possessor of the errant hemoglobin."

Presumably, this difference in constitution arose in the first place as a mutation in the gene controlling the formation of the hemoglobin molecule, or of the constituent peptide concerned. This mutation may have arisen as an alteration of the nucleotide triplet controlling the amino acid present in position 6 of the peptide under discussion. Table 4.1 contains two RNA code words for glutamic acid: AUG and AAG. The code word for valine is UUG. Hence the change from glutamic acid to valine in position 6 may have arisen as a change from AUG to UUG. Thus, a change in a single nucleotide in a DNA (and hence messenger RNA) molecule may result in a change in protein structure that has important phenotypic effects.

We may reasonably conclude that when Hb^A mutated to become the gene Hb^S, it did so by some such small change in the DNA molecule. A different change in the molecule resulted in a second type of mutant gene, Hb^C. This gene produces an abnormal hemoglobin called hemoglobin C, **Hb C.** It differs from **Hb A** (and **Hb S**) by having the amino acid lysine in the sixth position of the peptide we are discussing. One of the code words for lysine is AUA (Table 4.1). Hence the change from glutamic acid to lysine may have arisen as a code change from AUG to AUA, again substitution of a single nucleotide.

This is an appropriate place to note that the three genes Hb^A, Hb^S, and Hb^C constitute a series of **multiple alleles.** Alleles are genes that, alternatively, occupy the same position on a chromosome; they are each other's opposite number, so to speak. In Mendel's experiments (pp. 10–15), for example, we say that the gene Y is the allele of the gene y, and vice versa. At a certain location on a certain chromosome either Y or y may be found. Here we have a pair of alleles. A greater number of genes may be the alleles of each other—three in the present example. Multiple alleles commonly arise because a gene may mutate in several directions. Thus, at times, gene Hb^A mutates to Hb^S, with the result that valine is substituted for glutamic acid at one point in the hemoglobin molecule. At other times, gene Hb^A mutates to Hb^C, with the result that lysine is substituted for glutamic acid at the point in question. (Of course, there is no theoretical reason why one mutant gene may not mutate to form another mutant one, e.g., Hb^S to Hb^C: in this case, also, the result is a series of multiple alleles.)

In Chapter 9 we shall discuss multiple alleles more fully, particularly in connection with human blood groups. At present, we cannot give a better human example of the molecular basis of multiple allelism than that afforded by these three abnormal hemoglobins. The significance of these abnormal hemoglobins as they occur in human populations will be discussed later (pp. 272–273).

PROBLEMS

1. Using Table 4.1, translate the following sequence of RNA nucleotides into a sequence of amino acids forming part of a polypeptide chain:
C-U-G-U-U-U-U-G-G-A-U-A-G-U-G-G-U-U-G-U-C-A-G-U

2. The sequence of nucleotides given in No. 1 is a portion of a messenger RNA molecule. Write the sequence of nucleotides for the portion of a DNA molecule that served as a pattern or template for the formation of this messenger RNA.

3. A certain protein contains the following sequence of amino acids: isolucine-serine-arginine-glutamic acid-serine-proline-valine-glutamic acid. Using Table 4.1, write the sequence of RNA triplets that would code for this sequence of amino acids. Then write the sequence of DNA triplets that would code for the formation of the RNA.

4. Two normal parents produce a child suffering from sickle-cell anemia. What is the chance that their next child will also have this anemia?

REFERENCES

Benzer, S., 1957. "The elementary units of heredity." In W. D. McElroy and B. Glass (eds.). *A Symposium on the Chemical Basis of Heredity*. Baltimore: The Johns Hopkins Press. Pp. 70–93.

Gamow, G., 1954. "Possible relation between deoxyribonucleic acid and protein structures," *Nature*, **173**:318.

Ingram, V. M., 1956. "A specific chemical difference between the globins of normal human and sickle-cell anaemia haemoglobin," *Nature*, **178**:792–94.

Ingram, V. M., 1958. "How do genes act?" *Scientific American*, **198**:68–76.

Ingram, V. M., 1963. *The Hemoglobins in Genetics and Evolution*. New York: Columbia University Press.

McElroy, W. D., and B. Glass (eds.), 1957. *A Symposium on the Chemical Basis of Heredity*. Baltimore: The Johns Hopkins Press.

Neel, J. V., 1949. "The inheritance of sickle cell anemia," *Science*, **110**:64–66.

Neel, J. V., 1951. "The inheritance of the sickling phenomenon, with particular reference to sickle cell disease," *Blood*, **6**:389–412.

Nirenberg, M. W., 1963. "The genetic code: II," *Scientific American*, **208**:80–94.

Ochoa, S., 1964. "The chemical basis of heredity—the genetic code," *Experientia*, **20**:57–68; reprinted in *Bulletin of the New York Academy of Medicine*, 2nd series, **40**:387–413.

Pauling, L., H. A. Itano, S. J. Singer, and I. C. Wells, 1949. "Sickle cell anemia, a molecular disease," *Science*, **110**:543–48.

Sager, R., and F. J. Ryan, 1961. *Cell Heredity*. New York: John Wiley & Sons, Inc.

Strauss, B. S., 1960. *An Outline of Chemical Genetics*. Philadelphia: W. B. Saunders Company.

Sutton, H. E., 1961. *Genes, Enzymes, and Inherited Diseases*. New York: Holt, Rinehart and Winston.

Watson, J. D., and F. H. C. Crick, 1953. "The structure of DNA," *Cold Spring Harbor Symposia on Quantitative Biology*, **18**:123–31.

5.

MENDELIAN THINKING
APPLIED TO HUMAN FAMILIES

In Chapter 2 we discussed the fundamentals of thinking employed by Mendel and his successors in drawing conclusions from experimental data. We saw that obtaining a 3:1 (or a 1:2:1) ratio among F_2 offspring can be taken as evidence of single gene-pair inheritance if we assume the following: (1) Individual organisms possess genes in pairs. (2) In the production of germ cells, members of a pair of genes separate from each other so that each germ cell receives only one member of the pair. (3) A heterozygote produces two kinds of germ cells (for each gene pair) in equal numbers. (4) The laws of probability operate when the two kinds of sperm (or pollen grains) fertilize the two kinds of ova.

This interpretation arose from a need to explain data obtained in experiments with plants and animals. We must now transfer the interpretation to man himself.

Let us look at some of the ways in which human genetics necessarily differs from the genetics of lower organisms. In the first place, the geneticist cannot arrange the matings of the persons he is studying. It is a great advantage to be able to cross yellow peas with green peas, or black guinea pigs with white guinea pigs, at will. Unable to do the equivalent of this, the human geneticist always works "with one hand tied behind his back." He must be thankful for whatever the matrimonial whims of people provide in the way of "crosses."

Second, there is no such thing in human reproduction as an F_2 generation, as this term was employed in Chapter 2, and as it appears, for example, in Figure 2.1 (p. 16). In the experiments represented by this figure, homozygous black guinea pigs were mated to homozygous white ones. From the matings, F_1 males and females were produced and were mated among themselves (brother-sister matings) to produce the F_2 generation. Although brother-sister marriage has been practiced under exceptional conditions (e.g., the Pharaohs of an ancient Egyptian dynasty), it is not a social institution on which the modern human geneticist can rely for data.

What is the closest human approximation to an F_2 generation? We recall that the parents of an F_2 generation are both heterozygous. Therefore, when two individuals heterozygous for the same gene pair (e.g., both *Bb*) marry each other, we have the genetic equivalent of an $F_1 \times F_1$ mating, even though the wife is not the sister of her husband. The advantage of brother-sister matings lies in the certainty that each is indeed heterozygous for the same gene pair. When husband and wife are not brother and sister, an element of uncertainty is introduced; the genes under study may not in fact be identical even though phenotypic effects may be the same. There is more than one gene for albinism in man, for example. We shall see other examples of similar phenotypes caused by dissimilar genotypes. The element of uncertainty, however, is not so serious as to make impossible the obtaining of valuable data. Following Mendelian thinking, we should expect the children in such families to approximate a 3:1 ratio if the families are large (at least a score of children, preferably a hundred or more!).

That last statement points up another handicap for the human geneticist. In point of fact, human families are small. Families (at least those born to one wife) that a geneticist would consider large are practically nonexistent. Geneticists can overcome this handicap by pooling data—by finding just as many families as possible in which both parents seem to be heterozygous for the gene pair under study and then adding together all the children. Pooling data from many families does present some pitfalls, however. For example, not all individuals who seem to be heterozygous for the same gene pair are so in fact. This is a real problem of genetic identification, and it undoubtedly has produced errors.

We can now return to the question discussed in Chapter 2, but this time we will phrase it in terms of human genetics. *How can we determine whether or not a pair of alternative characteristics depends on the action of a single pair of alternative genes (alleles)?* There are several answers to this question, but the one of immediate interest at this point parallels Mendel's thinking: If a single pair of alleles is involved, pooled data of children in families in which both parents are of the presumed heterozygous type should approximate a 3:1 ratio (1:2:1 ratio if dominance is lacking).

An example will be helpful at this point. Blood types form a genetically simple example, although the phenotypes cannot be seen (like the color of cotyledons or hair) but can be discovered only by serological means.

The M-N Blood Types

The genetics of human blood groups and types receives much attention for many reasons. Human differences in blood type are important in clinical medicine (in blood transfusion and in the causation of erythroblastosis as a result of Rh-incompatibility of the parents, to mention two of the best-known instances). Of even more interest to the geneticist is the fact that the relationship between these genes and their products can be traced more readily than can the relationships between many other genes and their products. The products in the case of these genes are complex chemical compounds called **antigens**. Many typical antigens are proteins. As we saw in Chapter 4, the nature of proteins may be modified by altering the amino acids present, and the arrangement of amino acids, in turn, may depend on the sequence of nucleotide pairs in the DNA molecule. Here the road to be traversed between gene and product is a relatively short one.

An antigen is a substance that, under suitable circumstances, will induce the formation of **antibodies**, and then will react with these antibodies if brought into contact with them (in a test tube, for example). The antigens we are concerned with here are complex substances in (or more probably on the surface of) red blood cells (erythrocytes). The most widely known of these antigens are those designated A, B, and Rh; they will be discussed later (pp. 126–157). Two other antigens called M and N, were discovered by Landsteiner and Levine in 1927. They found that an individual's red blood cells may contain one or both of these antigens. If, for example, a suspension of red blood cells containing M is inoculated into a rabbit, it will form antibodies against the foreign cells. The antibodies are found in the serum (fluid portion) of the rabbit's blood. When some of the serum from this rabbit (called an **antiserum** because it contains antibodies) is mixed with human red blood cells containing antigen M, these cells will clump or agglutinate. An antigen such as M that causes the formation of antibodies which induce agglutination is called an **agglutinogen.** The antibodies formed by stimulus of an agglutinogen are called **agglutinins.**

In a similar manner, red blood cells containing agglutinogen N will cause a rabbit to form anti-N agglutinins. This serum is used to test for the presence of antigen N in unknown red blood cells, just as the serum from a rabbit inoculated with red blood cells containing agglutinogen M is used to test for the presence of antigen M. Using these two serums, a serologist can determine the blood type to which any individual belongs, on the basis of whether that individual's red cells react with (1) anti-M serum only, (2) anti-N serum only, or (3) both anti-M and anti-N serums. On this basis, as shown in Table 5.1, people may be divided into three categories or blood types: M, N, and MN.

Table 5.1 M-N blood types—Reactions of cells with antiserums.

If red blood cells contain—	Reaction with antiserums		Blood type of the donor of the cells
	Anti-M	Anti-N	
M only	+	—	M
M and N	+	+	MN
N only	—	+	N

$+$ = agglutination of the cells occurs.
$-$ = agglutination of the cells does not occur.

With this much serological background, let us inquire into the genetic basis of these blood types. Landsteiner and Levine advanced the hypothesis that antigens M and N depend on a single pair of alleles (and that, of course, is the reason we chose to use the example here). Following custom, we may designate the gene that results in M being present as L^M; the gene that results in N being present as L^N. If the hypothesis is correct, therefore, the genotypes are as follows: type M people are homozygous $L^M L^M$; type N people are homozygous $L^N L^N$; type MN people are heterozygous $L^M L^N$. Genes L^M and L^N are said to be codominant. If gene L^M is present, agglutinogen M is produced whether or not gene L^N is also present. Similarly, agglutinogen N is produced whenever gene L^N is present.

This hypothesis was tested in various ways, some of which we shall refer to later. At this time we are interested in studying the human equivalent of an F_2 generation. *If the hypothesis is correct, children in families of which both parents belong to type MN should approximate a 1:2:1 ratio.*

	Mother		Father
Genotype	$L^M L^N$		$L^M L^N$

Germ cells
$$\left\{ \begin{array}{c} L^M \to L^M \\ \searrow \nearrow \\ \nearrow \searrow \\ L^N \to L^N \end{array} \right\}$$

Children's genotypes	$L^M L^M$	$L^M L^N$	$L^M L^N$	$L^N L^N$
Phenotypes	M	MN		N
Ratio	1 :	2	:	1
Percentages	25	50		25

At the outset, Landsteiner and Levine (1928) had data from only 11 families having both parents of type MN. The children in these families were as follows: Type M = 17; Type MN = 31; Type N = 7.

Taken by itself, this would hardly suggest a 1:2:1 ratio. However, these data, plus those concerning children from other parental combinations (e.g., MN × N; MN × M; M × N, and so on), encouraged Landsteiner and Levine to conclude that they had support for their hypothesis.

As the years passed, many investigators in various countries accumulated additional data. By 1953, Wiener and his colleagues were able to amass information concerning 377 MN × MN matings (see Wiener and Wexler, 1958). The children of these matings were as follows:

Blood types	M	MN	N
Number	199	405	196
Percentages	24.7	50.8	24.5

We can see that this is indeed a close approximation to the ideal 1:2:1 ratio. Again we must emphasize that a close approximation to the Mendelian ratios is to be expected only when the numbers of offspring are large.

So far, we have discussed MN × MN matings because they directly parallel Mendel's experiments. Landsteiner and Levine, and their successors, also analyzed children from other parental combinations (see table on p. 43 of Wiener and Wexler, 1958). If single gene-pair inheritance is involved, other criteria, in addition to the one stressed above, should indicate it. Thus when both parents are of type M (L^M L^M × L^M L^M), all of the children should be of type M. When both parents are of type N all children should be of type N. When one parent is type M and the other type MN, half the children should be type M and half type MN.

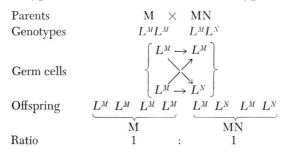

In plants and lower animals, this mating would be referred to as a back cross; see p. 17. In such families no type N children are to be expected. Similarly, in families in which one parent is of type N, the other of type MN, no type M children are to be expected.

Do the cumulative data indicate any exceptions to the expectations stated? The data recorded in the literature contain results for thousands of individuals; among them only six exceptions to the rules have been found. Why should there be any exceptions at all?

In the first place, there is always the possibility of human error in the serological tests. The testing procedures are somewhat complicated, and error is not impossible, particularly in testing for antigen N. Still, the tests were performed by experts, and the recent tests are not likely to be in error.

Another possibility is that a rare mutation was encountered in some particular case. For example, suppose that two type MM parents have a type MN child. What was the source of the gene L^N in the child? Perhaps during meiosis in one of the parents, one of the normally occurring L^M genes underwent chemical alteration, causing it to mutate to L^N. (Until we know more about the chemical difference between antigen M and antigen N we cannot say for sure, but such an alteration of the genes might conceivably involve only one or two nucleotide pairs in the DNA molecule.) Mutations are relatively rare events, but they do occur.

Finally we come to the explanation favored by the human geneticists engaged in this particular study. There is always the possibility, even the probability, that a small proportion of the children studied in any investigation are not the biological offspring of one or both of the parents. When adoption and illegitimacy are kept secret, as they frequently are, they introduce sources of error into the calculations of a geneticist. However, when allowance is made for them, conclusions can then be drawn.

Investigations of MN blood types are a fine example of the type of thinking involved in determining the mode of inheritance of human characteristics. On page 55 we set up this criterion: If a single pair of alleles is involved, pooled data of children in families in which both parents are of the presumed heterozygous type should approximate a 3:1 ratio (or a 1:2:1 ratio, if dominance is lacking). The MN blood types have one great advantage in enabling us to meet this criterion: the presumed heterozygous type ($L^M L^N$) can be clearly identified by serological tests. Consequently, when we say we have an MN × MN mating, we are sure that we do have one. The basis of this advantage is the fact that one allele is not dominant to the other. However, in a great many cases in which we are interested, one allele is dominant to the other.

Dominance and the Problem of Ascertainment

Dominance complicates the problem. Letting A and a represent a pair of alleles, we say that from pooled $Aa \times Aa$ matings we expect a 3:1 ratio (our criterion for single gene-pair inheritance). Now when one of the genes is dominant, how are we going to distinguish Aa individuals from

AA individuals? They may be just alike in phenotype. If so, how can we distinguish *Aa* × *Aa* matings from *AA* × *AA* matings, or from *Aa* × *AA* matings? In fact, there may be no way of doing so by examining the phenotypes of the parents. In many cases the only way to distinguish an *Aa* × *Aa* mating from the other two is by means of what in domestic animals is called a progeny test. *Aa* × *Aa* matings can produce *aa* children; the other two matings cannot. If a marriage between two people, both of whom possess the dominant phenotype, results in at least one child showing the recessive phenotype, we know that both parents are heterozygous (that it is in fact an *Aa* × *Aa* mating).

In such families, what ratio of dominant-phenotype to recessive-phenotype children can be expected? We must not be too quick to answer: 3:1. We can expect a 3:1 ratio in pooled data only when we have complete information about *Aa* × *Aa* matings among the people in the study. In the case of M-N blood types, we can identify all MN × MN matings regardless of the type of the children produced (or indeed of whether there are any children at all). Now, on the other hand, when we study genes that show dominance, such as our hypothetical *A* and *a*, we count only matings that have produced at least one *aa* child. We leave out all *Aa* × *Aa* matings in which all the children are *AA* or *Aa*. Thus we do not have an unbiased sample of all *Aa* × *Aa* matings; we have a truncate distribution. We must therefore rephrase our question: if inheritance is based on a single pair of alleles, what proportion of A-phenotype to *a*-phenotype children can be expected in *Aa* × *Aa* matings identified by having produced at least one *a*-phenotype child?

We can attack the problem most directly by asking: What proportion of *Aa* × *Aa* matings do in fact produce *no aa* children? Because the answer depends on the size of the sibship (number of children in the family), we inquire first: What proportion of one-child sibships will be expected to contain no *aa* child?

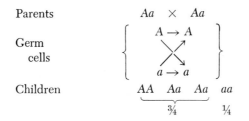

Parents   *Aa* × *Aa*

Germ cells

Children   *AA*   *Aa*   *Aa*   *aa*

For each child produced, the chance that he or she will show the dominant phenotype is 3/4; we therefore expect that in three fourths of the one-child sibships the one child will show that dominant phenotype. In other words, three fourths of one-child sibships (of *Aa* × *Aa* matings) will contain no *aa* child.

What proportion of two-child sibships will be expected to contain no

aa child? The chance that the older child will show the dominant phenotype is 3/4; the chance that the younger child will show the dominant
phenotype is also 3/4. Hence the chance that both will show the dominant
phenotype is $3/4 \times 3/4 = (3/4)^2 = 9/16$. In other words, 9/16 of two-
child sibships of *Aa* × *Aa* matings will contain no *aa* child.

Application of the Binomial Formula   What is the total expectation
with regard to two-child sibships born to *Aa* × *Aa* matings?

Let c = chances for one dominant-phenotype child = ¾
d = chances for one recessive-phenotype child = ¼°

Then expectation concerning a two-child family can be expressed by
squaring the binomial $(c + d)$ as follows:

$$(c + d)^2 = c^2 + 2cd + d^2$$

In this expansion:

c^2 = sibship of two dominant-phenotype children
$2cd$ = sibship of one dominant-phenotype and one recessive-
phenotype child.
The coefficient 2 indicates that the sibship can arise in
two ways: (1) the older child with dominant phenotype,
the younger child with recessive, or (2) the older child
with recessive phenotype, the younger child with dominant.
d^2 = sibship of two recessive-phenotype children.

Substituting the values of c and d, we obtain:

$c^2 = (¾)^2 = 9/16$ (two dominant-phenotype children)
$2cd = 2 \times ¾ \times ¼ = 6/16$ (one dominant, one recessive)
$d^2 = (¼)^2 = 1/16$ (two recessive-phenotype children)

Similarly, the proportion of three-child sibships expected to contain no
aa child can be found by raising the binomial $(c + d)$ to the third power:

$$(c + d)^3 = c^3 + 3c^2d + 3cd^2 + d^3$$

Here we have all possible kinds of sibships of three:

c^3 = all three children with dominant phenotype = $(¾)^3 = 27/64$
$3c^2d$ = two dominant-phenotype children and one recessive-
phenotype child = $3 \times (¾)^2 \times ¼ = 3 \times 9/16 \times ¼ = 27/64$†
And so on.

°The initials p and q are traditionally used here, but in this book p and q will always refer to gene frequencies in the Hardy-Weinberg formula.
†The coefficient 3 indicates that this sibship may arise in three ways (note that the
one *aa* child may be the oldest child, or the middle child, or the youngest child).

To find the proportion of four-child sibships that will be expected to contain no *aa* child, we raise $(c + d)$ to the fourth power:

$$(c \times d)^4 = c^4 + 4c^3d + 6c^2d^2 + 4cd^3 + d^4$$

In view of our discussion in Chapter 2 we may note especially the term $4c^3d$: three dominant-phenotype children and one recessive-phenotype child, the "perfect fit" in a family of four to the 3:1 ratio (see p. 21). In Chapter 2 we calculated this expectation; now we note that the binomial expansion states the same expectation: $4 \times (\frac{3}{4})^3 \times \frac{1}{4} = {}^{108}\!/_{256}$ or about $\frac{2}{5}$. The binomial expansion has two advantages: it is simple to calculate, and it makes a complete statement about expectations concerning all the possibilities in families of a given size.

The proportion of sibships of four that will contain no *aa* child is shown by the term c^4: $(\frac{3}{4})^4 = {}^{81}\!/_{256}$.

Now we are able to generalize a little concerning the proportion of sibships expected to contain no *aa* child.

$$
\begin{aligned}
&\text{1-child sibships, } c \ = \tfrac{3}{4} \\
&\text{2-child sibships, } c^2 = {}^{9}\!/_{16} \\
&\text{3-child sibships, } c^3 = {}^{27}\!/_{64} \\
&\text{4-child sibships, } c^4 = {}^{81}\!/_{256}
\end{aligned}
$$

In general, then, the proportion of sibships expected to contain no *aa* child is c^n, where n is the size of the sibship.

What we are really interested in is the proportion of $Aa \times Aa$ matings that are expected to produce at least one *aa* child. This is all $Aa \times Aa$ matings minus those that produce no *aa* child. Since c^n is a fraction, we can represent the total of $Aa \times Aa$ matings as 1 or unity. Then the proportion of matings expected to produce at least one *aa* child is $1 - c^n$. Notice how this works out in the case of the two-child sibships. Disregarding the $\frac{9}{16}$ of such sibships expected to consist of two dominant-phenotype children, we note that $\frac{6}{16}$ are expected to have one dominant-phenotype and one recessive-phenotype child, $\frac{1}{16}$ to have two recessive-phenotype children. Hence $\frac{6}{16} + \frac{1}{16} = \frac{7}{16}$ of the sibships will be expected to have at least one *aa* child. Note that $1 - c^n = 1 - (\frac{3}{4})^2 = 1 - \frac{9}{16} = \frac{7}{16}$ gives this value directly and easily.

Now we may return to the question: In $Aa \times Aa$ matings identified by producing at least one *aa* child, what proportion of the children will be expected to have the *aa* phenotype? If we had information concerning all $Aa \times Aa$ matings (regardless of children produced), this fraction would be $\frac{1}{4}$, or d. We may use the symbol d' to represent the fraction of recessive-phenotype children expected in sibships from $Aa \times Aa$ matings identified by having at least one such child.

If we knew of all $Aa \times Aa$ matings, d' would equal d (or $d/1$), but we can learn of only $(1 - c^n)$ of these matings.

Hence

$$d' = \frac{d}{1 - c^n} \tag{1}$$

For example, we apply this formula to a sibship of 4:

$$d' = \frac{d}{1 - c^n} = \frac{\frac{1}{4}}{1 - (\frac{3}{4})^4} = \frac{\frac{1}{4}}{1 - \frac{81}{256}} = \frac{\frac{1}{4}}{\frac{175}{256}} = \frac{1}{4} \times \frac{256}{175} =$$

$$\frac{64}{175} = 0.366 = 36.6\%$$

Thus, in sibships of four from $Aa \times Aa$ matings identified because they produced at least one aa child, 36.6 percent of the children will be expected to be aa (show the recessive phenotype). If we could include $Aa \times Aa$ matings that produced no aa children, 25 percent would be expected to be aa. The observed value, d', is always greater than d because of the fact that the dominant-phenotype children in sibships consisting only of such children cannot be counted in computing the ratio of dominant-phenotype to recessive-phenotype children in the pooled data. As a result, families that have more aa children than expected are not offset by families having more AA or Aa children than expected when these families have no aa children at all. Hence, in the observable families, the proportion of recessive-phenotype children to dominant-phenotype ones will be higher than it would be if knowledge of all $Aa \times Aa$ matings could be included.

Albinism   An example will help to make this clear. One of the human variants that have been recognized from time immemorial is **albinism**, complete lack of dark pigment (melanin) in skin, hair, and eyes (Fig. 5.1). Results of many investigations have indicated that the gene concerned is usually recessive. If A stands for the gene for normal pigmentation and a for the gene for albinism, albinos will have the genotype aa, and people of normal pigmentation will be either homozygous AA or heterozygous Aa. Most albino children are born to normally pigmented parents. When two normally pigmented parents produce an albino child, we know at once that the mating is $Aa \times Aa$.

Unlike the MN blood type situation, identifying Aa people (carriers of albinism) is not possible at present; only when an albino child is born can parents be identified as carriers. Tests, probably of a chemical nature, may be developed eventually to make identification possible. *Suppose* we had a chemical test now, and could identify *all $Aa \times Aa$ matings* in a given community or region.

For the sake of simplicity, let us suppose that all the sibships consist of four children, and that we learn of 256 such sibships. How many of the

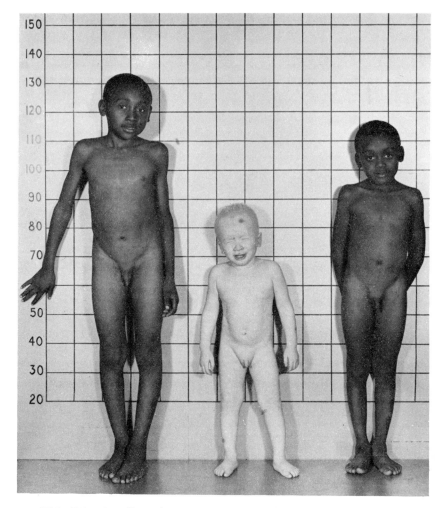

FIG. 5.1 An albino boy, 26 months of age, and his normally-pig-mented brothers. The albino brother probablv closed his eyes because the photographer's bright lights hurt them. Recall that albino eyes lack pigment. (Courtesy of Dr. Victor A. McKusick.)

256 would be expected to have no albino children, one albino child, two albino children, three albino children, four albino children? We can answer this question by raising the binomial $(c + d)$ to the fourth power

$$(c + d)^4 = c^4 + 4c^3d + 6c^2d^2 + 4cd^3 + d^4$$
$$= (\tfrac{3}{4})^4 + 4(\tfrac{3}{4})^3 \tfrac{1}{4} + 6(\tfrac{3}{4})^2(\tfrac{1}{4})^2 + 4(\tfrac{3}{4})(\tfrac{1}{4})^3 + (\tfrac{1}{4})^4$$

$$= \frac{81}{256} + \frac{108}{256} + \frac{54}{256} + \frac{12}{256} + \frac{1}{256}$$

The resulting expectations for 256 sibships of four children each can be tabulated as follows:

Children per sibship

Normal	Albino	No. of sibships	Total No. of children	Normal children	Albino children
4	0	81	324	324	0
3	1	108	432	324	108
2	2	54	216	108	108
1	3	12	48	12	36
0	4	1	4	0	4
		256	1024	768	256

$$3:1$$
$$\therefore \text{ albinos} = 25\%$$

This model presents an ideal situation, closely realized in the study of MN blood types. Actually, we cannot attain such complete data about albinism until we have some means of detecting heterozygotes (carriers) other than by production of albino children. Without such a test we must omit the first line of the table: families that have *no* albino children. Our data, then, would be as follows:

Children per sibship

Normal	Albino	No. of sibships	Total No. of children	Normal children	Albino children
3	1	108	432	324	108
2	2	54	216	108	108
1	3	12	48	12	36
0	4	1	4	0	4
		175	700	444	256

$$1.73:1$$
$$\therefore \text{ albinos} = 36.6\%$$

The only difference between the two tables is that the total number of normal sibs has been reduced by 324, whereas the number of albino sibs has not changed at all. As a result, the albinos now constitute 36.6 percent (instead of 25) of the total number of sibs. We recall that 36.6 percent was the percentage we obtained when we applied formula (1) to families of four (p. 63). Thus whether we use the formula or the model, we reach the conclusion that single gene-pair inheritance of albinism would be indicated by finding that 36.6 percent of the children in four-child sibships born to normal parents are albinos, when the sibships have been identified in the first place by having at least one albino child.

This percentage applies specifically to sibships of four. As indicated previously, the expected percentage varies with the size of the family and can be calculated by using formula (1). Values of d' for families of varying size are given in Table 5.2. Note that as the size of the sibship increases, the expected proportion of recessive-phenotype children approaches more and more closely to 25 percent. Thus, with sibships of twelve, only a fraction of a percentage more than 25 percent of the children is expected to consist of children having the recessive phenotype. This close approach to the ideal percentage reflects the fact that few $Aa \times Aa$ matings that produce twelve children will go undetected. The chance is very small that no one of the twelve children will be aa.

In the third column of Table 5.2, percentages are translated into the number of aa children expected per sibship. In Chapter 6 we shall see how these expectations are utilized in deciding whether or not actual data indicate that a conclusion of recessive inheritance is warranted (pp. 83–84)

TABLE 5.2. Expected occurrence of recessive-phenotype children in sibships identified by having at least one child with the recessive phenotype, *a priori* method.

Size of sibship n	Percentage of children expected to show recessive phenotype d'	No. of recessive-phenotype children expected per sibship $d' \cdot n$
1	100.00	1.000
2	57.14	1.143
3	43.24	1.297
4	36.57	1.463
5	32.78	1.639
6	30.41	1.825
7	28.85	2.020
8	27.78	2.222
9	27.03	2.433
10	26.49	2.649
11	26.10	2.871
12	25.82	3.098

This method of correcting pooled data is commonly called the **a priori method** because it starts with the assumption that if we had complete information concerning all relevant families, a 3:1 ratio would be approximated. To recapitulate, it is a way of compensating for the fact that when families of two heterozygous parents are identified only by virtue of having at least one child with the presumed recessive trait, *more* than one fourth of the children will be expected to show the recessive trait[*]

Why Actual Populations May Differ from Models   We should not leave this subject without noting that the correction of data given by formula

[*] Readers interested in further elaboration of the *a priori* method are referred to Stern, 1960 (Chap. 9); Li, 1961 (Chap. 5); Steinberg, 1959; Neel and Schull, 1954 (Chap. 14), and to the original paper by Bernstein, 1929.

1), or by our model, is not a perfect method applicable to all cases. As many students of the subject have emphasized, the efficacy of the method depends on obtaining the data in "correct" proportions. We can illustrate this from our model. We note that in the model, 108 of the 175 sibships are expected to have one albino child only, 54 are expected to have two albino children, 12 are expected to have three, 1 is expected to have four. Suppose that the proportions of the different types actually differ markedly from this. We can readily see that the results will be affected.

Why should the proportions observed differ markedly from the expected ones? To answer this we must bring up the subject of **ascertainment**, a thorn in the side of the human geneticist. There would be no problem if it were equally likely that a sibship having only one albino child, a sibship having two albino children, a sibship having three albino children, and a sibship having four would come to the attention of an investigator— "be ascertained." Such an equal chance of ascertainment could be realized if a complete canvass could be made (complete ascertainment). However, in most studies some method of sampling is employed. This may consist of asking people if they know of families in which there are albino children, or, in the case of pathological traits, it may consist of a study of medical records. In any method of sampling there is always the question of whether the sample is a true representation of the larger population. Is a sibship having only one albino child as likely to be brought to an investigator's attention as is a family in which all four sibs are albinos? Probably not. Some theorists postulate a mathematical regularity here: a sibship of four affected children is four times as likely to be ascertained as is a sibship in which only one of the four children is affected. At this point, all sorts of complications may enter the picture. Some inherited defects cause children to die young; in such cases, a sibship in which four children were affected is more likely to have at least one affected child still living at the time of an investigation than is a sibship in which only one child was affected (Roberts, 1963). We are touching here on a large and complicated problem; mathematical methods are available for correcting for bias in, or incompleteness of, ascertainment (see references listed on p. 71).

The Sibs of Propositi: Simple Sib Method

Although there are various means of ascertainment, the commonest is by looking for affected individuals (single ascertainment, Li, 1961). An investigator learns about a family by being told of an albino child or in a survey of school-children he may see an albino child and thus learn about the family of which the child is a member. An affected individual who attracts the investigator's attention to the family is called a **propositus** or **proband**. In our frame of reference, discovering a propositus is the way in which an investigator learns of the existence of a certain $Aa \times Aa$ mating.

In the preceding section, we applied a correction to pooled data to compensate for the fact that only $Aa \times Aa$ matings having a propositus could be included in the study. Another, and simpler, method of compensating for this fact is by counting the sibs of each propositus, omitting the propositus himself. Let us see how this would work in the case of sibships of four (p. 65). These observable families are of four kinds: (a) 1 albino, 3 normal; (b) 2 albino, 2 normal; (c) 3 albino, 1 normal; (d) 4 albino, 0 normal. Now let us regard one of the albino children in each family as a propositus. The four types can then be classified as follows:

(a) [1 albino propositus]; 3 normal sibs, 0 albino sibs.
(b) [1 albino propositus]; 2 normal sibs, 1 albino sib.
(c) [1 albino propositus]; 1 normal sib, 2 albino sibs.
(d) [1 albino propositus]; 0 normal sibs, 3 albino sibs.

Among the sibs, then, we have all possible combinations of three, from three normals only, to three albinos only. It is as if we had started out to study families of three in the first place and could in some way include sibships having only three normal children. We are able to do so because the one albino propositus has identified for us the fact that the mating is $Aa \times Aa$; that is the only purpose he serves in our computations this time. Among the other three children in each sibship, all possible combinations can occur, and among them single gene-pair inheritance should reveal itself by the occurrence of an approximation to a 3:1 ratio.

One other point should be mentioned in applying this sib method of correcting pooled data. When there are, for example, two albino children in a family, each one is regarded as a propositus in turn. Such a family may in fact be ascertained twice. One albino child may be in the fifth grade at school, the other in the eighth. When the investigator studies the fifth grade, he sees one child and so learns of the family. If he also studies the eighth grade, he sees the other child and learns of the family again. One child is just as much a propositus as is the other child, so in computations each is used as a propositus. This has the effect of counting one family twice (or three times if there are three albino children).

Perhaps we can visualize it as follows. Suppose the albino children are Mary and John, and the normally pigmented ones are Ted and Susan. Mary tells the investigator that among her brothers and sisters there are 1 albino (John) and 2 normals (Ted and Susan). John, in his turn, tells the investigator that among his brothers and sisters there are 1 albino (Mary)and 2 normals (Ted and Susan). So the investigator tabulates the sibs of the propositi as follows:

	normal	albino
(1)	2	1
(2)	2	1

Let us see how this method can be applied to the model we set up earlier (p. 65). We may reorganize the data in the table as follows:

Children per sibship: Albino Normal	No. of sibships	Total no. of children: Albino Normal	In each sibship:	Sibs of propositi: Albino Normal
1 3	108	108 324	1 propositus with 3 normal sibs (× 108)	0 324
2 2	54	108 108	2 propositi, each with 1 albino and 2 normal sibs (× 54)	108 216
3 1	12	36 12	3 propositi, each with 2 albino and 1 normal sibs (× 12)	72 36
4 0	1	4 0	4 propositi, each with 3 albino sibs (× 1)	12 0
	175	256 444		192 576

Thus we see that among the sibs of the propositi the 3:1 ratio is exhibited (576 normal : 192 albino), even though the total number of children including propositi (444 normal : 256 albino) does not demonstrate this ratio. We must not be confused by the fact that the total number of sibs of propositi (192 + 576 = 768) is greater than the total number of individual children (444 + 256 = 700). This situation arises because families having two albino children are counted twice; those having three albinos are counted three times, and so on (each albino child is regarded as a propositus).

In the ideal model of families of four children exhibiting single gene-pair inheritance, the underlying 3:1 ratio is laid bare by the simple sib method of correcting pooled data. Of course, actual data do not give exact 3:1 ratios with the precision revealed by our model, but the principle is the same.

This method of correcting pooled data, like the *a priori* method discussed earlier, has its sources of error. For example, it will only work well if complete information can be obtained about each sibship; sometimes this is difficult to achieve. Both methods will serve as examples of means by which human geneticists strive to overcome the handicap of being unable to carry out breeding experiments as do geneticists working with plants and lower animals. Despite this handicap, Mendelian thinking can be applied to human families, and reasonably secure conclusions concerning modes of inheritance can be drawn.

PROBLEMS

1. What blood types will the children belong to when the father is type M and the mother is type N? When the father is type MN, the mother type N?

2. The ability to taste phenylthiocarbamide (PTC) depends on a dominant gene, T, inability to taste the substance on its recessive allele, t. Persons with genotypes TT or Tt are called tasters, persons with the genotype tt, nontasters.

   (a) If a $Tt \times Tt$ mating results in four children, what is the chance that all four will be tasters? That all four will be nontasters? That three will be tasters, one a nontaster? That two will be tasters, two nontasters?

   (b) If a $Tt \times tt$ mating results in four children, what is the chance that all four will be tasters? That all four will be nontasters? That three will be tasters, one a nontaster? That two will be tasters, two nontasters?

   (c) If a $Tt \times tt$ mating results in eight children what is the chance that all eight will be tasters? That seven will be tasters and one a nontaster? That four will be tasters and four nontasters?

3. What proportion of sibships of six born to $Tt \times Tt$ matings (Question No. 2) will be expected to include no nontaster children? What proportion will be expected to include at least one nontaster child?

4. Let us imagine a trait called "forked eyelashes" and suppose that we wish to determine whether or not the trait depends on a recessive gene. We learn of 156 families that have at least one child with forked eyelashes. For simplicity, let us suppose that these are all families of five children each. Thus we learn of a total of 780 children; how many of them would you expect to have forked eyelashes if the trait is indeed recessive? (Work this without using Table 5.2, but check the correctness of your answer with that table.)

5. An investigator studying a certain trait learned of the following families:

   (a) 4 families of 2 children each, with 1 affected child in each family.

   (b) 8 families of 3 children each, with 1 affected child in each family.

   (c) 2 families of 3 children each, with 2 affected children in each family.

   (d) 1 family of 6 children, 3 of whom were affected.

   Use the simple sib method of correcting pooled data to determine whether or not these findings give evidence that the trait is inherited on the basis of a recessive autosomal gene. What is your conclusion, and why?

REFERENCES

Bernstein, F., 1929. "Variations– und Erblichkeitsstatistik." In E. Baur and M. Hartmann (eds.). *Handbuch der Vererbungswissenschaft,* Lieferung 8 (1, C), Bd. 1, pp. 1–96. Berlin: Gebrüder Borntraeger.

Landsteiner, K., and P. Levine, 1928. "On the inheritance of agglutinogens of human blood demonstrable by immune agglutinins," *Journal of Experimental Medicine,* 48:731–49.

Li, C. C., 1961. *Human Genetics.* New York: McGraw-Hill Book Company, Inc.

Neel, J. V., and W. J. Schull, 1954. *Human Heredity.* Chicago: The University of Chicago Press.

Roberts, J. A. F., 1963. *An Introduction to Medical Genetics,* 3rd. ed. London: Oxford University Press.

Steinberg, A. G., 1959. "Methodology in human genetics," *Journal of Medical Education,* 34:315–34.

Stern, C., 1960. *Principles of Human Genetics,* 2nd. ed. San Francisco: W. H. Freeman & Company.

Wiener, A. S., and I. B. Wexler, 1958. *Heredity of the Human Blood Groups.* New York: Grune & Stratton Inc.

6.

STUDYING HUMAN PEDIGREES

Tracing the inheritance of a trait through generations of an ancestral line is a time-honored method of studying human genetics. Such a line is called a family tree, or more properly, a family pedigree. The construction of family trees was based on early genealogical records, which were kept for reasons very different from genetic ones. However, the observation that certain physical traits reappeared from time to time within a family aroused interest, and this interest marked the beginnings of the study of human genetics.

In the preceding chapter we considered methods of analyzing pooled data so that we could draw as direct a parallel as possible with the Mendelian method of experimentation and formulation of conclusions. Now we will turn to an older and, until recently, a more widely used method of attempting to ascertain the mode of inheritance of human traits. How does the study of family pedigrees enable us to decide whether a trait is dominant or recessive in inheritance?

Dominant Inheritance

If a characteristic depends on a dominant gene, how will this fact manifest itself in a pedigree?

As a first approximation, we may make this statement: *A trait determined by a dominant gene will not appear in an offspring unless it also appears in one or both parents.* If the offspring shows the dominant phenotype A, his genotype must be AA or Aa. Therefore, he must have received

an *A* from at least one parent, and that parent (being *AA* or *Aa*) will show
the trait, too. This fact is sometimes stated by saying that a dominant trait
never "skips."

Figure 6.1 is an abbreviated version of a very large pedigree chart of a
kindred (a family in the larger and continuing sense) in which Huntington's chorea has been inherited for at least six generations. **Huntington's
chorea** is a mental disorder in which mental deterioration is accompanied
by uncontrollable, involuntary muscular movements. At the present time,
it is always fatal.

Figure 6.1 follows certain generally accepted conventions of genetic
chart-making. Circles represent females; squares represent males. Solid or
shaded squares and circles represent individuals who show the trait in

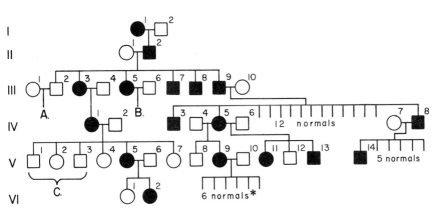

FIG. 6.1   Inheritance of Huntington's chorea. Black squares and
circles represent males and females, respectively, who had the disease.
A. This couple had 9 children and 53 grandchildren, all normal.   B.
This couple had 11 children, 3 with Huntington's chorea. These three
married but did not pass on the trait, although they had families of 6,
8, and 8 children, respectively.   C. These three married, and produced
a total of 19 children, all normal.

* It is possible that some members were young at the time of investigation, and that symptoms may have developed later in life. (Abbreviated
from a pedigree chart prepared by the Eugenics Survey of Vermont.)

question. A horizontal line connecting a circle to a square represents a
marriage, and a vertical line extending downward from the horizontal
one connects to the child or children produced by that marriage. If there
are several children, the vertical line ends in another horizontal one, from
which the squares and circles representing the children dangle like apples
from a branch. The generations are numbered at the left with Roman
numerals, and each individual in a generation is designated by an Arabic
numeral. Thus every individual can be referred to without the use of

names. For example, the earliest known ancestral couple shown in Figure 6.1 was I-1 and I-2.

I-1 was a woman in whom Huntington's chorea developed. Her husband, I-2, did not have the disorder. They had one son, II-2, who showed the trait. He married a woman, II-1, who did not. They, in turn, had 6 children: a boy, III-2, who did not have the trait, and 2 daughters and 3 sons who did (III-3; III-5; III-7; III-8; III-9).

Let us consider III-2, for he and his normal wife, III-1, illustrate a most important corollary of the general statement we have made about dominant inheritance. *If the trait depends on a dominant gene, a marriage of two people who do not show the trait will produce only normal descendants,* barring the rare occurrence of a new mutation. If we let H represent the gene for Huntington's chorea, and h the gene for normality, then III-1 and III-2 must have had the genotypes $hh \times hh$. In that case, all descendants would be hh, too, unless the gene H were brought in by marriage from "outside the family." As Figure 6.1 shows, III-1 and III-2 had 9 children, all normal, and these in turn married and produced 53 grandchildren, all normal. In no case did two normal parents produce a child who later had Huntington's chorea.

In contrast to the descendants of III-2, consider those of his sister III-3. She married a normal man and they had one daughter, IV-1 in whom the trait developed. She married and produced a family of 6, only one of whom, V-5 became choreic. V-5 married and produced 2 daughters, one of whom (VI-2) developed the disorder. In this line we have six generations of Huntington's chorea, extending without a skip from I-1 to VI-2. Note again that the normal individuals of V generation who married (V-1, V-2, V-3) had only normal children.

Huntington's chorea thus satisfies the criterion of never skipping, which is indicative of dominant inheritance. Many pedigrees have been published giving the same results; the fact that Huntington's chorea depends on a dominant gene may be regarded as well established. Unlike some other types of mental disorder, little if any environmental influence is involved. The trait will develop in persons who have the gene (if they live long enough), regardless of good or bad environment.

Another expectation for simple dominant-gene inheritance is satisfied by the data in Figure 6.1. *The trait shows up with about equal frequency in males and in females.*

However, the pedigree chart does not show the ratio of affected to normal children that we might expect. We note that in no case did an affected individual marry another affected individual; all had normal spouses. (This is almost invariably the case when a dominant gene is rare—as that for Huntington's chorea fortunately is, outside of certain families). Thus the matings were $Hh \times hh$. In such families, we should expect affected (Hh) and normal (hh) children in equal numbers—the

1:1 ratio. However, inspection of Figure 6.1 shows that the number of offspring, from *Hh* × *hh* matings, classified as normal far exceeds the number of affected offspring. For example, the family of 15 born to III-9 and III-10 included only 3 choreics. And III-5 × III-6 produced 11 children, of whom 3 were affected; these three married and produced a total of 22 children, all classified as normal.

How can we explain this discrepancy between expectation and actuality? In the first place, Huntington's chorea has one complicating aspect: although people may develop the symptoms at any age, they normally do not do so until at least middle age (the average age of onset is in the 40's). This means, then, that an investigator often cannot accurately classify children and young people. Hence, too many young people are likely to be classified as normal.

Similarly, the family of III-9 × III-10, for example, lived about four generations ago, a long time in terms of human memory and of the history of medicine. It seems possible that some of the 12 children classified as normal may have died young (of childhood diseases, tuberculosis, cancer) before they were likely to have manifested choreic symptoms. Therefore, some people may have been classified as normal when in fact they had the *Hh* genotype and would have become choreic had they lived long enough.

This is a complication that arises when a hereditary trait has a late onset. Fortunately, many traits are detectable at birth or soon after. In such cases, the children of *Aa* × *aa* matings usually approximate the expected 1:1 ratio very closely (when data from several or many such matings are pooled, of course).

Steinberg (1959) cited an example that is applicable here. The trait is called **retinoblastoma,** a cancer of the retina of the eye in children, and it is quickly fatal unless the affected eye is removed. If the eye is removed in time, the child may live to adulthood, marry, and have children of his own. Much evidence indicates that retinoblastoma depends on a dominant gene. If we represent the gene by *R* and the normal allele by *r*, then persons who have retinoblastoma have the genotype *Rr*. If they survive the disease and marry a normal mate, we have an example of an *Rr* × *rr* mating. (In theory, of course, a person with retinoblastoma could also be homozygous, *RR*. But an *RR* genotype could only arise if two persons who survived retinoblastoma married each other. To date, there is no record of such a marriage.)

Reese (1954) gathered data concerning 15 families, in each of which one parent had survived retinoblastoma. Figure 6.2 presents two of the pedigrees studied by Reese (1954). Note that there is no skipping.

The numerical results of the data assembled by Reese were analyzed by Steinberg (1959). In the 15 families there were 30 children, 23 affected and 7 not affected. One of the families was discovered by accident, but the

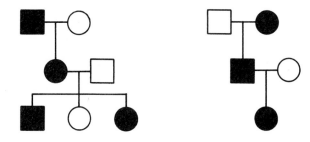

FIG. 6.2 Two pedigrees of inheritance of retinoblastoma. Black squares and circles represent males and females, respectively, in whom retinoblastoma developed. (Redrawn from Reese, A. B., 1954 (December). "Frequency of retinoblastoma in the progeny of parents who have survived the disease," *Archives of Ophthalmology*, **52**:815–18.)

other 14 were discovered because an affected child had been brought for treatment. Such a child, we recall, is designated as a propositus (p. 68). We have here an example of the sort of biased ascertainment that we discussed in Chapter 5; we do not have proper representation of families in which there are no affected children. Interestingly, the sibship discovered by accident consisted of 3 unaffected children. Steinberg applied the sib method of correction. He stated: "It is clear that no family selected via an affected child can have fewer than one affected child. Hence, families of one child each will have 100 percent of the children affected when only 50 percent were expected." Subtracting the 14 propositi from the 23 affected children leaves 9 affected. The ratio of 9 affected to 7 unaffected is as close to 8:8 as we can expect when numbers are so small. The evidence is that survivors of retinoblastoma married to normal mates produced affected and normal children in a 1:1 ratio as expected.

In summary, the following are the hallmarks of dominant, autosomal inheritance. (1) Children do not show the trait unless at least one parent does. As a corollary, the trait never develops in the descendants of two normal parents unless a new mutation occurs or unless the gene is introduced from an outside source by marriage. (2) The trait appears with equal frequency in males and females. (3) If the trait is rare, most, if not all, persons who have it will be heterozygotes. (4) When such heterozygotes marry unaffected mates, half the children, on the average, can be expected to show the trait and half can be expected not to do so.

Mention should also be made of another hallmark of a *completely* dominant gene: homozygotes for the gene (*AA*) have the same phenotype as do heterozygotes (*Aa*). The emphasis here is on the word "completely." In fact, in plants and experimental animals all degrees of dominance are found. Sometimes homozygotes seem to be exactly like heterozygotes. Sometimes heterozygotes differ from homozygotes—slightly or more distinctly. If the difference is great enough, we say that dominance is lacking (as in Blue Andalusian fowls, p. 19).

In the case of man, we can apply this criterion only with dominant genes that are common. People who belong to blood group A, for example, may be homozygous or heterozygous (I^AI^A or I^AI^O, p. 131). Ordinary testing serums do not distinguish between the red blood cells of homozygotes and heterozygotes. Therefore, we may say that I^A is completely dominant to I^O. In the future, however, more refined testing methods may enable us to distinguish between the two. When that becomes possible, we shall no longer regard I^A as completely dominant to I^O. This illustrates the point that the distinction between dominant and recessive genes is somewhat arbitrary and varies with the ability to distinguish homozygotes from heterozygotes.

Because most of the dominant genes studied in man are rare, the criterion of homozygotes being indistinguishable from heterozygotes cannot be applied. This is because all, or almost all, persons showing the dominant trait are heterozygotes. As noted in the case of retinoblastoma (p. 75), homozygotes can occur only when heterozygotes marry each other (e.g., $Aa \times Aa$). When such a mating occurs, only one fourth of the children, on the average, are expected to be homozygous AA; the small size of human families adds to the unlikelihood of actually finding AA individuals. Thus, many dominant genes are known only from their effects in heterozygotes. Because we do not know what the phenotype of homozygotes would be, in these cases we have no evidence as to whether or not the gene is completely dominant as defined above.

There are some reasons for suspecting that where harmful genes are concerned symptoms are more severe in homozygotes than in heterozygotes. For example, the first dominant gene identified in man was that for **brachydactyly**. The phenotype consists of markedly shortened fingers. In one form (sometimes called brachyphalangy or minor brachydactyly), only the index finger is shortened. In an extensive study of this trait, Mohr and Wriedt (1919) demonstrated the dominant inheritance of this gene. In one instance, a brachydactylous man married his first cousin, who was probably also brachydactylous although the investigators could not be certain of this (dependence on old photographs and people's memories frequently leaves one in doubt in such studies). At any rate, her father had been brachydactylous; if she also was, this was a $Bb \times Bb$ mating. The couple had two daughters; one was brachydactylous, the other was a cripple, lacking fingers and toes, who died at one year of age. She may have been homozygous (BB) although we cannot be sure. However, whether she was or not, proved cases of homozygotes for rare dominant genes are virtually nonexistent.

Partial Penetrance   Let us return to the first criterion, that of a dominant trait not skipping. Suppose that we collected information about a certain trait, inherited in a kindred for several generations, and then constructed a pedigree chart resembling Figure 6.1. In this study a child usually does not show the trait unless one parent does, but suppose there are occasional exceptions. What conclusion should we draw? Although in most respects the criteria for a dominant gene are satisfied, must we conclude because of these exceptions that the gene is not dominant at all? How can we account for these exceptions?

We mentioned previously three possible reasons for exceptions: adoption, illegitimacy, and the occurrence of new mutations. However, mutation of any one gene is a rare event. Let us suppose that the exceptions in our pedigree are numerous enough so that the explanation that each one represents a new mutation is extremely unlikely.

After ruling out mutation, adoption, or illegitimacy as an explanation, we are left with the fact that, at times a gene does not produce its usual phenotypic effect. Gene A usually results in phenotype A, but sometimes the phenotype fails to appear although gene A is present. We then say that gene A has incomplete or **partial penetrance.** When a dominant gene is completely penetrant, every possessor of the gene shows the trait. The gene for Huntington's chorea seems to be completely penetrant, or very nearly so; the symptoms develop in every possessor of the gene, if he lives long enough. In contrast, the gene for retinoblastoma is calculated to have about 90 percent penetrance (Neel and Schull, 1954); malignant tumors of the retina develop in about 90 percent of the children who have the gene.

Why is it that a dominant gene does not always produce the effect it usually does? A phenotype is the result of complicated processes conditioned by both heredity and environment. In environment we include all the factors that may impinge on an embryo during its development from ovum to birth. At times, environmental factors may override genetic factors, rendering impossible the usual outcome of a genetic endowment. Undoubtedly tumors of the retina have requirements in addition to the mere presence of gene R. Perhaps when tumors do not develop in possessors of gene R, the failure (a happy one) is due to lack of some essential constituent for tumor formation, or to the development of some inhibitor to tumor formation. Future research will undoubtedly yield much more information than we have at present on this point.

We have mentioned absence of essential constituents and presence of inhibitors as examples of environmental factors that can modify the action of genes. In fact, however, so inextricably are heredity and environment interwoven that essential constituents and inhibitors may themselves be under genetic control. Here we are referring again to what are usually called modifying genes (p. 176). The phenotype is the result of the action of all genes present (plus environmental factors); no gene operates all by itself. If a gene is to produce its usual effect, complicated systems of enzymes must operate during development. Some of these enzymes are under the control of other genes. Hence, changes in these other genes may lead to failure of the main gene to produce its usual phenotype.

For example, let us examine the genes for color in mice. Mice possess the alleles *B* and *b*. Normally, mice having gene *B* are black, and homozygotes for gene *b* are brown. The pigment (melanin) in both black and brown mice is produced from amino acids (especially tyrosine) by a long chain of reactions, and each link in the chain is controlled by an enzyme. An essential link in the chain is the conversion of tyrosine to an intermediate product "on the way toward" melanin. The enzyme tyrosinase is necessary for this conversion; it is under the control of a gene designated as *C* (Silvers, 1961). In the absence of *C* (i.e., in *cc* individuals), no pigment is produced, and therefore the gene *B* or *b* can have no effect at all. Thus the absence of gene *C* reduces the penetrance of *B* (or *b*) to zero.

Modifying genes are so common that probably we should always find them if our investigation were intensive enough. To return to the subject of Huntington's chorea, there is evidence that modifying genes control the age of onset of the symptoms (Neel and Schull, 1954). It seems to be genetically determined in some families that the symptoms shall appear in early life, whereas the genes present in other families determine that the symptoms shall appear later in life. In this case, we are not dealing with lack of penetrance although we might use our imaginations to picture how an apparent lack of penetrance might arise from the situation. Suppose that in the modifying genes in a certain kindred there should be a change (a mutation, perhaps), causing the symptoms to appear in possessors of the mutation only after age 90. In that kindred we should then have examples of people with the *Hh* genotype who married, had children, and died of heart disease or cancer *before* they reached the age of 90 and developed choreic symptoms. However, if some of their children became choreic, we should have an example of apparent skipping, in other words, an apparent lack of penetrance. Although this example is imaginary, it is entirely in line with known genetic principles.

We shall have occasion to refer to partial penetrance from time to time in subsequent discussions. Its existence complicates the work of the human geneticist. How much simpler it would be if a certain genotype produced its corresponding phenotype in all the individuals possessing it.

Variable Expressivity   To parallel the last statement: How much simpler if a certain genotype always produced the *same* phenotype. As a matter of fact, even when the gene does produce a detectable effect, the expression of the gene may vary. (Of course, if the gene does not express itself at all, we have lack of penetrance.) Thus a gene may produce somewhat different effects in one individual than a gene of the same kind produces in another individual.

An apparent example is afforded by the study of Lutman and Neel (1945) on juvenile cataract of the eyes. When cataracts develop, the crystalline lens of the eye gradually becomes more and more opaque, with

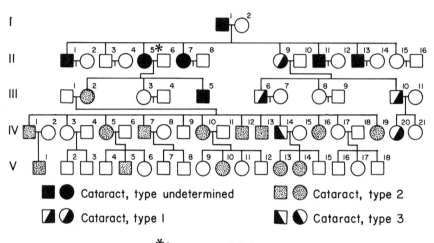

FIG. 6.3 Variable expressivity in inherited cataract. (Based on a chart in Lutman, F. C., and J. V. Neel, 1945 (May). "Inherited cataract in the B. genealogy," *Archives of Ophthalmology,* 33:341–57.)

the result that vision is progressively impaired. Removal of the cloudy lens restores vision. We usually think of cataracts as an accompaniment of old age, but occasionally cataracts develop in the eyes of young children. Figure 6.3 represents a portion of a large kindred of this kind studied by Lutman and Neel. The presence of juvenile cataract seems to be determined by a dominant gene. Analysis of the entire pedigree (of which Fig. 6.3 is only a portion) shows that the trait never skips: no child has cataracts unless one of the parents has. There were 24 marriages in which one parent was cataractous. As no two cataractous persons married each other, all persons with cataract must have been heterozygotes. Hence, if we represent the gene for the trait by C, their marriages were $Cc \times cc$ matings. From such matings we expect a 1:1 ratio. The 24 marriages produced 79 children. The nature of 2 of these was undeterminable, but of the remaining 77, 34 were normal and 43 cataractous. This agrees fairly well with the expectation, which would be 38:39. Of the 43 affected individuals, 23 were males, 20 females.

When an ophthalmologist examines a cataract, the opacity is seen to be caused by more-or-less densely packed white flakes and granules, which form a pattern. The patterns may differ greatly from individual to individual.* Despite the diversity of these patterns, Lutman and Neel were able to classify the cataracts into three types. In type 1 the opacities were flakelike and fenestrated (like tiny irregular doughnuts) and were concentrated toward the front of the lens. As you will see from Figure 6.3, this type was confined to II-9 and her descendants. Type 2, characterized by solider flakes massed in the center of the lens, was more common; it was possessed by III-2 and most of her numerous cataractous descendants. Yet one of her sons was the only individual investigated who had a type 3 cataract. In him the opacity was feather-like and fibrous, rather than flakelike as in the other two types. Nevertheless his cataractous daughters (V-13 and 14) displayed the more usual type 2.

What caused the variability? Probably we should look for the cause in modifying genes. It seems likely that II-9 and her descendants were characterized by certain modifiers of the main gene, III-2 and her descendants by different modifiers. The authors pointed out that the simplest explanation would be that II-9 had a dominant modifying gene (by mutation?) not present in her brothers and sisters. If we represent this gene by M, then she and her cataractous descendants would have the genotype $CcMm$ (whereas III-2 and her cataractous descendants, lacking M, would be $Ccmm$).

There is, of course, the additional possibility of the influence of environmental factors operating during embryonic development. Perhaps such factors might account for the strange case of IV-14, who differed so markedly from his mother, sibs, and daughters. However, further conclusions on this point must await additional research.

A recent extensive investigation of patients with Huntington's chorea has emphasized the great diversity of symptoms displayed by different individuals (Oepen, 1961). Actually such variable expressivity should not surprise us. Without fear of contradiction we can state that individual differences will be found in any trait whatsoever if that trait is analyzed intensively enough. We have stated that the phenotype depends on the sum-total of genes present (plus environmental factors), all interacting together. No two human individuals (with the possible exception of identical twins) are exactly alike in all genes (let alone in environmental factors). Therefore, we should expect variations in pheno-

*The original paper contains excellent drawings of these varied patterns.

type to be the rule, even among individuals who share certain main genes.

Because of the complexity of genetic and environmental interaction, the genes whose actions are most favorable for study are those separated from their phenotypic effects by the shortest possible route, as Penrose (1959) has emphasized. Best of all are the instances in which we can demonstrate that a gene determines the nature of a given enzyme. Nevertheless, many of the human traits that are of great interest to us are so complex that the gene-to-enzyme relationships are not yet known. We may expect future research to reveal them but in the meantime we must draw what conclusions we can from the data available to us.

Recessive Inheritance

To a large extent as we study human pedigrees, we identify recessive traits by virtue of the fact that they do *not* follow the rules that we have laid down for dominant traits. Dominant traits do not skip (children do not show the trait unless a parent did); recessive traits commonly skip (although they may not do so).

Figure 6.4 presents a pedigree of the inheritance of albinism based on a study by Pearson, Nettleship, and Usher (1911-1913.) Generation II was the first one about which the authors obtained definite information. In this generation, we find a family consisting of two normally pigmented brothers (II-2 and II-4) and their albino sister (II-3). Evidently, then, if neither parent (I-1 and I-2) was an albino, both must have been heterozygous ($Aa \times Aa$). Both brothers married, and each marriage started a line of descent in which no albinos appeared until the fifth generation. A great-granddaughter (V-1) of II-2 was an albino, and three of the great-grandchildren of II-4 were also albinos. This is a fine example of skipping generations. Moreover, if the families had not known that there was an albino great-aunt, the appearance of albino children would have been a complete surprise, for there was no indication that the gene was in the family. Because not only two, but three, four, or more generations may be skipped, albino children often are born to parents who had no idea that they or their relatives and ancestors possessed the gene.

As far as the records indicated, none of the fathers (IV-2, IV-6, IV-8) of the fifth-generation albino children were related to each other or to their wives. Thus it was probably coincidence that these three women (IV-1, IV-5, IV-7), carriers of albinism, happened to marry men who were also heterozygous. The chances are small that a person who does not marry a relative will happen to marry a carrier of the gene for albinism, and the chance that it will happen three times in one generation of one kindred is, of course, much smaller.

If, on the other hand, a person marries a relative (e.g., a first cousin), the chances that he will be marrying a carrier for albinism (or for any other recessive gene he may have) are considerably increased. In many kindreds in which homozygotes for rare recessive traits appear, the amount of consanguinity is greater than it is in the population at large. This increase of consanguinity as a hallmark of a recessive gene was recognized long ago by the British geneticist Bateson and has been re-emphasized by Penrose (1959). It will be discussed further in Chapter 8.

Another way in which pedigrees showing recessive inheritance usually differ from those showing dominant inheritance is in the smaller number of affected individuals. Commonly, homozygous recessives are the children of two heterozygotes. In Figure 6.4, the matings of IV-1 × IV-2, IV-5 × IV-6, and IV-7 × IV-8 were surely of this kind, and the mating of

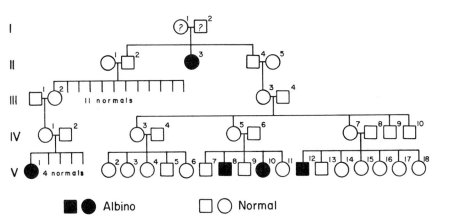

FIG. 6.4 Inheritance of albinism. (Based on a chart in Pearson, K., E. Nettleship, and C. H. Usher, 1911–1913. "A monograph on albinism in man," *Drapers' Company Research Memoirs, Biometric Series,* **6, 8, 9.** London: Dulau & Company Ltd. Used by permission of Galton Laboratory, University College, London.)

I-1 × I-2 probably was, also. From the four matings, the numbers of normal and of albino children are, respectively, 4 + 1; 3 + 2; 6 + 1; 2 + 1. Thus, among 20 children, 5 are albinos. How many albino children would be expected in these four families which were selected because they had at least one albino child?

Here we may make use of the *a priori* method of correcting pooled data (p. 63).We note that the four families may be classified as follows: one family of 3 children, two families of 5 children, one family of 7 children. How many children in each family would be expected to be albinos? The expected number varies with size of the family and is obtained by multiplying d' by n (where n is the number of children in the family). The values of $d' \cdot n$ are given in Table 5.2 (p. 66). We may organize the material as follows.:

Size of Sibship	No. of Sibships	$d' \cdot n$	$d' \cdot n \cdot$ No. of Sibships
3	1	1.297	$1.297 \times 1 = 1.297$
5	2	1.639	$1.639 \times 2 = 3.278$
7	1	2.020	$2.020 \times 1 = 2.020$
		Total number of albino children expected	$= \overline{6.595}$

Thus, in the four families selected, we should expect 6 or 7 sibs to be albinos. The number actually observed, 5, is below expectation but not far below, considering the small number of children involved.

Another criterion of a recessive trait is that when two persons showing the phenotype marry each other (e.g., $aa \times aa$) all their children will show this phenotype. Thus, if two people belonging to blood group O marry each other ($I^o I^o \times I^o I^o$), all the children are found to belong to group O, also. Albinos seldom marry each other but when they do, all the children are usually albinos. Thus Snyder and David (1957) showed a pedigree in which two albino parents had a family of three: two albino boys and one albino girl.

Occasionally, however, two albino parents will have normally pigmented children. When adoption and illegitimacy are ruled out, how can this result be explained? In general, partial penetrance applies to recessive traits as it does to dominant ones. However, in this instance we can be a little more specific in analyzing the situation. We noted earlier (p. 79) that albino mice lack the enzyme tyrosinase, which in pigmented individuals acts on the amino acid tyrosine, a precursor of melanin (the pigment itself): no tyrosinase, no pigment. We also noted that albino mice are homozygous for a recessive gene (cc). Do human albinos also lack tyrosinase? Witkop, Van Scott, and Jacoby (1961) took hair bulbs from the skin of albinos and incubated them in a solution of tyrosine. Hair bulbs from most albinos produced melanin, showing that they have the necessary tyrosinase to act on the tyrosine. However, hair bulbs from some albinos did not produce melanin, which seems to indicate that tyrosinase is absent (as it is in albino mice and in the hair bulbs of normally gray human hair). These findings suggest that there are at least two kinds of albinos: those who lack tyrosinase (they all have tyrosine itself) and those who have some other deficiency in the melanin-producing mechanism. (Witkop *et al.* suggested the possibility of some deficiency in the mechanism by which tyrosine enters the pigment-forming cells from the blood.) These studies are illustrative of the recent methods of genetic research and point up the fact, observable in other cases, too, that a given phenotype is not always the result of the same genotype. If two persons who are albinos for different reasons marry each other, the deficiency of the wife's pigment-forming mechanism may be compensated for by the husband's genetic endowment, and vice versa. As a result, the children may be normally pigmented.

As frequently happens, analogous situations are found in experimental plants and animals. In sweet peas, for example, the pigment in colored flowers is anthocyanin. This complex compound is synthesized in a chain reaction, each link of the chain being catalyzed by an enzyme. If any one of the enzymes is lacking, anthocyanin is not produced. Hence, white varieties of sweet peas may be white for different reasons. Two of the genes controlling production of the essential enzymes have been designated by *C* and *P;* both are necessary for the production of color. One white variety of sweet peas may have the genotype *CCpp* (it is white because *P* is lacking). Another white variety may have the genotype *ccPP.* If these two varieties are crossed, the offspring have colored flowers; the *P* missing in one parent is supplied by the other; the *C* missing in one parent is supplied by the other (genotype *CcPp*).

These are called **complementary genes**; they may be defined as two (or more) dominant genes that interact to produce a phenotype although neither gene produces a phenotypic effect by itself. Because most, if not all, synthetic processes are complex chain reactions, we may expect to find more and more individuals (or varieties) similar in phenotype but not in genotype as our knowledge of the basic biochemical process underlying phenotypes increases. Just as the two varieties of white sweet peas were white for different reasons, so many human individuals showing a certain phenotype have that phenotype for different genetic reasons. We discovered the difference in genotype between the varieties of white sweet peas by crossing them. Since we cannot make comparable crosses of human beings, our knowledge of human genetic differences will grow more slowly. An albino husband and wife, who are albinos for different genetic reasons and so produce normally pigmented children, are a case in point.

Hereditary deafness is probably another example. Sometimes two deaf parents have only deaf children. In other cases, two deaf parents have children with normal hearing. We can explain this if we assume that two genes, usually designated *D* and *E*, are necessary for normal hearing. If two deaf people having the genotype *DDee* marry each other, all the children (lacking *E*) will be deaf. However, two deaf people having the genotypes *DDee* and *ddEE*, respectively, will have children with normal hearing (*DdEe*).

In summary, we note three criteria of recessive inheritance to be looked for in studying pedigrees: (1) Traits dependent on recessive genes frequently skip one or more generations in a direct ancestral line. (2) When two parents showing a phenotype dependent on recessive genes have the same genotype, all children show the phenotype of the parents. (3) In a pedigree showing inheritance of an otherwise rare recessive trait, the amount of consanguinity is frequently greater than it is in the population at large (see Chap. 8).

PROBLEMS

1. The individuals represented by solid squares and circles in the accompanying pedigree chart show a certain trait.

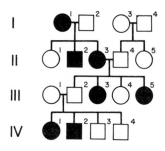

(a) Could the trait be inherited on the basis of a dominant gene with complete penetrance? A dominant gene with partial penetrance? A recessive gene?

(b) Assuming that the trait depends on a dominant gene, A, having partial penetrance, give the genotypes of III-2, IV-1, IV-2, IV-3, IV-4. (Assume that III-1 does not have the gene.)

(c) Assuming that the trait depends on a recessive gene, a, give the genotypes of III-1, III-2, IV-1, IV-2, IV-3, IV-4. (If more than one genotype is possible, give all genotypes that the individual may have.)

2. If black mice having the genotype $CcBb$ are mated to white (pigmentless) mice having the genotype $ccbb$, what colors will be expected in the offspring and in what proportions will the different colors be expected to occur?

3. If the suggestion of Lutman and Neel (p. 81) is correct, would it have been possible for II-9 (Fig. 6.3) to have had a child with type 2 cataract? (Assume that II-10 had the genotype $ccmm$ and that independent assortment occurred.)

4. If II-3 (Fig. 6.4) had married a heterozygous man and they had produced four children, what would have been the chances that *at least one* child would have been an albino? (Chap. 5; but recall that in this case the chance for a normal child is ½ rather than ¾.)

5. If sweet peas having colored flowers and the genotype $CcPp$ are crossed with white sweet peas having the genotype $ccpp$, what types of progeny will be expected and in what proportions will the different types be expected to occur?

6. Suppose that you discover a rare defect and wish to determine its mode of inheritance. You make as extensive a survey as you can and obtain the following data. In every case the parents are normal.

Size of sibship	No. of sibships	No. of affected children per sibship	Total number of affected children
1	2	1	2
2	4	1	4
2	2	2	4
3	8	1	8
4	6	1	6
4	6	2	12
			36

Use the *a priori* method of correcting pooled data to determine whether the incidence of affected children in these families is evidence for or against the hypothesis that the trait is inherited as a simple Mendelian recessive (Table

5.2, p. 66). What do you conclude, and why?
7. Following the hypothesis concerning hereditary deafness stated on page 85, explain the following cases:
   (a) Two deaf parents whose children are all deaf. Give possible genotypes of parents and children.
   (b) Two deaf parents whose children all have normal hearing. Give possible genotypes of parents and children.
   (c) Father with normal hearing, mother deaf; half of the children deaf, half normal. Give possible genotypes of parents and children.

REFERENCES

Lutman, F. C., and J. V. Neel, 1945. "Inherited cataract in the B. genealogy," *Archives of Ophthalmology*, 33:341–57.

Mohr, O. L., and C. Wriedt, 1919. "A new type of hereditary brachyphalangy in man," *Carnegie Institution of Washington*, Publ. 295:1–64.

Neel, J. V., and W. J. Schull, 1954. *Human Heredity*. Chicago: The University of Chicago Press.

Oepen, H., 1961. "The specificity and expressivity of the Huntington gene exemplified by paroxysmal disturbances." *Second International Congress of Human Genetics*. International Congress Series No. 32, p. E 167. New York: Excerpta Medica Foundation.

Pearson, K., E. Nettleship, and C. H. Usher, 1911–1913. "A monograph on albinism in man," *Drapers' Company Research Memoirs, Biometric Series*, 6, 8, 9. London: Dulau & Company Ltd.

Penrose, L. S., 1959. "Genetical analysis in man." In G. E. W. Wolstenholme and C. M. O'Connor (eds.). *Biochemistry of Human Genetics*. Ciba Foundation Symposium. Boston: Little, Brown & Company.

Reese, A. B., 1954. "Frequency of retinoblastoma in the progeny of parents who have survived the disease," *Archives of Ophthalmology*, 52:815–18.

Silvers, W. K., 1961. "Genes and the pigment cells of mammals," *Science*, 134:368–73.

Snyder, L. H., and P. R. David, 1957. *The Principles of Heredity*, 5th ed. Boston: D. C. Heath & Company.

Steinberg, A. G., 1959. "Methodology in human genetics," *Journal of Medical Education*, 34:315–34.

Witkop, C. J., E. J. Van Scott, and G. A. Jacoby, 1961. "Evidence for two forms of autosomal recessive albinism in man." *Second International Congress of Human Genetics*. International Congress Series No. 32, p. E 169. New York: Excerpta Medica Foundation.

7.

MENDELIAN THINKING
APPLIED TO POPULATIONS

Some people will object to use of the term "Mendelian thinking" as a title for the subject matter to be presented in this chapter. Admittedly, Mendel did not think, or at least write, about the subject we shall discuss. However, what we mean by "Mendelian thinking" is the operation of the laws of probability in genetic phenomena. In Chapter 2 we emphasized the point that they operate (a) in the production by heterozygotes of two equally numerous types of germ cells, and (b) in the production of fertilized ova, when two equally numerous kinds of sperm combine with two equally numerous kinds of ova. We saw that application of the laws of probability at these two points results in the classic 3:1 (or 1:2:1) ratio.

Random Mating

Now we wish to apply the laws of probability to a third point: the arrangement of matings. Mendel arranged his matings of peas very carefully, leaving nothing to chance. Suppose that matings *are* left to chance; what may we then expect?

In the interest of clarity, let us talk in terms of a specific example. In Figure 2.1, p. 16, we showed a cross between homozygous black guinea pigs and white ones. The F_1 offspring are black and heterozygous. When they are mated among themselves, the F_2 offspring are ¼ BB (homozygous black), ½ Bb (heterozygous black), and ¼ bb (homozygous white).

At this point, it is customary to observe that if the homozygous blacks are mated together, all their offspring will be black, and that similarly if the whites are mated together, they will breed true for whiteness. On the other hand, if the heterozygous blacks are mated together, their offspring again will approximate the 3:1 phenotypic ratio. All this is correct, but it is not the point we wish to make at present.

Suppose that the experimenter does *not* arrange the matings—that he lets the guinea pigs themselves do the choosing. What will be the result?

As we approach this question, we shall make two simplifying assumptions at the outset. The first is that all three genotypes (*BB, Bb,* and *bb*) are equally healthy and fertile. This is probably true in this case, but it is not true of all examples we might cite.

Our second assumption is that in their matings the guinea pigs have no preference based on color. If black guinea pigs preferred to mate with black ones, and white guinea pigs with white ones, this would be an example of **assortative mating**. Assortative mating frequently occurs, as we shall see later, but let us assume that it is not present in the case under consideration. The opposite of assortative mating is **random mating**, or **panmixis**, to use a more technical term. Let us assume that guinea pigs are panmictic as far as color is concerned, no preference being shown.

Suppose that we have a large group of these F_2 guinea pigs in the proportions stated above—¼ *BB*, ²⁄₄ *Bb*, ¼ *bb* (and that these proportions apply to both sexes). Now we let nature take its course. How will the matings occur if breeding is truly random? If it is, the chance that a given male will mate with a black female or a white female is determined by the relative frequencies of these two kinds of females in the population. If black females and white females were equally numerous, the chance that a given male would mate with a black female would be ½; the chance that he would mate with a white female would also be ½. However, this is not true of the present population; there are three times as many black females as there are white ones. Hence the chance that a given male will mate with a black female is ¾ and the chance that he will mate with a white female is ¼. In terms of genotypes, the chance that a given male will mate with a *BB* female is ¼, that he will mate with a *Bb* female is ²⁄₄, that he will mate with a *bb* female is ¼. And, of course, we can turn the whole thing around and state that the chance that a given female will mate with a *BB* male is ¼, that she will mate with a *Bb* male is ²⁄₄, that she will mate with a *bb* male is ¼.

The various types of matings and their expected relative frequencies can be shown by a checkerboard diagram:

		Females		
		¼ *BB*	²⁄₄ *Bb*	¼ *bb*
Males	¼ *BB*	¹⁄₁₆ *BB* × *BB*	²⁄₁₆ *BB* × *Bb*	¹⁄₁₆ *BB* × *bb*
	²⁄₄ *Bb*	²⁄₁₆ *Bb* × *BB*	⁴⁄₁₆ *Bb* × *Bb*	²⁄₁₆ *Bb* × *bb*
	¼ *bb*	¹⁄₁₆ *bb* × *BB*	²⁄₁₆ *bb* × *Bb*	¹⁄₁₆ *bb* × *bb*

(The fraction in each space is obtained by multiplying the fraction at the head of that column by the fraction at the left of that horizontal row.) These different matings and their relative frequencies are extracted from the checkerboard and listed as the first column of Table 7.1. This table gives the expectation with regard to the offspring, assuming as we do that all matings are equally fertile. If they are, the *BB* × *BB* matings, for example (first horizontal row in the table), will be expected to produce 1⁄16 of the offspring, and these will all be *BB*, as shown. Again, 4⁄16 of the matings will be *BB* × *Bb* (second horizontal row), but in this case half of the offspring (2⁄16 of the total) will be *BB*, half will be *Bb*. And so on for the remainder of the table (note the 1:2:1 ratio from the *Bb* × *Bb* matings).

Table 7.1 Random mating in a population composed of 1⁄4 *BB*, 2⁄4 *Bb*, 1⁄4 *bb*.

Matings	Offspring		
	BB	Bb	bb
1/16 BB × BB	1/16	0	0
4/16 BB × Bb	2/16	2/16	0
2/16 BB × bb	0	2/16	0
4/16 Bb × Bb	1/16	2/16	1/16
4/16 Bb × bb	0	2/16	2/16
1/16 bb × bb	0	0	1/16
Totals	4/16 = 1/4	8/16 = 2/4	4/16 = 1/4

From the totals at the bottom of Table 7.1 we note that the offspring, like their parents, will be expected to be 1⁄4 *BB*, 2⁄4 *Bb*, 1⁄4 *bb*. When random mating occurs in a population and the relative frequencies of the different genotypes remain unchanged from generation to generation, we say that the population is in **genetic equilibrium**. In this case, equilibrium depends on the laws of probability operating in the arrangement of matings, as well as in the production of germ cells and the union of germ cells to produce fertilized ova (zygotes). In other cases, equilibrium may result from the operation of other forces, as we shall see later.

Let us now simplify our methods of computation somewhat. We started with females occurring in the proportions 1⁄4 *BB*, 2⁄4 *Bb*, 1⁄4 *bb*. Let us concentrate on the ova they produce. The *BB* females will produce only ova containing *B*, and these will constitute one fourth of the total ova produced. The *Bb* females will produce *B*-containing and *b*-containing ova in equal numbers; because they produce two fourths of the total number of ova, they will contribute one fourth of the total as *B*-containing ova and one fourth as *b*-containing ones. Finally, the *bb* females will produce only *b*-containing ova, which will constitute one fourth of the whole number of ova. In summary, in this population, half of the ova contain *B* (one fourth from *BB* females plus one fourth from *Bb* females) and half of the ova contain *b* (one fourth from *Bb* females plus one fourth from *bb* females).

The parental males also occur as ¼ *BB*, 2/4 *Bb*, ¼ *bb*. By the same line of reasoning, half of the sperm will contain *B*, half will contain *b*.

So when the ova and sperm form zygotes, we can expect the following:

		Ova	
		½ *B*	½ *b*
Sperm	½ *B*	¼ *BB*	¼ *Bb*
	½ *b*	¼ *Bb*	¼ *bb*

The offspring (in the body of the checkerboard) are immediately seen to be ¼ *BB*, 2/4 *Bb*, ¼ *bb*, the same result we obtained by more complex diagrams before.

The Hardy-Weinberg Formula

In general, we can speak of the total of all genes in ova and sperm produced by the parents in a population as constituting the **gene pool** of that population. This is a very useful concept, which we shall use frequently. In our present example, half of the genes in the gene pool are *B* and half are *b* (here we need not distinguish between *B* genes contained in ova and *B* genes contained in sperm; the same applies to *b* genes). Hence, we can generalize and summarize by saying that in a population whose gene pool is composed of ½ *B* genes and ½ *b* genes, the offspring will be expected to occur in the proportions of ¼ *BB*, 2/4 *Bb*, ¼ *bb* (and the population is in equilibrium).

Another way of expressing this is as follows:

Let p = the relative frequency of gene *B*
q = the relative frequency of gene *b*

Then $(p+q)^2$ = the expected frequencies of the different types of offspring.

In our present example:

$$
\begin{aligned}
p &= \tfrac{1}{2} \\
q &= \tfrac{1}{2} \\
(p+q)^2 &= p^2 \quad + \quad 2\,pq \quad + \quad q^2 \\
&= (\tfrac{1}{2})^2 \quad + \quad 2\,\tfrac{1}{2} \times \tfrac{1}{2} \quad + \quad (\tfrac{1}{2})^2 \\
&= \tfrac{1}{4} \quad + \quad \tfrac{2}{4} \quad + \quad \tfrac{1}{4}
\end{aligned}
$$

Note that p^2 is BB, pq is Bb, q^2 is bb. So we obtain at once ¼ BB, ¾ Bb, ¼ bb.

Parenthetically, we may note that this formula is simply an algebraic way of expressing what is shown in the little checkerboard above. In that diagram, the sperm are of two types: ½ B + ½ b. In terms of our formula this is "$p + q$." In the same way, the ova are of two types: ½ B + ½ b. This also is "$p + q$." In filling in the checkerboard we did diagrammatically the equivalent of multiplying "½ B + ½b" by "½ B + ½ b," or in other words of multiplying "$p + q$" by "$p + q$," which equals, of course, $(p + q)^2$.

The application of the squared binomial, $(p + q)^2$, to panmictic populations was stated independently and almost simultaneously by two men, Hardy and Weinberg (Hardy, 1908; Weinberg, 1908). Hence it has come to be referred to as the **Hardy-Weinberg law** or **formula**.

We have introduced the Hardy-Weinberg law by discussing a hypothetical population of guinea pigs having a gene pool in which the relative frequency of the dominant gene and the relative frequency of the recessive gene are equal—in which $p = $ ½ and $q = $ ½, in other words. Note that $p + q = 1$. This must necessarily be so; the number of dominant genes plus the number of recessive genes must equal the total number of genes of that allelic pair present in the gene pool.

However, p and q need not be equal; in fact, they probably seldom are equal in actual populations. Suppose, for example, that $p = 0.9$ and $q = 0.1$; in a panmictic population of guinea pigs having this gene pool, what proportions of the different types of offspring can be expected?

$$(p + q)^2 \quad = \quad p^2 \qquad + \quad 2\,pq \qquad + \quad q^2$$

	$(0.9)^2$	$2(0.9)(0.1)$	$(0.1)^2$
	0.81	0.18	0.01
Answer:	81% BB	18% Bb	1% bb

Similarly, we can determine expectations with regard to any values of p and q we wish.

However, in actual investigations the situation usually is reversed. We know the phenotypes, and if we are fortunate the genotypes, of individuals in a population, and wish to determine the constitution of the gene pool—the values of p and q.

For an example, let us return to the MN blood types where, as we saw (pp. 57–58), we have the advantage of being able to distinguish heterozygotes from homozygotes by serological tests. An investigator tested 1000 inhabitants of the city of Frankfurt am Main. His findings were: 52.9 percent of type MN, 27.0 percent of type M, 20.1 percent of type N (data of Laubenheimer, from Wiener, 1943–1962). Translating the data into genotypes we have:

$$27.0\% \text{ or } 0.270 = L^M L^M$$
$$52.9\% \text{ or } 0.529 = L^M L^N$$
$$20.1\% \text{ or } 0.201 = L^N L^N$$

In this group of 1000 people, what is the relative frequency of gene L^M? Of gene L^N?

$$p = \text{frequency of } L^M$$
$$q = \text{frequency of } L^N$$

Then p is composed of all the genes produced by type M people plus half the genes produced by type MN people. Similarly, q is composed of all the genes produced by type N people plus the other half of the genes produced by type MN people. Thus,

$$p = 0.270 + \frac{0.529}{2} = 0.5345 = \text{approx. } 0.53$$

$$q = 0.201 + \frac{0.529}{2} = 0.4655 = \text{approx. } 0.47$$

This means that in the gene pool of these 1000 people, about 53 percent of the genes are L^M genes and 47 percent are L^N genes.

Having determined this, we can now ask a further question: Do these 1000 people in Frankfurt constitute a population in equilibrium? If they do, the Hardy-Weinberg formula, using these values of p and q, should give the same proportions of M, MN, and N individuals as those actually observed.

$$p = 0.53$$
$$q = 0.47$$

$$
\begin{aligned}
(p+q)^2 &= p^2 &&+ 2pq &&+ q^2 \\
&= (0.53)^2 &&+ 2(0.53)(0.47) &&+ (0.47)^2 \\
&= 0.2809 &&+ 0.4982 &&+ 0.2209 \\
&= 28.09\% \, L^M L^M &&+ 49.82\% \, L^M L^N &&+ 22.09\% \, L^N L^N
\end{aligned}
$$

These percentages are to be compared to the observed percentages: 27.0% $L^M L^M$, 52.9% $L^M L^N$, 20.1% $L^N L^N$. The agreement is fairly good (probably it would have been better if we had not rounded off the values of p and q as we did). Apparently the population is in equilibrium or nearly so. If there were any point in determining the probability of whether the difference between observed and expected values is or is not significant (i.e., is or is not caused by chance sampling error), we could apply statistical methods, such as the chi-square test. However, it would not contribute to our present line of thought.

Thus far, the examples we have given have been of populations that at least approximated genetic equilibrium at the outset. Let us see what happens when this is not the case. Here we can make good use of the population geneticist's old friend, the "uninhabited island."

Suppose that a group of 500 people decide to migrate to an uninhabited island. A serologist tests them and finds that they are assorted as follows: 50 are type M; 300 are type MN; 150 are type N. Do they constitute a population in equilibrium?

First, we calculate the values of p and q. In doing so, we shall translate numbers into percentages expressed as decimal fractions, and we shall remember that the value of p, for example, consists of all the genes contributed by M people plus half those contributed by MN people.

$$\text{Genotype } L^M L^M = 50 \text{ (of 500)} = 0.1 \ (10\%)$$
$$L^M L^N = 300 \text{ (of 500)} = 0.6 \ (60\%)$$
$$L^N L^N = 150 \text{ (of 500)} = 0.3 \ (30\%)$$

$$p = 0.1 + \frac{0.6}{2} = 0.4$$

$$q = 0.3 + \frac{0.6}{2} = 0.6$$

$$
\begin{array}{rcccccc}
(p+q)^2 &=& p^2 &+& 2pq &+& q^2 \\
&=& (0.4)^2 &+& 2(0.4)(0.6) &+& (0.6)^2 \\
&=& 0.16 &+& 0.48 &+& 0.36
\end{array}
$$

Hence a population with these gene frequencies ($p = 0.4$; $q = 0.6$) would be expected to have the following proportions of the different types: type M, 16 percent; type MN, 48 percent; type N, 36 percent. Because the actual percentages among the migrants were 10, 60, and 30, respectively, we can see that the migrants were not a population in equilibrum at the outset.

The use of the Hardy-Weinberg formula tells us something else, also. It tells us the proportions of the different types to be expected among the children of the migrants if the parents marry at random as far as the L^M and L^N genes are concerned. This is likely to be the case, for most people do not know their M-N type—and if they did, who would choose his or her marriage partner on the basis of it?

We may expect that the children born on our imaginary island will occur in the proportions of 16 percent M, 48 percent MN, 36 percent N. Do these children in their turn constitute a population in equilibrium? When they grow up and marry, what proportions of the different types will be expected among their children (the grandchildren of the original migrants)? In answering this we proceed as before:

$$p = 0.16 + \frac{0.48}{2} = 0.4$$

$$q = 0.36 + \frac{0.48}{2} = 0.6$$

$$(p+q)^2 = p^2 \quad + \quad 2pq \quad + \quad q^2$$
$$= (0.4)^2 \quad + \quad 2(0.4)(0.6) \quad + \quad (0.6)^2$$
$$= 0.16 \quad + \quad 0.48 \quad + \quad 0.36$$

Therefore: 16% $L^M L^M$, 48% $L^M L^N$, 36% $L^N L^N$

The proportions among the grandchildren are the same as those among the children. This demonstrates that the children themselves constituted a population in equilibrium. Here we see an example of an important corollary of the Hardy-Weinberg law: *If a population is not in equilibrium, it will reach that state by one generation of random mating (panmixis).*

We note that the persistence of an equilibrium, once established, is in this case caused by the fact that the values of p and q do not change. This is to say that the relative proportions of L^M and L^N genes in the gene pool remain the same, generation after generation. We may compare the gene pool to a deck of cards. Unless someone is dishonest, the cards in the deck remain the same, game after game.

To look ahead a bit, we may ask the question: Under what conditions may the gene pool itself change? If one allele mutates to form the other occasionally, the relative proportions of the two will be altered. If the possessors of one allele have some disadvantage affecting fertility, as compared to the possessors of the other, the proportions will change from generation to generation. We are touching here on subjects that we shall discuss later in other connections. Change in the gene pool is essential if evolution is to occur (Chap. 24).

To summarize: The Hardy-Weinberg law states in algebraic form the fact that a panmictic population tends to attain genetic equilibrium, with regard to a pair of alleles, in one generation, and to maintain that equilibrium thereafter. This is a statement of an ideal situation; it assumes (a) that mating is truly random as far as the alleles in question are concerned, and (b) that the alleles do not differ in their effects on viability and fertility. To the extent that these conditions are not met in actual populations, these populations do not conform to the Hardy-Weinberg law.

Estimating the Frequency of Heterozygotes

Of what practical use is the Hardy-Weinberg formula? One important use lies in the estimation of the relative frequency of heterozygotes in cases in which heterozygotes cannot be detected directly. As we have noted, in many human traits heterozygotes are like one of the homozygotes in phenotype. Here we may return to the example of recessive albinism. People with the genotype *Aa* have as normal pigmentation as do people with the genotype *AA*. However, it is of interest to estimate how many people have the *Aa* genotype (i.e., are carriers of albinism), and here the Hardy-Weinberg formula is helpful.

In our general population what proportion of people are albinos? Results of various investigations differ, but 1 in 20,000 seems to be a good approximation. Albinos have the genotype *aa*.

Let p = relative frequency of *A*
q = relative frequency of *a*
Then $(p + q)^2 = p^2 + 2pq + q^2$
in which p^2 is *AA*
$2pq$ is *Aa*
q^2 is *aa*

This means that *if* we can consider our population as panmictic with regard to genes *A* and *a*, we can say that $q^2 = 1/20,000$. Let us examine that "if." In a truly panmictic population, being an albino or not being an albino would have no influence on one's likelihood of marriage and parenthood. That may not be true in the present instance. Even if it is not, albinos constitute such a small proportion of the population that the total gene pool will be little affected by a possible difference between them and normally pigmented people in the proportion in which genes are passed on to children. In the population as a whole, 19,999/20,000 of people are normally pigmented. Because very few of these people know before they marry whether or not they are carriers of gene *a*, it seems safe to say that among these normally pigmented people, mating is at random as far as these alleles are concerned. (Possibly an occasional person may hesitate to marry someone who has an albino sib, but this must be rare enough so that it has little total effect on the country's gene pool). We can say, then, that we are reasonably justified in applying the Hardy-Weinberg formula to recessive albinism.

Hence $q^2 = 1/20,000$
$q = \sqrt{1/20,000}$ = approx. $\frac{1}{141}$
Since $p + q = 1$
$p = 1 - q = 1 - \frac{1}{141} = \frac{140}{141}$

We recall that the heterozygotes are represented by the "$2pq$" of the formula:

$$2pq = 2 \times \frac{140}{141} \times \frac{1}{141} = \frac{2}{141} \text{ or approx. } \frac{1}{70}$$

In calculating this estimation we disregarded the $\frac{140}{141}$ since it is so close to 1 that multiplying by it would make no significant difference in what is at best only an approximation.

We conclude from this that in a population in which only one person in 20,000 is an albino, one person in 70 is a carrier. This high proportion of carriers may seem rather surprising. If it is correct, why are albinos so rare? Because the chances are small that one carrier will happen to marry another one (moreover, if two carriers do marry, only one fourth of their children, on the average, are expected to be albinos). As we intimated previously (p. 83) and will discuss later (Chap. 8), the chance of a carrier marrying another carrier is greatly increased if the spouse is a relative (e.g., a cousin).

This fraction, $\frac{1}{70}$, representing the proportion of heterozygotes for albinism, is a useful estimate that will enter into our calculations from time to time. Useful as it is, we admit frankly that we should prefer to have a direct method of detecting carriers for albinism, perhaps by some sort of biochemical test. If and when someone develops such a test, our present method of estimation will be rendered obsolete, but in the meantime it is the best method we have.

When that hoped-for test is developed, we shall be interested to see whether or not it shows us that carriers for albinism really do constitute about $\frac{1}{70}$ of the population. We may predict with some confidence that the order of magnitude of the estimate is correct, at least. As evidence on this point, let us return to the data on MN blood types in Frankfurt (p. 92). Suppose that in this case we knew the number of type N people but for some reason could not determine directly the number of type MN people. If this were the case, how closely could we estimate the number of type MN people, using the formula?

We equate the percentage of type N people ($L^N L^N$) to q^2:

$$q^2 = 0.201$$
$$q = \sqrt{0.201} = \text{approx. } 0.45$$
$$p = 1 - q = 1 - 0.45 = 0.55$$
$$2pq = 2 \times (0.55)(0.45) = 0.495 \text{ or } 49.5\%$$

Thus, use of the method would lead us to expect that 49.5 percent of the population would be MN, whereas the investigator found that 52.9 percent of them actually are. The difference of slightly less than 3 percent is not great. We may agree that the estimate is close enough so that it would be useful if we could not make actual counts of the number of carriers.

Evidence Concerning Single Allele Inheritance

A second area in which the Hardy-Weinberg formula is useful relates to the question that has been a recurrent theme throughout the book thus far. How do we determine whether a certain characteristic in which we may be interested depends on a single gene or on a more complicated genetic arrangement? In Chapter 2, we discussed at length just how and why obtaining a 3:1 (or 1:2:1) ratio in an F_2 generation gives evidence of single gene-pair inheritance. In Chapter 5, we saw how this same interpretation could be placed on pooled data of human matings if we used suitable methods of correcting for incomplete ascertainment. Now we ask a further question: How can similar interpretations be drawn from data relating to whole populations? How does single-gene inheritance manifest itself in a population? Or, more specifically, if a characteristic depends on a single recessive gene, what proportion of the population will be expected to show the corresponding phenotype (i.e., to be homozygous for the presumed recessive gene)?

Because most of the traits about which we ask this question are relatively rare, marriages between people who show the trait are so infrequent that they produce few useful data (as we noted earlier concerning the marriages of albinos to each other). Hence we can narrow the question still further and divide it into two parts: (1) From matings in which one parent shows the dominant trait and the other the recessive trait, what proportion of the children will be expected to show the recessive trait? (2) From matings in which both parents show the dominant trait, what proportion of the children will be expected to show the recessive trait? The Hardy-Weinberg formula can be applied to answer these questions (Snyder, 1934; Stern, 1960; Li, 1961).

The first question relates to families in which one parent shows the dominant phenotype and the other the recessive phenotype. Using familiar symbols, we note that such matings may be of two types: $AA \times aa$, or $Aa \times aa$. In terms of the Hardy-Weinberg formula, what proportion of matings will be expected to be of each type? We recall that in the formula:

$$AA = p^2$$
$$Aa = 2pq$$
$$aa = q^2$$

Hence we can express the expected frequencies of the matings as follows:

Mating	Expected frequency
$AA \times aa$	$2\,[p^2 \times q^2] = 2\,p^2q^2$
$Aa \times aa$	$2\,[2\,pq \times q^2] = 4\,pq^3$

Why do we multiply the expression in the square brackets by 2 in each case? Because the mating can arise in two ways. For example, an $AA \times aa$ mating can mean either (1) mother AA, father aa, or (2) mother aa, father AA.

What of the offspring expected from these matings?

| | | Offspring | | |
Mating	Frequency	Total	Dominant	Recessive
$AA \times aa$	$2\,p^2q^2$	$2\,p^2q^2$	$2\,p^2q^2$	0
$Aa \times aa$	$4\,pq^3$	$4\,pq^3$	$2\,pq^3$	$2\,pq^3$

These frequencies express the fact that from $AA \times aa$ matings we expect all the children to show the dominant phenotype, whereas from $Aa \times aa$ matings we expect half of the children to show the dominant phenotype, half to show the recessive phenotype.

The total offspring of these marriages can then be represented by the expected frequencies: $2\,p^2q^2 + 4\,pq^3$. Of this total, what proportion is expected to show the recessive phenotype? From the table we see that this is $2\,pq^3$.

Hence, the expected frequency of recessive offspring relative to the total offspring is:

$$\frac{2\,pq^3}{2\,p^2q^2 + 4\,pq^3}$$

We then proceed to simplify. Dividing both numerator and denominator by $2\,pq^2$, we have:

$$\frac{q}{p + 2\,q}$$

Because $p = 1 - q$, we write this as $\dfrac{q}{1 - q + 2\,q}$, which then becomes

$$\frac{q}{1 + q}. \tag{1}*$$

If we know the frequency, q, of a recessive gene in the population, we can use this formula to predict the proportion of recessive-phenotype children to be expected from matings in which one parent shows the dominant phenotype, the other the recessive.

Let us illustrate its use by referring to albinism again. If albinism is indeed inherited as a simple Mendelian recessive, what proportion of albino children will be expected in families in which one parent is normally pigmented, the other an albino? On page 96 we noted that for albinism $q = \frac{1}{141}$ (based on the fact that albinos constitute about 1/20,000 of our population). We substitute this fraction in the formula:

$$\frac{q}{1 + q} = \frac{\dfrac{1}{141}}{\dfrac{141}{141} + \dfrac{1}{141}} = \frac{\dfrac{1}{141}}{\dfrac{142}{141}} = \frac{1}{141} \times \frac{141}{142} = \frac{1}{142} \text{ or } 0.007 = 0.7\%$$

*Formulas (1) and (2) are sometimes called Snyder's formulas, after Dr. Laurence H. Snyder, prominent American geneticist, who set them forth in substantially their present form (Snyder, 1934).

This means that if inheritance is of the type indicated, about 7 children in a thousand born of normal × albino matings will be expected to be albinos.

We now turn to the second type of family mentioned at the outset, that in which both parents show the dominant trait. What proportion of their children will be expected to show the recessive trait? This is really a more useful question than the first one, for in the case of rare recessive traits, almost all children showing the trait are born to parents who do not show it.

Three types of matings are involved here. These matings with their expected frequencies and the expected frequencies of the offspring, are shown in Table 7.2; the expressions for each were worked out in the manner employed above.

TABLE 7.2 Expected relative frequencies of different types of off-spring from matings in which both parents show the dominant phenotype.

Mating	Frequency	Offspring		
		Total	Dominant	Recessive
AA × AA	$p^2 \times p^2 = p^4$	p^4	p^4	0
AA × Aa	$2\,[p^2 \times 2\,pq] = 4\,p^3q$	$4\,p^3q$	$4\,p^3q$	0
Aa × Aa	$2\,pq \times 2\,pq = 4\,p^2q^2$	$4\,p^2q^2$	$3\,p^2q^2$	p^2q^2

What fraction of the offspring will be expected to show the recessive phenotype?

$$\frac{p^2q^2}{p^4 + 4\,p^3q + 4\,p^2q^2}$$

Dividing numerator and denominator by p^2, we have

$$\frac{q^2}{p^2 + 4\,pq + 4\,q^2} = \left(\frac{q}{p + 2\,q}\right)^2$$

Now we substitute $1 - q$ for p:

$$\left(\frac{q}{1 - q + 2\,q}\right)^2 = \left(\frac{q}{1 + q}\right)^2 \qquad (2)°$$

This formula will enable us to predict the proportion of recessive-phenotype children to be expected from matings in which both parents show the dominant phenotype.

Returning to the example of albinism, we recall that we determined that

$$\frac{q}{1 + q} = \frac{1}{142} \text{ or } 0.007$$

Hence:

$$\left(\frac{q}{1 + q} \right)^2 = (0.007)^2 = 0.000049 \text{ or } 0.0049\%$$

This means that if albinism is inherited as a simple recessive, we should expect 49 out of a million children born to normal parents to be albinos.

We should note here that we have come nearly full circle. Our value of q is based on the observed fact that about one person in 20,000 is an albino. One person in 20,000 is the same as 50 persons in a million. How do we account for the difference between 49 and 50 per million (aside from the arithmetic effects of rounding off decimal fractions)? The 50/1,000,000 includes children having at least one albino parent; the 49/1,000,000 does not. Thus we have a numerical illustration of the fact stated previously that in our population as a whole most albino children are born to parents both of whom are normally pigmented. Similar statements apply to other relatively rare recessive traits.

Although in many respects albinism is a good example to use, it lacks all elements of suspense. We know how the story is coming out before we tell it. Many lines of evidence have indicated for years that albinism depends on a recessive gene (although as noted previously—p. 84—the recessive gene may not be the same one in all people, and, as not mentioned previously, dominant genes may occasionally be involved).

Accordingly, it is instructive and interesting to see how our formulas (1) and (2) can help us to reach a decision concerning the mode of inheritance of a "new" trait, one not analyzed hitherto. Such a new characteristic is exemplified by a double-jointedness of the thumbs which some people possess (Fig. 7.1) and which is called *distal hyperextensibility*. Its inheritance has been studied by Glass and Kistler (1953) of Johns Hopkins University.

These investigators devised a simple method of measuring distal hyperextensibility (Fig. 7.2). "A transparent plastic protractor was reddened along the straight edge and two lines were drawn parallel to this edge and respectively 0.5 and 1.0 cm from it. These assisted in aligning the straight edge of the protractor parallel to the posterior (dorsal) surface of the thumb, the hand being held palm upwards, and the midpoint of the protractor being placed on the end of the palmar skin folds, at the center of the distal joint of the thumb. The angle was then read along the line from this point to the corner or most laterally projecting part of the thumbnail. All persons who had either thumb extensible to a 50° angle or greater were classified as possessors of the trait, all others as nonaffected."

Interest in this rather trivial trait, which Glass and Kistler have dubbed "hitchhiker's thumb," centers around the possibility that it may be an

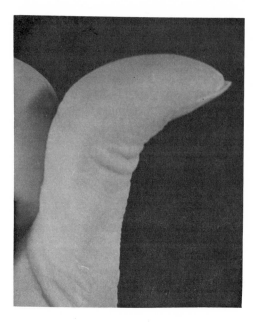

FIG. 7.1 The distally hyperextensible thumb of J. I. M. (Photo by James Benton).

easily observed characteristic with a simple genetic basis. Traits of this kind are most useful in studies of the genetics of human populations and in the field of physical anthropology.

Investigation of 895 white persons and 157 Negroes indicated that the trait is quite common; it was evident in approximately one fourth (24.7 percent) of the white population and one third of the Negro population.

The authors investigated the possibility that distal hyperextensibility (*dht*) may depend on a single recessive gene for which, of course, people showing the *dht* phenotype are homozygous.

If a single recessive gene is involved, the 24.7 percent incidence of *dht* in the "white" sample can be equated to q^2 of the Hardy-Weinberg formula.

$$q^2 = 0.247 \qquad q = \sqrt{0.247} = 0.496$$

In the preceding chapter we discussed lack of penetrance. Part of the present data lent itself to determination of what the degree of penetrance might be in this case. Among 85 college students showing the trait, 60 percent showed it in both thumbs; 27 percent had hyperextensible right thumbs only; 13 percent had hyperextensible left thumbs only. Apparently those who showed the trait in only one thumb had the genetic basis for the trait, but for some reason this genetic basis only affected one

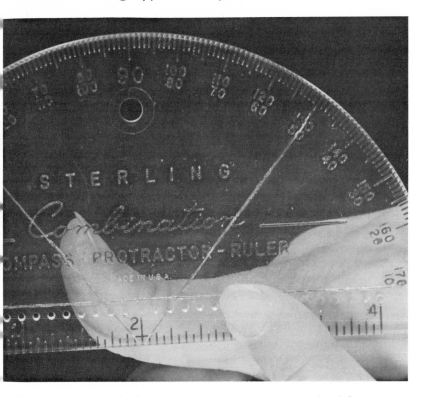

*FIG. 7.2 Method of using a protractor to measure distal hyperextensibility of the thumb. (Photo by James Benton).

thumb. If 27 percent of people having the genes for *dht* showed the trait in the right thumb only, and 13 percent showed it in the left thumb only, what percentage of people having the genes for *dht* would be expected not to show the trait in *either* thumb (i.e., to exhibit lack of penetrance)? The answer would be the two percentages multiplied together: $0.27 \times 0.13 = 0.035$. Thus 3.5 percent of people would be expected to lack the trait although they had the genes for it. In other words, the penetrance would be 100 percent minus 3.5 percent, or 96.5 percent.

The investigators then studied the offspring of various types of matings. They found 11 families in which both parents showed the trait (*dht* × *dht*). There were 24 children in these families; all but one was *dht*. If the trait depends on a recessive gene, *all* children in families born to two homozygous recessive parents must be homozygous recessive. How can we account for the one *non-dht* child in 24? The authors are probably correct in ascribing the occurrence to the incomplete penetrance just discussed; doubtless the child had the homozygous recessive genotype but failed to develop the *dht* phenotype.

Glass and Kistler found 48 families in which one parent showed the trait, whereas the other did not (*dht* × *non-dht*). There were 108 children; 37 were *dht*; 71 were *non-dht*. Using formula (1) and the frequency *q* of the presumed recessive gene, they calculated the number of *dht* children to be expected in such families.

$$\frac{q}{1 + q} = \frac{0.496}{1.496} = 0.3315$$

$$0.3315 \times 108 = 35.8 = \text{Number of } dht \text{ children expected.}$$

Obviously 35.8 is very close to the 37 actually observed. Even without employing the chi-square test as the authors did, we can see the close agreement.

The investigation included 132 families in which both parents lacked the trait (*non-dht* × *non-dht*). There were 313 children: 32 were *dht*, 281 *non-dht*. Using formula (2), the authors calculated the expectation for such families.

$$\left(\frac{q}{1 + q} \right)^2 = (0.3315)^2 = 0.1099$$

$$0.1099 \times 313 = 34.4 = \text{Number of } dht \text{ children expected.}$$

Again this is in good agreement with the 32 *dht* children actually observed.

Just by way of checking we may ask: How would it look if we turned the whole thing around and assumed that *dht* depends on a *dominant* gene? That would mean that *non-dht* would depend on the corresponding recessive allele. We mentioned above that 24.7 percent of the people tested were *dht*; that means that 75.3 percent were *non-dht*. Under this assumption, then,

$$q^2 = 0.753 \qquad q = \sqrt{0.753} = 0.867$$

Then in *dht* × *non-dht* matings:

$$\frac{q}{1 + q} = \frac{0.867}{1.867} = 0.4643$$

$$0.4643 \times 108 = 50.1 = \text{Number of } non\text{-}dht \text{ children expected.}$$

However, 71 *non-dht* offspring were observed; even without statistical analysis we can see that this agreement is far from good.

Turning to *dht* × *dht* matings:

$$\left(\frac{q}{1 + q} \right)^2 = (0.4643)^2 = 0.2156$$

$$0.2156 \times 24 = 5.2 = \text{Number of } non\text{-}dht \text{ children expected.}$$

We recall that in such families 1 *non-dht* child was actually observed. Here the numbers are small, but such as they are they indicate lack of agreement.

Even more damaging to the hypothesis that *non-dht* depends on a recessive gene are the results from the *non-dht* × *non-dht* matings cited above. All children would be expected to be *non-dht*; actually 32 out of 313 were not. If the gene were recessive, we should have to assume that its penetrance was quite low to account for so many exceptions to expectation.

Thus we see that the analysis of families reveals close agreement with expectation based on the assumption of recessive inheritance, and very poor agreement with expectation based on the assumption of dominant inheritance.

Glass and Kistler employed another interesting test based on the Hardy-Weinberg formula. This is a method, developed by several earlier investigators, in which recessive propositi are classified according to the type of mating represented by their parents. Propositi from the three types of matings (*non-dht* × *non-dht*; *non-dht* × *dht*; *dht* × *dht*) are to be expected in the ratio of p^2 : $2\,pq$: q^2 (*if dht* depends on a single recessive gene). The reason for this is shown in Table 7.3, where A represents a dominant gene, a its recessive allele.

TABLE 7.3 Expected frequencies of recessives from different types of matings.

Mating	Frequency of mating	Expected frequency of Recessives
Aa × Aa	$2\,pq \times 2\,pq = 4\,p^2q^2$	p^2q^2 (¼ of offspring)
Aa × aa	$2\,[2\,pq \times q^2] = 4\,pq^3$	$2\,pq^3$ (½ of offspring)
aa × aa	$q^2 \times q^2 = q^4$	q^4 (all offspring)

Thus:
p^2q^2 : $2\,pq^3$: $q^4 = p^2$: $2\,pq$: q^2 (by removing q^2 from each term)

In the present instance, this means that if *dht* depends on a recessive gene, propositi showing *dht* should arise from the three types of matings in the ratio of p^2 : $2\,pq$: q^2.

$$q = 0.496 \qquad p = 1 - q = 0.504$$
$$p^2 = 0.254 \qquad 2\,pq = 0.499 \qquad q^2 = 0.247 \text{ (p. 102)}$$

The authors had at their disposal 94 cases, forming a random sampling of propositi.

$0.254 \times 94 = 23.9 =$ Number of *dht* propositi expected to have arisen from *non-dht* × *non-dht* matings.

$0.499 \times 94 = 46.9 =$ Number of *dht* propositi expected from *non-dht* × *dht* matings.

$0.247 \times 94 = 23.2 =$ Number of *dht* propositi expected from *dht* × *dht* matings.

The authors applied a correction for partial penetrance, changing the respective numbers to 25.6 : 46.8 : 21.6. The actual numbers of propositi observed to have arisen from the three types of matings were 26, 53, and 15, respectively. We see that the agreement here is not as close as it was in the preceding test, particularly in the number of propositi who were the children of *dht* × *dht* matings. The authors attribute this to two factors: "first, chance, because the expected size of this class is small enough to be affected considerably by sampling error; and second, the fact that this particular class will be especially affected by the incomplete penetrance of the trait."

Additional investigation revealed that *dht* is not sex-linked (Chap. 12) and is not explainable on a basis of multiple, cumulative genes (Chap. 11).

Glass and Kistler point out that Li and Steinberg have shown, independently, that the methods we have described, based on the Hardy-Weinberg formula, will not distinguish between inheritance dependent on a single recessive gene and inheritance dependent on two recessive genes. Following the principle of parsimony (p. 14), however, we may well agree with the authors that, until someone demonstrates otherwise, distal hyperextensibility of the thumb may be considered a simple recessive trait, and, as such, will be useful in genetic investigations and physical anthropology.

The Hardy-Weinberg law, as an expression of the laws of probability operating in populations, forms the basis of population genetics. We shall make frequent use of it in our subsequent discussions.

At this time we remind ourselves that a population will not conform closely to the principle unless (a) mating is random with respect to the genes under consideration, and (b) the alternative genotypes do not affect viability and fertility differentially. We shall reserve until later consideration of the second point, turning our attention to the effect of non-random mating.

Assortative Mating

When people are influenced in their choice of mates by the genetic trait being studied, the conditions of random mating assumed by the Hardy-Weinberg formula are not met. There is evidence, for example, that tall men and women are more inclined to marry each other than they are to choose short partners. Although many exceptions are encountered, the tendency is present, and to the extent that it exists, it affords an example of assortative mating. In its most common form, assortative mating is positive—"like mating with like," although it may also be negative—unlike individuals choosing each other as mates. The mathematics of assortative mating, both positive and negative, was worked out by the late Dr. Gunnar Dahlberg (1948), a leading human geneticist in Sweden.

What is the effect of positive assortative mating on a population? For the sake of simplicity, we shall picture a situation in which the tendency of like to marry like is complete, a condition seldom if ever encountered in actual examples. Furthermore, the effect is most clearly discernible when heterozygotes differ from both types of homozygotes, as in the MN blood types. Let us inquire into the consequences of complete assortative mating based on MN blood types. In doing so, we picture the possible, although highly improbable, situation in which type M people would marry only type M people, type MN people would marry each other exclusively, and type N people would choose only type N people as mates.

Let us start with a population having the constitution: ¼ M, 2/4 MN, ¼ N. From our previous discussion we know that if mating were random, this population would be in equilibrium, maintaining the same relative proportions generation after generation. However, in this case we postulate complete assortative mating. Under these conditions, what will be the nature of the next generation?

The type M people will mate among themselves ($L^M L^M \times L^M L^M$), producing only type M children to constitute one fourth of this next generation.

The type N people will also produce only type N children, to constitute one fourth of the next generation.

The type MN people will mate together ($L^M L^N \times L^M L^N$), but in this case three types of children will be produced. Of these children, one fourth will be M, two fourths will be MN, one fourth will be N. The type MN people will produce one half of the total number of children. Of this half, one fourth will be M, thus, $\frac{1}{2} \times \frac{1}{4} = \frac{1}{8}$—therefore, ⅛ of the total number of children will be of type M derived from MN parents. Similarly, $\frac{1}{2} \times \frac{2}{4} = \frac{2}{8}$ of the total number of children will be of type MN derived from MN parents, and $\frac{1}{2} \times \frac{1}{4} = \frac{1}{8}$ will be of type N derived from MN parents.

The total result will be as follows:

Type M children:
- ¼ from M parents
- ⅛ from MN parents
- ⅜ Total

Type MN children:
- 2/8 from MN parents

Type N children:
- ⅛ from MN parents
- ¼ from N parents
- ⅜ Total

Hence, in one generation of assortative mating, the fraction of M individuals has increased from ¼ to ⅜, the fraction of N individuals has increased to the same extent, but the fraction of MN individuals has *decreased* from $\frac{3}{4}$ to $\frac{5}{8}$.

What will happen if assortative mating is continued for a second generation? The production of grandchildren of the original population will occur as follows:

Parents: $\frac{3}{8}$ M $\frac{2}{8}$ MN $\frac{3}{8}$ N

           $\frac{3}{8}$ M $\frac{2}{32}$ M $\frac{4}{32}$ MN $\frac{2}{32}$ N $\frac{3}{8}$ N

       $\frac{3}{8} + \frac{2}{32} = \frac{14}{32}$ $\frac{4}{32}$ $\frac{2}{32} + \frac{3}{8} = \frac{14}{32}$

Children: $\frac{7}{16}$ M $\frac{2}{16}$ MN $\frac{7}{16}$ N

Again we note that the proportions of M and N individuals have increased at the expense of the proportion of MN individuals.

The same trend will continue as long as assortative mating is practiced (Fig. 7.3). Although our model is oversimplified, it illustrates the effects

Generations

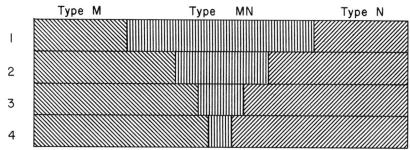

FIG. 7.3 Effect of assortative mating on the relative proportions of homozygotes and heterozygotes. Four generations of a model assuming complete, positive assortative mating based on MN blood types, and starting with a population in which $\frac{1}{4}$ are of type M, $\frac{2}{4}$ of type MN, $\frac{1}{4}$ of type N.

of positive assortative mating: *the number of homozygotes tends to increase, the number of heterozygotes tends to decrease.* If assortative mating is only partial, the effects will be less striking than those in our model, but the tendency will be present. This tendency to change in the relative proportions of homozygotes and heterozygotes stands in marked contrast to the tendency to maintenance of the *status quo* when mating is random. Thus, the tendency of populations to reach and maintain an equilibrium is upset if assortative mating occurs.

In the next chapter we shall direct our attention to the manner in which consanguinity or inbreeding modifies expectations based on random mating.

PROBLEMS

1. A certain group of 300 people is constituted as follows: 150 *AA*, 120 *Aa*, 30 *aa*. Do these people form a panmictic population at equilibrium? If not, what number of individuals would have been expected to have had each of the three genotypes if the population *had* been in equilibrium?
   NOTE: When it is not known whether or not a population is in equilibrium, the values of p and q are calculated as follows. The *AA* people contribute to the gene pool only *A* genes, whereas *half* of the genes contributed by the *Aa* people are *A* genes. Hence the value of p equals the proportion of people who are *AA* plus half of the proportion of people who are *Aa*; in this case:

$$p = \frac{150}{300} + \frac{1}{2}\left(\frac{120}{300}\right) = \frac{210}{300} = 0.7$$

   Similarly, the value of q equals half the proportion of people who are *Aa* plus the proportion of people who are *aa*:

$$q = \frac{1}{2}\left(\frac{120}{300}\right) + \frac{30}{300} = \frac{90}{300} = 0.3$$

   Or, if you have determined the value of p you may obtain the value of q by subtraction, since $1 - p = q$. Alternatively, if you have determined the value of q, $p = 1 - q$.

2. A hitherto uninhabited island was colonized by a group of 475 people. When these people were blood typed, 304 were found to belong to type M, 19 to type N, and 152 to type MN. Did this group of people constitute a population in equilibrium? If not, what number of individuals would have been expected to have belonged to each of the three types if the population *had* been in equilibrum?

3. During the eighteenth century a group of 100 colonists migrated to a previously uninhabited island. They had the following blood type distribution: 34 were of type M, 58 of type MN, 8 of type N. Today their descendants number 2000. If we can assume that mutation and migration during the intervening years have not significantly altered the gene pool, how many of the 2000 will be expected to be of each blood type?

4. Is this population of 500 individuals in genetic equilibrium: 310 *AA*, 150 *Aa*, 40 *aa*? If not, what numbers would have been expected for each of the three genotypes if the population *had* been in equilibrium?

5. In terms of the Hardy-Weinberg formula, what proportion of children in a panmictic population is expected to consist of heterozygotes born to parents both of whom are heterozygous?

6. Suppose that you discover a "new" human trait that you suspect of being inherited as a Mendelian recessive. You find that one person in 10,000 shows the trait. If you are correct in your hypothesis as to the nature of the heredity, what percentage of children, born to parents only one of whom shows the trait, will be expected to exhibit the trait?

7. Suppose that a national census reveals that one person in 400 has forked eyelashes. In a certain city of that nation there are 10,000 children. If "forked eyelashes" depends on a recessive autosomal gene, how many of the children will be expected to have forked eyelashes but to be the children of parents neither of whom shows the trait?

8. In a population panmictic for a certain pair of autosomal alleles, what proportion of the marriages is expected to occur between individuals both of whom show the dominant trait? (Answer in terms of p and q.)

9. In a certain panmictic population, 16 percent of the people are homozygous for a recessive gene. What percentage of the people in this population are heterozygous (carriers)?

10. In our example of assortative mating applied to the M-N blood types (pp. 107–108), we noted that a second generation of assortative mating resulted in the proportions: $\frac{7}{16}$ M, $\frac{2}{16}$ MN, $\frac{7}{16}$ N. What would be the proportions of the three types following an additional generation of complete assortative mating?

11. What proportion of the total number of children in a panmictic population will be expected to belong to blood type N and to be the offspring of parents both of whom belong to type MN? (Answer in terms of p and q.)

REFERENCES

Dahlberg, G., 1948. *Mathematical Methods for Population Genetics*. New York: Interscience Publishers.

Glass, B., and J. C. Kistler, 1953. "Distal hyperextensibility of the thumbs," *Acta Genetica et Statistica Medica*, 4:192–206.

Hardy, G. H., 1908. "Mendelian proportions in a mixed population," *Science*, 28:49–50. Reprinted in J. A. Peters (ed.), 1959. *Classic Papers in Genetics*. Englewood Cliffs, N. J.: Prentice-Hall, Inc. Pp. 60–62.

Li, C. C., 1961. *Human Genetics*. New York: McGraw-Hill Book Company, Inc.

Snyder, L. H., 1934. "Studies in human inheritance. X. A table to determine the proportion of recessives to be expected in various matings involving a unit character," *Genetics*, 19:1–17.

Stern, C., 1960. *Principles of Human Genetics*, 2nd ed. San Francisco: W. H. Freeman & Company.

Weinberg, W., 1908. "Über den Nachweis der Vererbung beim Menschen." *Jahreshefte des Vereins für Vaterländische Naturkunde in Württemberg, Stuttgart*, 64:368–82. (English translation: "On the demonstration of heredity in man," in S. H. Boyer, IV, 1963. *Papers on Human Genetics*. Englewood Cliffs, N. J.: Prentice-Hall, Inc. Pp. 4–15.)

Wiener, A. S., 1943–1962. *Blood Groups and Transfusion*, 3rd ed. Springfield, Ill.: Charles C Thomas. Reprinted—New York: Hafner Publishing Company.

8.

CONSANGUINITY OR INBREEDING

The term **consanguinity** refers to marriage between relatives. Without intending a pun, we point out immediately that consanguinity is a relative term. Actually all human beings are related to each other. We all had ancestors in common if we go back far enough in our study, and for people in the same racial group it is not necessary to go back very far. It has been estimated (Dahlberg, 1948a), for example, that if there had been *no* consanguinity, each individual living today would have had 1 billion ancestors who lived 30 generations ago (about 750 years ago). We surmise that there were not 1 billion people in existence in the thirteenth century; certainly there were not 1 billion for every person alive today.

How closely must two people be related for their marriage to be considered consanguineous? In modern society, the term refers principally to the marriage of first cousins. In this case, one parent of the husband is a sib of one of his wife's parents (there are rarely "double first cousins," in which case both parents of the husband are sibs, respectively, of his wife's parents). In certain times and societies brother-sister marriage, a still closer consanguinity, has been practiced; occasionally marriage between uncle and niece occurs. Although marriage of second cousins, the children of first cousins, is also considered consanguineous, it has so little genetic effect that we shall largely ignore it. For present purposes, consanguinity will refer principally to first-cousin matings.

We shall begin by asking the question: If a man has a certain recessive gene, what are the chances that his first cousin has the same recessive gene? To give concreteness to our question we may return to our example of recessive albinism. If a man is a carrier (heterozygous) for albinism, what are the chances that his first cousin is also a carrier? The pedigree in Figure 8.1 represents such a situation. Here the siblings shared as parents by the man and his cousin are represented as sisters; the result would be the same if they were brothers or if they were a brother-sister

111

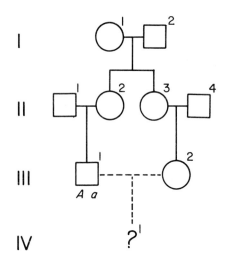

FIG. 8.1 Consanguinity. Proposed marriage of first cousins, one of whom (III-1) is known to be heterozygous for a certain pair of alleles.

pair (for we are not discussing a sex-linked gene; see Chap. 12).

The man in question, III-1, is represented as being heterozygous; what are the chances that his cousin, III-2, also is?

(1) What are the chances that III-1 inherited the *a* gene from his mother (the parent related to III-2) rather than from his father (the parent not related to III-2)? This chance is ½ (as far as we know he was equally likely to have inherited it from either parent). If he inherited *a* from his mother, II-2, that means that she was heterozygous, *Aa*.

(2) If II-2 was heterozygous, she must have received *a* from one of her parents, I-1 × I-2. Thus their mating must have been *Aa* × *AA* (without designating which was which). If so, what are the chances that II-3, sister of II-2, is also *Aa*? Because she had an equal chance of receiving *A* or *a* from her heterozygous parent in generation I, the chance is ½.

(3) If II-3 is *Aa*, what are the chances that she will pass on gene *a* to her daughter, III-2? Clearly the chance is ½.

At three points as we pass through our pedigree from III-1 to III-2, we encounter chances of ½. Because each is an independent event, the chance that all three will occur is ½ × ½ × ½ = ⅛. This means that if a man who is a carrier for a certain recessive gene marries his first cousin, the chances are 1 in 8 that he will be marrying another carrier.

What are the chances that he will be marrying another carrier if he marries someone who is *not* his cousin? This depends on the relative frequency of the gene in the gene pool. In the case of albinism, we found (p. 96) that about 1 person in 70 is a carrier. If his wife is not his cousin, there is 1 chance in 70 that she is a carrier. This means that in this particular case he is about 9 times as likely to marry a carrier if he marries his cousin as he is if he marries "outside the family." (However, the difference in likelihood varies with difference in the gene frequency, becoming less if the gene is common, so that the random chance of marrying a carrier is greater.)

Going one step further we ask, if III-1 marries III-2 what are the chances that a child (e.g., the first one) will be an albino. From $Aa \times Aa$ matings one fourth of the children are expected to be *aa*. Hence the total chance that any one child will be an albino is $\frac{1}{8} \times \frac{1}{4} = \frac{1}{32}$.

For comparison we ask, if III-1 does not marry his cousin what are the chances that he will have an albino child? The chance is $\frac{1}{70} \times \frac{1}{4} = \frac{1}{280}$ (the chance that his wife is a carrier multiplied by the chance of an *aa* child from an $Aa \times Aa$ mating). Again we note the approximately ninefold difference.

In our calculations so far we have made one simplifying assumption: that the *a* gene entered the pedigree only once—that if it came from I-1 or I-2 it did not *also* come from II-1 or II-4, the husbands of the sisters II-2 and II-3. With rare genes, such a simplifying assumption is usually warranted, but if the gene is common there is greater likelihood that unrelated spouses may be carriers.

The Effects of Consanguinity

We see then that inbreeding increases the chance that homozygous offspring will be produced. Conversely, it follows that consanguinity tends to decrease the percentage of heterozygotes. Parenthetically, we note that inbreeding does not change the gene pool itself, any more than a deck of cards is changed by a change in the method of dealing. Inbreeding simply alters the manner in which the genes are dealt out to offspring.

We might pause for a moment to note that an increase in the relative frequency of homozygotes is the only effect of consanguinity. Some people have the idea that in some rather mystical way inbreeding in itself is essentially harmful. We are in a position to understand that this is not true. Inbreeding only increases homozygosity. This is not bad in itself; it is only harmful if the genes for which offspring become homozygous are harmful genes. After all, in certain times and societies in human history the extreme inbreeding involved in brother-sister matings has been practiced with success—for example, among the Egyptian Pharaohs and the Incas of Peru. The fact remains, however, that most of us (probably all of us) are heterozygous for genes that have a detrimental effect when present in a double dose. Therefore, inbreeding tends to increase the proportion of offspring showing hereditary defects.

We should note at once that this tendency to increased homozygosity varies inversely with the gene frequency. The more frequent the gene, the less effect consanguinity has. This is logical, for what consanguinity does is to increase the chance that heterozygotes will marry each other. If the gene is abundant, there will be many heterozygotes, with the result that they will marry each other frequently just by chance in the absence of inbreeding.

→To make this point clear with an example, we recall that if the frequency, q, of a recessive gene is 0.5, we expect that 25 percent of a random-breeding population will be homozygous recessive (p. 90). Suppose that a dictator should issue an edict that henceforth everyone must marry a first cousin. What effect would the resulting consanguinity have on homozygosity among the offspring?

If all matings are first-cousin matings, the percentage of homozygous recessives among the offspring is given by the formula:

$$\frac{q}{16} (1 + 15\ q)$$

(See Appendix A (pp. 399–400) for the derivation and explanation of this formula.)

Applying the formula to a population in which $q = 0.5$, we have

$$\frac{q}{16} (1 + 15\ q) = \frac{0.5}{16} (1 + 7.5) = \frac{4.25}{16} = 0.265 = 26.5\%$$

Thus we see that a complete program of first-cousin mating would only increase the percentage of homozygous recessives from 25 percent to 26.5 percent. To put it another way: In a panmictic population of 10,000, 2500 offspring are expected to be homozygous recessive. In a population of 10,000 in which everyone marries his first cousin, 2650 offspring are expected to be homozygous recessive. (In both cases we assume that the total size of the population is not increasing from generation to generation.) Thus the increase is 150, and this increase is only 6 percent of the number of homozygous recessives (2500) we should expect if there were no inbreeding.

In a population in which $q = 0.5$, the heterozygotes constitute 50 percent of the population (p. 90) and hence they will frequently marry each other even without inbreeding. We may well point out here that random mating or panmixis assumes the occurrence of some inbreeding. Recalling our discussion of the Hardy-Weinberg law, we realize that a basic assumption of that law is that mating follows the laws of probability. This means that the relative frequency of different types of mating depends entirely on the relative frequencies of the different genotypes in the population. This is assumed to be entirely independent of whether or not the females in question are related to the males. Thus, *by chance,* a male would sometimes marry a cousin, sometimes not. This is what we mean when we say that the Hardy-Weinberg law provides for some inbreeding, occurring by chance.

Now let us look at a population in which $q = 0.1$. As we saw earlier (p. 92), if this population is panmictic, 1 percent of the offspring are expected to be homozygous recessive. What percentage would be expected to be homozygous recessive if everyone married his first cousin?

$$\frac{q}{16} (1 + 15 \ q) = \frac{0.1}{16} (1 + 1.5) = \frac{0.25}{16} = 0.0156 = 1.56\%$$

The percentage has increased from 1 percent to 1.56 percent. Although this may seem to be a negligible increase, let us think of it in terms of a population of 10,000. With panmixis, 100 homozygous recessives are expected; with complete first-cousin mating 156 homozygous recessives are expected. This is an increase of 56, which, of course, is a 56 percent increase over the 100 we would have expected to result from panmixis.

Summarizing, we note that when $q = 0.5$, complete first-cousin mating results in only a 6 percent increase in homozygous recessives. When $q = 0.1$, complete first-cousin mating results in a 56 percent increase in homozygous recessives. This illustrates the principle that the effect of inbreeding in producing homozygous recessives varies inversely with the gene frequency.

New Mutations and Consanguinity It will be instructive to consider the extreme case, that of a new mutation which results in a gene not otherwise present in a population. By way of example, imagine a population in which everyone has the genotype *AA*. Suppose that in the germ cells of one individual a mutation from *A* to *a* occurred, so that some of his germ cells contained this new mutant gene. How could an *aa* individual be produced in the shortest possible time? Only through consanguinity, as illustrated in Figure 8.2. In this pedigree, we have represented two daughters, II-2 and II-3, as both containing the new gene. Then we have shown them passing the gene on to their respective offspring, III-1 and III-2. If these latter (first cousins) marry, each child has ¼ chance of being *aa*.

The new gene, *a*, remained hidden for three generations. If it is completely recessive, the first person who could show its phenotype would be a great-grandchild of the person in whom the mutation occurred, and then it could only come to light so quickly if consanguinity were involved. We recognize immediately, of course, that the new mutation may remain hidden for many generations, an *aa* individual first being produced when remote descendants of I-2 happen to marry each other. However, we have deliberately set out to demonstrate the quickest production of an *aa* individual.

Incidentally, we might notice that the many years that separate great-grandfather from great-grandchild have a delaying effect on investigations such as those concerned with new mutations produced by atomic bombs. If only the great-grandchildren of persons who experienced the blast can show the phenotypic effects—and then only if inbreeding occurs,

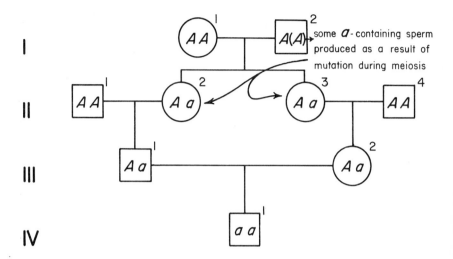

FIG. 8.2 Consanguinity as the means by which a homozygote for a "new" mutation can arise in the smallest possible number of generations.

such investigations must be long-term ones. Fortunately for investigators, although unfortunately for the victims themselves, many new mutations have some degree of dominance, meaning that they *do* produce some detectable effect in heterozygotes. Also, new sex-linked mutations do not remain hidden for as long a time as does the type indicated in our hypothetical pedigree (Chap. 12).

Increased Consanguinity Among Parents of Offspring Showing Rare Recessive Traits   If a gene is not completely new (as in our hypothetical model) but is nevertheless very rare, heterozygotes for the gene will seldom marry each other unless they are cousins.

To illustrate: What are the chances that you, if you are a young person of marriageable age, will have an albino child? In answering the question I shall assume that you have no albino relatives, and that the person you marry has no albino relatives. What are the chances that you are a carrier of the gene for albinism? As we have seen (p. 96), this chance is 2 pq, which is about $\frac{1}{70}$. What are the chances that your spouse, if not a cousin, is a carrier? This is also 2 $pq = \frac{1}{70}$. If you are both carriers, a given offspring has $\frac{1}{4}$ chance of being an albino. Therefore, the total chance that your first child will be an albino is

$$\frac{1}{70} \times \frac{1}{70} \times \frac{1}{4} = 1/19,600$$

Suppose you do marry a first cousin. The chance that you are a carrier is still $\frac{1}{70}$. However, the chance that your spouse is also a carrier is now not $\frac{1}{70}$, but $\frac{1}{8}$. Consequently, the chance that your first child will be an albino is

$$\frac{1}{70} \times \frac{1}{8} \times \frac{1}{4} = 1/2240$$

Thus by marrying a cousin you have increased more than eightfold the likelihood of having an albino child.

We recall that our calculations with regard to albinism are based on data indicating that $q = \frac{1}{141}$. Suppose we consider a gene much rarer than this: $q = \frac{1}{1000}$. Then $2\,pq = $ approximately $\frac{1}{500}$.

What are the chances that a man who is heterozygous for this rarer gene will have a homozygous recessive child if he does not marry a first cousin?

(1) Chance that he is a carrier $= \frac{1}{500}$

(2) Chance that his wife is a carrier $= \frac{1}{500}$

(3) Chance for a homozygous recessive child of two carrier parents $= \frac{1}{4}$

$$\frac{1}{500} \times \frac{1}{500} \times \frac{1}{4} = \frac{1}{1,000,000}$$

Now suppose that he does marry his first cousin:

(1) Chance that he is a carrier $= \frac{1}{500}$

(2) Chance that his wife is a carrier $= \frac{1}{8}$

(Note that this remains constant, not changing with gene frequency.)

(3) Chance for a homozygous recessive child of two carrier parents $= \frac{1}{4}$

$$\frac{1}{500} \times \frac{1}{8} \times \frac{1}{4} = \frac{1}{16,000}$$

In the case of this rarer gene, marrying a cousin has increased the likelihood of a homozygous recessive child, not eightfold, but more than sixty-twofold.

In Chapter 6 (p. 85) we noted that increased consanguinity among the parents is a hallmark of a rare recessive gene. Now we understand why this is. When a gene is really rare, a heterozygote will seldom happen to marry a heterozygote unless he marries a cousin.

An interesting case in point is afforded by a rare defect in which fibrinogen is lacking from the blood plasma. Fibrinogen is a plasma protein that is converted to fibrin in a cut or wound, forming a meshwork of fibers throughout a blood clot. Because blood cannot clot without fibrinogen, its absence is extremely serious. The defect is known as congenital **afibrinogenemia**. Fortunately the trait is rare. Frick and McQuarrie (1954) reported that 12 cases were known in which information about the parents was available. In 5 of the 12 cases, the parents were first cousins. Thus, in these 12 cases, the incidence of consanguinity was over 41 percent (as compared to an incidence of about 1 percent in the population at large). Here we have a fine example of increased consanguinity as a hallmark of a rare recessive gene.

In the paper just cited, the authors presented an interesting pedigree of a case the paper described in detail (Fig. 8.3). The afibrinogenemic propositus is IV-2. His parents were first cousins. The other interesting aspect of this study is the indication that carriers can be detected by virtue of

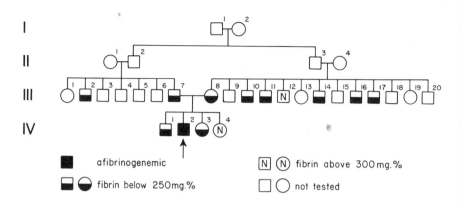

FIG. 8.3 Consanguinity in the ancestry of an afibrinogenemic child. (Redrawn from Frick, P. G., and I. McQuarrie, 1954. "Congenital afibrinogenemia," *Pediatrics,* **13**:44–58.)

the fact that they have less fibrinogen, and therefore less fibrin, than do other people (although the fibrin is sufficient for the formation of adequate clots). Thus the patient's parents (III-7 and III-8) both had a low fibrin level, as did some of their sibs. From their offspring, we surmise that II-2 and II-3 were heterozygous; unfortunately, they were not living at the time of the investigation and so could not be tested for fibrin level.

If we represent the rare recessive gene by *f* and its normal allele by *F*, the parents (III-7 and III-8) were *Ff* × *Ff*. Then their children were, in sequence *Ff, ff, Ff,* and *FF*. The authors pointed out the interested coincidence of this perfect tally with the 1:2:1 ratio.

Another human trait dependent on a rare recessive gene is **alkaptonuria**. In the chain of reactions by which amino acids are broken down in the body and the products excreted, one of the intermediate products is *homogentisic acid* (alkaptone). In most people this is broken down further, eventually to CO_2 and H_2O. However, alkaptonurics (people homozygous for the recessive gene in question) are unable to metabolize homogentisic acid, with the result that it collects in their urine. The urine turns black on exposure to the air. The trait usually has no seriously detrimental effects although arthritis sometimes seems to accompany it.

Although the trait is rare, some years ago a team of investigators learned that a substantial number of alkaptonurics were living in a certain region of Georgia (Hall, Hawkins, and Child, 1950). Investigation disclosed 16 cases, 15 of whom belonged to one large kindred, which could be traced back for seven generations.

Figure 8.4 is based on a portion of the large pedigree chart published by these authors. This portion includes 12 of the 15 alkaptonurics and goes back five generations. It is interesting not only for the number of affected individuals but also for the varying degrees of consanguinity displayed by

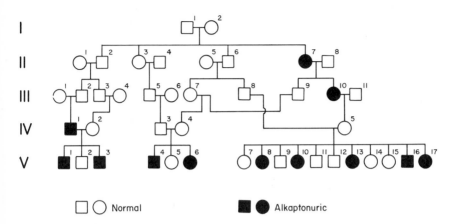

FIG. 8.4 Inheritance of alkaptonuria in a kindred characterized by consanguinity. (Based on a chart in Hall, W. K., K. R. Hawkins, and G. P. Child, 1950. "The inheritance of alkaptonuria in a large human family," *Journal of Heredity*, 41:23–25.)

the parents of the three families in the latest generation.

If we use *a* to represent the gene for alkaptonuria, and *A* to represent its normal allele, affected persons have the genotype *aa*. IV-1 represents such a person; his parents must both have been carriers (descendants did not know whether his mother, III-1, was related to the family or not). As the pedigree shows, IV-1 married his first cousin, daughter of his father's brother; of their three children, two were affected, whereas one was not.

Individuals IV-3 and IV-4, both carriers, were double second cousins. The father of IV-3 (III-5) was the first cousin of *both* of his wife's parents (III-7 and III-9). Such an arrangement is well calculated to concentrate recessive genes.

The parents of the largest family in the last generation (III-8 × IV-5) were first cousins once removed. The husband married his first cousin's daughter. Judging from the nature of their large family, both were carriers.

The authors mentioned that gathering data was facilitated by the fact that one branch of the family had monthly family reunions. We might comment that such family socializing if long continued would tend to encourage consanguinity itself.

Many studies have been made of the increased incidence of consanguinity among the parents of persons showing rare recessive defects. Without attempting a complete cataloguing, we may mention one or two typical investigations of this kind. Neel, Kodani, Brewer, and Anderson (1949) studied consanguineous matings in Japan. In the general population, first-cousin marriages occur about 6 percent of the time, but among parents of albinos the incidence of first-cousin marriage is between 37 and 59 percent. Among parents of children suffering from infantile amaurotic idiocy the incidence of first-cousin marriage is between 55 and 85 percent. Comparable figures for ichthyosis congenita are 67 to 93 percent; for congenital total color blindness, 39 to 51 percent; for xeroderma pigmentosum, 37 to 43 percent.

The authors quoted comparable figures for Caucasian populations, in which the general level of first-cousin marriage is about 1 percent. The percentages of first-cousin marriages for the parents of children affected with the five traits mentioned are as follows: albinism, 18 to 24 percent; infantile amaurotic idiocy, 27 to 53 percent; ichthyosis congenita, 30 to 40 percent; congenital total color blindness, 11 to 21 percent; xeroderma pigmentosum, 20 to 26 percent. More recent analysis of inbreeding in Japan is found in Schull and Neel, 1965.

Many more data might be cited but those given will suffice to illustrate the principle of increased consanguinity among parents as a hallmark of rare recessive traits.

Total Risk   Another way of looking at the significance of consanguinity is to ask the question: What is the total risk that some abnormality will occur in the children from first-cousin marriages? Studies have included a wide variety of congenital abnormalities, including many for which the genetic bases have not yet been analyzed. For example, from an extensive study of consanguinity in Japan, Schull (1958) concluded that whereas one or another of a long list of major congenital abnormalities occurs in about 1 percent of children born to nonconsanguineous marriages, it occurs in about 1.7 percent of children born of first-cousin marriages. Thus the risk of abnormality is 70 percent greater when the parents are related.

Other studies have indicated similar increases in risk; details of conclusions vary depending on the abnormalities included in the study. For example, Slatis, Reis, and Hoene (1958) studied 109 consanguineous marriages in the Chicago region. They concluded that the rate of abnormalities among children of consanguineous marriages was somewhat less than twice as great as the rate among children of unrelated parents, "but if only major abnormalities are considered, the added risk of consanguinity is exceedingly great, i.e., 8 of 192 living consanguineous children have had serious abnormalities, whereas 0 of 163 living control children have suffered serious abnormalities."

Genetic Isolates

As we mentioned earlier, the Hardy-Weinberg law assumes the existence of a population in which breeding is entirely random. If we apply the formula to the population of the United States, we make the tacit assumption that a certain man of marriageable age is equally likely to marry any one of all the women of marriageable age in the United States. The moment we make such a statement we realize that it does not describe an actual situation. A man in Maine *may* marry a woman in California, but the chances are greater that he will marry a woman in Maine. A man of one race *may* marry a woman of another race, but the chances are greater that he will marry a woman of his own race. A man of one religion *may* marry a woman of another religion, but the chances are greater that he will marry a coreligionist. And so it goes; many factors operate to interfere with random mating in the ideal sense.

Of these factors, the easiest ones to visualize are geographic. In mentioning Maine and California we have indicated the importance of distance in preventing true panmixis. How much distance is required? The answer depends on the means of communication available. A century ago, people in Maine had much less contact with people in California than they do today. In fact, before the days of automobiles and good roads, people in northern Maine had much less contact with people in southern Maine than they do today. Even today, statistics would probably show that a citizen of Presque Isle is more likely to marry another citizen of that city than he is to marry a citizen of Portland. All of which illustrates the fact that our theoretical, large, interbreeding population is in reality greatly subdivided into smaller units, which we call **genetic isolates.** The adjective "genetic" refers to the fact that the people in the isolate possess a common gene pool that is more or less separate from the gene pools of other isolates.

The classic example of an isolate can be seen in the inhabitants of a mountain valley, or "cove" as it is called in the southern Appalachians, connected to the outside world by a narrow, rough road, seldom used. Here, the mountain ranges combined with distance to form the isolating factors. In times past, more than today, such isolated communities were self-contained units, economically and socially. Generation after generation, marriages occurred between members of the community, seldom with an "outlander." Therefore, especially if the community was small, many or most of the people in later generations came to be more or less related to each other, with the result that marriage between relatives was frequent.

Many studies have indicated that there is an inverse correlation between the size of the isolate and the amount of consanguinity. The smaller the isolate the greater the amount of inbreeding. This relationship has been given mathematical expression, and formulas have been proposed for use in estimating the size of an isolate from the amount of consanguinity within it (see especially Dahlberg, 1948a and b). Although we note the general tendency, we shall not pursue the matter more precisely. In fact, precision is not attainable. Isolates seldom, if ever, have clear-cut boundaries, and, as Dahlberg stated, we can often say that "every person has his or her own isolate" (equating "isolate" with one's circle of acquaint-anceship).

Returning to our isolated mountain valley, we recall that occasionally such communities are characterized by an unusually high incidence of hereditary defects. In the light of our discussion of the action of con-sanguinity in increasing the production of homozygous individuals, we understand why this is so. With modern means of communication, these geographic isolates are fast disappearing. The mountaineers' circle of acquaintanceship is expanding, with the result that more of the marriages are with persons outside the isolate and hence fewer are consanguineous. This breaking of isolates results in a decreased production of children homozygous for recessive defects, as genes from the isolate mingle with genes outside it. This is the way the breaking of isolates should work in theory. Because of inadequate records, it is difficult to acquire accurate data, but the information we have indicates that the expected changes have, in fact, occurred.

Not all genetic isolates are geographic; some are social or religious. For example, when our mountaineer moves to the city, he is likely to find him-self still a member of an isolate, but an isolate defined in social and reli-gious terms. Thus, if he is white and Protestant and has a low income, he is more likely to marry a woman with these same attributes than he is a woman who is dark-skinned, Catholic, and wealthy. In Chapter 24 we shall discuss genetic phenomena in a religious isolate studied by Dr. Bentley Glass and his coworkers. This isolate consists of an Old Order Dunker community, founded by immigrants in Pennsylvania over two centuries ago. Members of the order seldom marry outside their own group and if they do, they leave the group.

Thus we see that the large, randomly breeding population postulated by the Hardy-Weinberg formula is to some extent a fictitious concept. Nevertheless it remains a useful one; although isolates *may* differ in genetic constitution, they do not necessarily differ with regard to the genes in which we may be interested in a given study. Catholics, for example, do not differ from Protestants in frequencies of the blood-group genes (unless the Catholics and Protestants belong to different racial or ethnic groups).

As we shall see in our discussion of forces operative in human evolu-tion (Chap. 24), the fact that early human populations were probably divided into rather small isolates is believed to have been a potent factor in the origin of human diversity.

In summary, we note that consanguinity tends to modify the Hardy-Weinberg equilibrium by increasing the proportion of homozygotes (with a concomitant decrease in the proportion of heterozygotes). Its effect is most marked on rare recessive genes. Indeed, increased consanguinity among parents forms a distinguishing criterion of a rare recessive gene.

Formation of genetic isolates increases the incidence of consanguinity, whereas breaking of such isolates decreases the amount of consanguinity. We expect this decrease to be accompanied by a decrease in persons homozygous for rare recessive defects.

PROBLEMS

1. In the gene pool of a certain population, the frequency, q, of the recessive gene b is 0.001 (0.1 percent). If a man having the genotype Bb marries his first cousin, what is the chance that their first child will have the genotype bb? If the man marries a woman unrelated to him, what is the chance that their first child will have the genotype bb? Hence, how many times more likely is production of a bb child if the man marries a first cousin than it is if he marries an unrelated woman?

2. In the population mentioned in question No. 1, what percentage of the offspring will be bb under a system of random mating? What percentage of the offspring would be bb if all marriages were first-cousin matings? By how many times is the occurrence of bb children increased through a uniform practice of first-cousin mating?

3. As we have seen, the frequency, q, of the gene for albinism is $\frac{1}{141}$. If a normally pigmented man picked at random in the population marries his niece, his sister's daughter, what is the chance that their first child will be an albino? (Assume that the sister's husband is not heterozygous.)
   What would be the chance for an albino child if this man married a first cousin? From the standpoint of producing recessive-phenotype children, is it more "dangerous" to marry one's niece or one's first cousin? How many times more?

4. Members of a pair of identical (monozygotic) twins have the same genotype. Identical-twin brothers married identical-twin sisters. The brothers were albinos. One couple produced a normally pigmented daughter and the other couple a normally pigmented son. If these first cousins marry each other, what is the chance that their first child will be an albino?

5. In the accompanying pedigree chart, I-2 is an albino; all other persons in the first three generations have normal pigmentation. What is the chance that IV-1, yet unborn, will be an albino? (Assume that II-1, and II-4 are not heterozygous.)

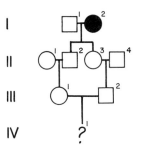

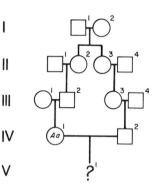

6. In the accompanying pedigree chart, if IV-1, known to be heterozygous *Aa*, marries her second cousin, IV-2, what is the chance that their first child will have the genotype *aa*? (Assume that gene *a* enters the kindred only once.)

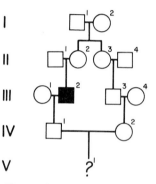

7. In the accompanying pedigree, III-2 is an albino; all other persons in the first four generations have normal pigmentation. What is the chance that V-1, yet unborn, will be albino? (Assume that I-1, II-4, III-1, and III-4 are not heterozygous.)

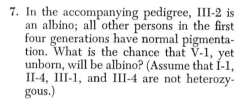

8. John Doe's mother has a brother who is an albino, the only person in the kindred who is. If John marries his cousin, the daughter of his mother's sister, what is the chance that their first child will be an albino? (Assume that the gene for albinism does not enter the kindred from unrelated spouses in later generations.)

REFERENCES

Dahlberg, G., 1948a. *Mathematical Methods for Population Genetics*. New York: Interscience Publishers.

Dahlberg, G., 1948b. "Genetics of human populations." In M. Demerec (ed.), *Advances in Genetics*, 2:67–98.

Frick, P. G., and I. McQuarrie, 1954. "Congenital afibrinogenemia," *Pediatrics*, 13:44–58.

Hall, W. K., K. R. Hawkins, and G. P. Child, 1950. "The inheritance of alkaptonuria in a large human family," *Journal of Heredity*, 41:23–25.

Neel, J. V., M. Kodani, R. Brewer, and R. C. Anderson, 1949. "The incidence of consanguineous matings in Japan," *American Journal of Human Genetics*, 1:156–78.

Schull, W. J., 1958. "Empirical risks in consanguineous marriages: sex ratio, malformation, and viability," *American Journal of Human Genetics,* **10:**294–343.

Schull, W. J., and J. V. Neel, 1965. *The Effects of Inbreeding on Japanese Children.* New York: Harper & Row, Publishers.

Slatis, H. M., R. H. Reis, and R. E. Hoene, 1958. "Consanguineous marriages in the Chicago region," *American Journal of Human Genetics,* **10:**446–64.

9.

MULTIPLE ALLELES:
ABO BLOOD GROUPS

In preceding chapters, we have made frequent reference to red blood cell antigens (agglutinogens) M and N, and their inheritance. These antigens were not the first ones discovered. We chose to discuss them first because they illustrate inheritance under conditions in which heterozygotes are directly determinable by serological tests. We now turn our attention to the more widely known ABO blood groups.

The ABO Blood Groups

These "classic" blood groups were discovered by Dr. Karl Landsteiner at the beginning of this century. In his initial investigation, he collected blood samples from 22 individuals and separated the cells from the fluid portion or serum (Landsteiner, 1901). Then by cross-matching (mixing the serum of one person with the blood cells of another person), he found that the serum of some people contains antibodies that will clump or agglutinate the red blood cells of other people. By such cross-matching, he classified his 22 people into three groups:

Group A—the serum of these people reacted with cells of people in group B, but not with cells of people in group A.

Group B—the serum reacted with cells from group A, but not with cells from group B.

Group C (or, as we call it today, group O)—the serum of these people agglutinated cells of people in both group A and group B, but group C cells were not agglutinated by group A or B serums.

Landsteiner's initial sample of 22 people did not include a person whose serum failed to agglutinate all three of the other kinds of cells (groups A, B, and C) and whose cells were agglutinated by serums from all three of these groups. Such people were soon discovered, however; today we classify them as group AB.

We note immediately some differences between these groups and the MN types. (1) People do not have naturally occurring antibodies against antigen M or N when they lack the antigen in their cells (e.g., a type M person does not have anti-N antibodies in his serum). On the other hand, people *do* have naturally occurring antibodies against antigen A or B when they lack the antigen in their cells. (2) People have in their red blood cells antigen M, antigen N, or both antigens; no one lacks both. On the other hand, some people *do* lack both A and B (people of group O). Table 9.1 summarizes the relationships of cellular antigens A and B to antibodies in the serum.

TABLE 9.1   ABO blood groups.

Blood group	Antigens in red blood cells	Antibodies in serum
A	A	anti-B
B	B	anti-A
AB	A and B	neither
O	neither	anti-A and anti-B

As we noted earlier, test fluids for detecting M and N are prepared by inoculating rabbits, which then form antibodies. Test fluids for A and B may be prepared in the same manner, but normally, human serums are employed. From Table 9.1 we can readily see that serum from a person who belongs to group A forms a test fluid that will react with cells containing B, and serum from a person belonging to group B forms a test fluid for cells containing A. Using these two serums, we can determine the group to which any person belongs, by testing his red blood cells as shown in Table 9.2.

The Von Dungern-Hirschfeld Hypothesis

With this much serological background we now ask: How are agglutinogens A and B inherited? Some ten years after Landsteiner's discovery, von Dungern and Hirschfeld (1910) proposed the hypothesis that each is dependent on a dominant gene, which we may designate as A and B, respectively. We are now confident that this interpretation is correct. What is the relationship of A to B? The authors proposed that A and not-A

TABLE 9.2   ABO blood groups—Reactions of cells with antiserums.

If red blood cells contain	Reaction with antiserums		Blood group of donor of the cells
	Anti-A	Anti-B	
A only	+	−	A
B only	−	+	B
both A and B	+	+	AB
neither A nor B	−	−	O

$+ =$ Clumping of cells.
$- =$ No clumping of cells.

behave as a dominant-versus-recessive Mendelian pair, and that B and not-B form a second such pair, independent of the first pair in inheritance. (We may represent the gene for absence of antigen A by the initial a, the gene for absence of B by b.) If this idea is correct, we have an example of two pairs of genes with independent assortment (pp. 37–38).

In point of fact, this hypothesis has been disproved. Why bother with it then? Because the way in which it was disproved is a valuable case history of the manner in which human geneticists solve their problems, and it is therefore well worth our attention.

According to the von Dungern and Hirschfeld theory, people who belong to group A have at least one A but are homozygous bb; people who belong to group B are homozygous aa but have at least one B; people who belong to group AB have at least one A and at least one B; and people who belong to group O have the genotype $aabb$. The groups and all possible genotypes in each are listed in Table 9.3. We might note parenthetically that it is the antigens A and B for whose inheritance we have to account. The antibodies in the serum (anti-B and anti-A) accompany the antigens but do not seem to be inherited separately. Discussion of the

TABLE 9.3   The von Dungern-Hirschfeld hypothesis of ABO inheritance.

Blood groups	Genotypes
A	AAbb, Aabb
B	aaBB, aaBb
AB	AABB, AaBB, AABb, AaBb
O	aabb

origin of the antibodies is not pertinent here (see Wiener, 1943–1962, for a discussion of the subject).

This theory accounts satisfactorily for many observed facts. For example, if both parents belong to group O, so do all the children. This would be expected from an *aabb* × *aabb* mating. Again, two group A parents may have a group O child. If, as might well be the case, the parents are heterozygous, this would work out as follows:

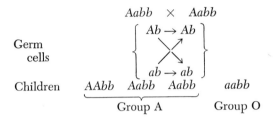

Similarly, two group B parents may have a group O child.

However, according to this theory, two group AB parents also can have a group O child:

$$Aabb \times AabB$$

Germ cells	AB AB
	Ab Ab
	aB aB
	ab ⟶ ab

The arrow indicates formation of the zygote that could result in a group O child. Actual observation shows, however, that group AB parents do not, in fact, have group O children (or vice versa, for that matter). Here, then, is a finding that the theory of two independent pairs of genes does not explain.

The theory ran into further trouble when the distribution of blood groups in whole populations was studied. Data of this kind have been accumulated in tremendous number. In 1925, Bernstein pointed out that if the theory were valid, the following equation should be correct:

$$(\overline{A} + \overline{AB}) \cdot (\overline{B} + \overline{AB}) = \overline{AB}$$

This may be translated as follows: In a population, the number of people who belong to group A added to the number who belong to group AB, if multiplied by the number who belong to group B added to the number who belong to group AB, should equal the number who belong to group AB. We may not understand at first glance why this equation should apply if the two-gene-pair theory is correct. The equation is derived by simple algebra, employing reasoning of the type encountered in applications of the Hardy-Weinberg formula. The derivation of the equation is given in Appendix B (pp. 401–402).

The results of large numbers of investigations have shown that this equation does not represent the actual situation encountered in populations. Typical of these findings are results that have historical interest because they were cited in Bernstein's original paper. The data used were collected by Kirihara, who tested 502 Japanese living in Korea. Bernstein analyzed his data as follows:

$$\overline{A} + \overline{AB} = 50\% = 0.5$$
$$\overline{B} + \overline{AB} = 28.4\% = 0.284$$
$$(\overline{A} + \overline{AB}) \cdot (\overline{B} + \overline{AB}) = 0.5 \times 0.284 = 0.142 \text{ or } 14.2\%$$

This means that, according to the theory, 14.2 percent of the population would be expected to belong to group AB. Actually only 7.8 percent did. This sort of discrepancy between expectation and reality was encountered so regularly that doubt was cast on the correctness of the theory.

The Multiple Allele Hypothesis

In the same paper, Bernstein proposed an alternative theory: that a set of multiple alleles forms the basis of inheritance. In Chapter 4 we mentioned multiple alleles in connection with abnormal hemoglobins. The idea of multiple alleles is that only one gene-location (locus) in only one pair of chromosomes is involved. This locus may be occupied by any one of a series of genes, which are said to constitute a series of multiple alleles. In the present instance, with the groups as stated, we have a series of three alleles. These are designated in various ways by different writers; we shall follow the precedent of those who employ the initial I (for **isoagglutinogen**—a normally occurring antigen) with appropriate superscripts. Thus:

$$I^A = \text{gene for antigen A}$$
$$I^B = \text{gene for antigen B}$$
$$I^O = \text{gene recessive to both } I^A \text{ and } I^B$$

In Figure 9.1 we represent by two straight lines the pair of chromosomes concerned. The short crossline represents the locus in question. This locus in any one chromosome may be occupied by any one of the three genes. Because the chromosomes occur as a pair, any individual may have any two of the three genes. The figure shows the genotypes possible in persons belonging to each group.

Does the multiple allele hypothesis explain observed facts better than did the theory of two independently assorting gene pairs? We noted above that people belonging to blood group AB do not, in fact, have children belonging to group O. The present theory, unlike the former one, explains this:

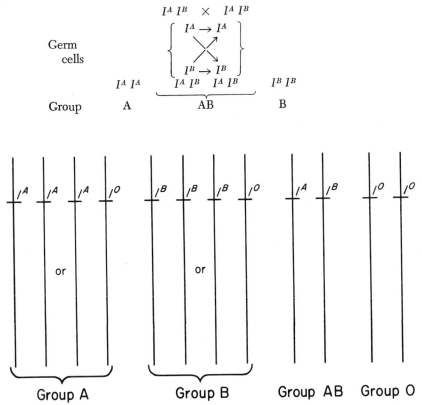

FIG. 9.1 All possible pairings of the blood group alleles I^A, I^B, and I^O. Each pair of vertical lines represents a pair of chromosomes. The short cross line represents the locus of the multiple alleles concerned.

In fact, even if one parent belongs to group O, it is still impossible for a group AB parent to have a group O child:

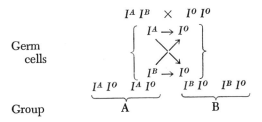

This last diagram also demonstrates the converse: a group O parent (even when married to a group AB person) cannot have a group AB child.

Here the multiple allele theory agrees with observation. What does the study of populations reveal as to the adequacy of the multiple allele theory?

We answer this question by calculating the relative proportions of the different groups to be expected in a panmictic population *if* the theory is correct. To do this, we employ the Hardy-Weinberg formula extended to include three alleles.

Let p = relative frequency of gene I^A
q = relative frequency of gene I^B
r = relative frequency of gene I^O
$p + q + r = 1$

Then:

$$(p + q + r)^2 = p^2 + 2\,pq + 2\,pr + q^2 + 2\,qr + r^2$$

This means that in a panmictic population:

the relative frequency of $I^A\,I^A$ persons is p^2
the relative frequency of $I^A\,I^O$ persons is $2\,pr$
the relative frequency of $I^B\,I^B$ persons is q^2
the relative frequency of $I^B\,I^O$ persons is $2\,qr$
the relative frequency of $I^A\,I^B$ persons is $2\,pq$
the relative frequency of $I^O\,I^O$ persons is r^2

Hence the frequency of:

group A persons $(I^A\,I^A + I^A\,I^O)$ is $p^2 + 2\,pr$
group B persons $(I^B\,I^B + I^B\,I^O)$ is $q^2 + 2\,qr$
group AB persons $(I^A\,I^B)$ is $2\,pq$
group O persons $(I^O\,I^O)$ is r^2

Group A + group O = $p^2 + 2\,pr + r^2 = (p + r)^2$
Group B + group O = $q^2 + 2\,qr + r^2 = (q + r)^2$
Then $p + r = \sqrt{\overline{A} + \overline{O}}$ (Where $\overline{A}$ is the number of group A
people, $\overline{O}$ the number in group O)

and $q + r = \sqrt{\overline{B} + \overline{O}}$
Since $p + q + r = 1$
$p = 1 - (q + r) = 1 - \sqrt{\overline{B} + \overline{O}}$ and
$q = 1 - (p + r) = 1 - \sqrt{\overline{A} + \overline{O}}$
$r = \sqrt{\overline{O}}$

Hence:

$$p + q + r = (1 - \sqrt{\overline{B} + \overline{O}}) + (1 - \sqrt{\overline{A} + \overline{O}}) + \sqrt{\overline{O}} = 1$$

This is usually simplified and written as:

$$\sqrt{\overline{O} + \overline{B}} + \sqrt{\overline{O} + \overline{A}} - \sqrt{\overline{O}} = 1$$

(The square root of the frequency of group O persons added to group B persons, plus the square root of the frequency of group O persons plus group A persons, minus the square root of the frequency of group O persons, equals 1.)

This is the expectation; do observed facts fit it? Tests on large numbers of populations, including thousands of individuals, demonstrate that the expectation expressed by the formula fits very precisely indeed (see Wiener, 1943–1962, for detailed results). Agreement has been so close and so uniformly attained that the multiple allele theory is now established beyond reasonable doubt.

Some of the tests of the theory have involved applications of the Hardy-Weinberg formula that are of theoretical interest to us. To use an example given by Wiener (1943–1962), we may ask: If the theory is correct, how frequently should the combination of group O mother and group O child be encountered in a population?

Group O children can arise from group O mothers in the following ways:

Expected Frequency

Mother $I^O I^O$ × Father $I^O I^O$ $\quad r^2 \times r^2 = r^4$ (all children O)

Mother $I^O I^O$ × Father $I^A I^O$ $\quad r^2 \times 2\,pr = 2\,pr^3$ (½ of children O)

Mother $I^O I^O$ × Father $I^B I^O$ $\quad r^2 \times 2\,qr = 2\,qr^3$ (½ of children O)

Hence the combination of group O mother and group O child has the expectation:

$$r^4 + \frac{2\,pr^3}{2} + \frac{2\,qr^3}{2} = r^4 + pr^3 + qr^3 = r^3\,(r + p + q) = r^3$$
$$\text{(since } p + q + r = 1\text{)}$$

So an investigator collects data on a population and computes the value of r (which equals $\sqrt{\bar{O}}$ as we saw above). Then if the theory is correct, the frequency of the combination group O mother and group O child should approximate r^3. Repeated testing in this manner has substantiated the correctness of the theory.

The example chosen above is simply a sample. We can ask questions about expectation concerning other parent-child combinations, and then test expectation against actual findings. For example, in what proportion of cases would we expect a group O mother and group A child? Expectation may be calculated in the manner of the preceding example.

Medico-Legal or Forensic Applications

With the multiple allele theory firmly established, we can now determine what types of children are possible, and what types impossible, in any mating in which we may be interested. For example, we determined that when one parent is AB and the other is O, the children may be A or B, but cannot be AB or O. Many books (e.g., Snyder and David, 1957; Stern, 1960; Wiener, 1943–1962) contain tables from which one can read quickly the types of "possible" and "impossible" offspring from every type of mating, but we can easily calculate expectations for any mating in which we may be interested.

We can readily see that the ability to determine such expectations enables us to decide some disputes concerning family relationships. In most actual instances, these are cases of disputed paternity (although occasionally, in hope of financial gain from a deceased woman's estate, a person may make fraudulent claim to being her descendant).

In one instance, for example, a woman hailed a man into court, claiming that he was the father of her child. Serological tests were performed. The mother belonged to group A, the child to group B; the accused man belonged to group O. Hence his innocence was established. Even without writing out the genotypes, we understand that the actual father must have contributed antigen B (which the mother did not have). The accused man did not have this antigen either. The mother's genotype was $I^A I^O$ (note that if she had been $I^A I^A$ she could not have had a group B child). The child was $I^B I^O$ (he must have inherited I^O from his mother). The accused man was $I^O I^O$; hence he could not have an $I^B I^O$ child by an $I^A I^O$ woman. The true father must have been $I^B I^B$ or $I^B I^O$ or $I^A I^B$.

Suppose that the accused man *had* belonged to group B. What would that have indicated? Actually nothing, taken by itself, since any group B man could have been the father. The evidence in these cases is of an excluding variety: in a proportion of cases men wrongly accused of paternity can prove their innocence by means of blood tests. Of course, if they are *not* wrongly accused, the tests will be of no avail to them, and in some cases, as suggested, even if they are innocent the blood tests will not help them prove they are. The chance of proving innocence is increased by making use, in addition to the A and B antigens, of the M and N antigens discussed earlier, of the various Rh antigens to be discussed presently, and of a variety of other antigens known to serologists. When one set of antigens does not prove innocence, another set may do so.

If, for example, the mother is of group A, type M, and her child is of group O, type M, we know that an accused man of group O, type N, could not have been the father. The A and O groups do not show his innocence, but the MN types do. The child had the genotype $L^M L^M$; he received one L^M from his mother, and he received the other L^M from his father. The accused man, being $L^N L^N$, could not have contributed that second L^M.

As we bring more and more antigens to bear on a given case, we increase the chances of proving innocence. We also increase the chances of proving guilt. It is customary to say that the blood tests cannot prove guilt—that any man of the designated type could have been the father. This is true, but if we increase the number of antigens and still find that the accused man agrees in every detail with the genetic constitution that the true father must have had, we progressively decrease the likelihood that some *other* man of this exact genetic constitution may have been present under the proper circumstances to father the child in question.

In this respect, almost the ultimate has been reached in cattle, in which some 40 pairs of antigens are known. The chance that two unrelated bulls will agree perfectly with regard to all these pairs is of the order of $(\frac{1}{2})^{40}$— a vanishingly small chance. For all practical purposes, an individual bull can be "fingerprinted" by means of his blood, and the fact that he sired a certain calf established beyond all reasonable doubt. This is obviously important with pedigreed cattle.

The number of identified human antigens has increased so rapidly in recent years that the positive individual identification possible today in cattle may soon be attainable in man.

Not all medico-legal cases involve disputed paternity. Sometimes babies are wrongly identified in hospitals, or at least parents think that they have been. From the standpoint of genetics, a particularly instructive case occurred in a large midwestern city some years ago. Two ladies, whom we shall call Mrs. Smith and Mrs. Jones, went to the same hospital and gave birth to baby girls on the same day. A few days later, they left the hospital on the same day, taking their babies with them.

When she reached home, Mrs. Smith discovered that her baby was labelled "Jones," and Mrs. Jones discovered that her baby was labelled "Smith". What to do? Were the babies correctly labelled but somehow accidentally exchanged in the flurry of leaving the hospital? Or were the labels incorrect, so that each mother had, indeed, taken home her own baby? Solving the problem was not helped by the fact that both mothers claimed the same baby.

Blood tests were performed and cleared up the whole matter. By fortunate chance, Mr. Smith was AB and Mrs. Smith was O. The baby they took home, labelled "Jones," was group O. As we know, such a parent-child combination is impossible. The baby labelled "Smith" (whom the Joneses had taken home) belonged to group A, so the Smiths could have been her parents.

Mr. and Mrs. Jones both belonged to group O, as did the baby marked "Jones" (whom the Smiths took home). Thus, the Joneses could not have been the parents of the baby labelled "Smith" (group A).

Evidently, then, the labels were correct. The families exchanged the babies and everyone was satisfied. The happy outcome was due in large measure to the fact that one parent happened to belong to group AB. Under other circumstances, such clear-cut conclusions might not have been possible.

Applications to Anthropology

We noted in our discussion of distal hyperextensibility of the thumb
(p. 102) that geneticists and physical anthropologists are constantly seeking human traits that have a clearly established, and preferably simple,
genetic basis. Such traits are of great value in comparing populations and
in tracing the relationships of different groups to one another. Because of
the relatively direct relationship between genes and the antigens they
produce or control, red blood cell antigens form the best traits of this
kind known at present.

The anthropological literature is filled with serological data. Blood tests
have been performed on an amazing number of varied populations from
all parts of the earth. Readers interested in the blood group distribution
of almost any people will find pertinent data in the huge tables compiled
by Wiener (1943–1962) and Mourant (1954).

Extensive discussion of the anthropological implications of the blood
groups is found in Boyd's *Genetics and the Races of Man* (1950). At
present, we can find space for only a few examples to illustrate the manner
in which serological data can be useful in the study of human diversity
and the formation of races.

At the outset we may note that, on the whole, although populations
differ in the *proportions* in which the different blood groups occur, rarely,
if ever, is one antigen completely lacking in one population. A comparison
of the blood group distribution of western Europeans with that of eastern
Asiatics demonstrates this. A typical study of Englishmen in London
shows the following distribution (Boyd, 1950):

Group A = 42.4%; B = 8.3%; AB = 1.4%; O = 47.9%

We may compare these figures with results of a study of a Chinese
population:

A = 30.8%; B = 27.7%; AB = 7.3%; O= 34.2%

We note that a smaller proportion of Chinese have antigen A, as compared to the number of Englishmen who have it (30.8% + 7.3% = 38.1% of
Chinese have it, alone or combined with B; whereas 42.4% + 1.4% = 43.8%
of Englishmen have it, alone or combined with B). The largest contrast
is in the possession of antigen B. Among Englishmen, 8.3% + 1.4% = 9.7%
have B, alone or combined with A; among Chinese, 27.7% + 7.3% = 35%
have B, alone or combined with A.

A genetically preferable way of saying this is to use formulas, such as
those we mentioned on the preceding pages (132-133), to calculate the

frequencies of genes I^A, I^B, and I^O in the two gene pools. For these frequencies we employ the initials p, q, and r, respectively, as before.

In this manner, the data concerning the English population sample reveal a gene pool in which the approximate gene frequencies are (Boyd, 1950):

$$p = 0.250 \qquad q = 0.050 \qquad r = 0.692$$

whereas the data concerning the Chinese population sample reveal a gene pool in which the approximate frequencies are:

$$p = 0.220 \qquad q = 0.201 \qquad r = 0.587$$

The q's tell the story: among the English, 5 percent of the genes are I^B, whereas among the Chinese, 20 percent of the genes are I^B. Geneticists look forward to the day when *all* differences between populations, and racial groups, can be expressed in terms of gene frequencies.

England and China are at the two extremes of the Eurasian continent. Long ago it was pointed out (by H. and L. Hirschfeld; see Wiener, 1943–1962) that there are progressive differences in populations lying between these two extremes. As one travels eastward on the continent of Eurasia, one successively encounters populations having less and less antigen A and more and more antigen B. Although this geographic trend is interesting, we are still far from explaining how it originated. We might imagine that antigen A originated in Europe and antigen B in the Far East, and that as people migrated back and forth, the I^A gene gradually spread eastward and I^B spread westward. Such a hypothesis has the appeal of simplicity, but it leaves many questions unanswered. Much evidence suggests that both antigens A and B are very ancient; in fact, they are probably older than man himself, for they are found in subhuman primates such as the great apes (see Moody, 1962) and even in some lower mammals. They may have arisen by mutation of genes more than once in evolutionary history, a fact that complicates our attempts to trace that history by serological means.

At times, however, blood grouping may enable an investigator to determine the affinities and probable origin of some groups of people. The following well-known case is of value because we have independent knowledge of the history of the group in question. Several hundred years ago a group of gypsies migrated from their native India to Hungary. They lived among the Hungarian people but did not intermarry with them (thus they constituted a genetic isolate, pp. 120–123). Serological tests demonstrate that they still retain the blood group distribution of their ancestors (Table 9.4), which differs markedly from that of their Hungarian neighbors. If we did not know the history of these people, but concluded from the blood group distribution that they were of Indian, or at least Asiatic, origin, we should have drawn a correct conclusion. In cases in which we do not know the history, then, conclusions based on the blood groups may frequently be of value.

The anthropological literature in this field is almost unimaginably voluminous. Hardly an issue of the *American Journal of Physical Anthropology* is without data on the blood groups of peoples in some region of the earth.

Students of human genetics and evolution are very interested in the exchange of genes between populations, and in the related problem of how mutations are distributed from the center in which they first occur. Gene pools are mingled whenever diverse peoples come into contact, either through migration or even through such casual contact as when soldiers of one country are stationed for a time in another country. The mixed phenotypes of the children produced give evidence of the genetic mixing, although many traits of coloring, facial features, and other characteristics by which we usually distinguish one people from another have

TABLE 9.4   ABO blood group frequencies of Hungarians, Hungarian gypsies and people in India.

| | Percent in group | | | |
	A	B	AB	O
Gypsies (in Hungary)	21.1	38.4	8.5	34.2
People in India	19.0	41.2	8.5	31.3
Hungarians	38.0	18.8	12.2	31.0

From a larger table in Wiener, A. S., *Blood Groups and Transfusion*, 3rd ed., 1943. Courtesy of the author and of Charles C Thomas, Publisher, Springfield, Illinois.

not yet been thoroughly analyzed genetically. In this respect, blood groups offer an advantage, as we have already noted. An interesting case in point is afforded by the Australian aborigines and their neighbors to the north (Fig. 9.2). These neighbors possess the B gene (I^B), but the gene seems to be lacking among the natives of Australia except for a few individuals in the extreme northern portion (Cape York Peninsula and the region adjacent to the Gulf of Carpentaria). Birdsell (1950) concluded that the infiltration of I^B into these regions is to be explained by contacts between the aborigines and (a) Papuan populations from the islands in the strait between Australia and New Guinea, and (b) Malays of Indonesia, who in early historic times are known to have sent fishing fleets into Australian waters.

Incidentally, the student of human blood groups has many interesting riddles to solve. How shall we explain the fact that Australian aborigines originally lacked I^B, if our evidence is correct? And how shall we explain the fact that American Indians are almost lacking in I^B (some groups tested lack it entirely; others have gene pools in which q is about 1 percent)? The ancestors of the American Indians presumably migrated from

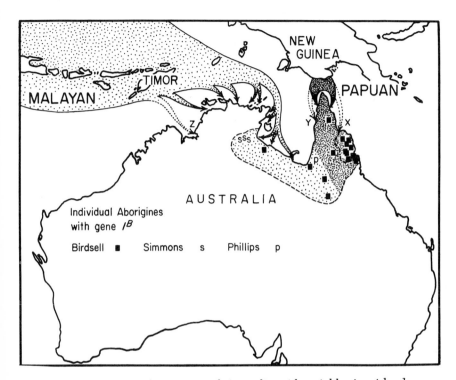

FIG. 9.2 The northern coast of Australia with neighboring islands. Shading shows regions in which some of the aborigines possess antigen B. The shaded arrows show probable routes by which visitors in times past brought the I^B gene to Australia. (After Birdsell, J. B., 1950. "Some implications of the genetical concept of race in terms of spatial analysis," *Cold Spring Harbor Symposia on Quantitative Biology,* 15:259–311.)

Asia across a land bridge spanning what is now Bering Strait, yet modern Asiatics have a high percentage of I^B! Did the ancestors of the Indians migrate before I^B became abundant in Asiatic gene pools? Did the ancestors belong to a different racial stock from that represented by the modern inhabitants of Asia? Perhaps chance, in the form of "genetic drift" (pp. 360–366), determined that the ancestral migrants included very few individuals having I^B. Perhaps differential susceptibility to disease played a role (see pp. 156–157).

These are typical of the fascinating problems presented to the student of blood group distributions.

Some Allied Considerations   We have spoken of the genes concerned in the ABO blood groups as constituting a series of three multiple alleles:

I^A, I^B, I^O. Actually there are four or five, and possibly more. For many years it has been known that antigen A is not a single entity but that there are two serologically distinct forms of it, called A_1 and A_2. Correspondingly, there are two "A-genes": I^{A_1} and I^{A_2}. More recently an A_3 antigen has been discovered, and even an A_4, but these two are very rare.

Recognition of subgroup A_1 and subgroup A_2 increases the list of multiple alleles to four. Persons in subgroup A_1 may have any one of three genotypes: $I^{A_1} I^{A_1}$, $I^{A_1} I^{A_2}$ (I^{A_1} is dominant to I^{A_2}), or $I^{A_1} I^O$. People in subgroup A_2 are $I^{A_2} I^{A_2}$ or $I^{A_2} I^O$. The AB group is similarly divided: $I^{A_1} I^B$ or $I^{A_2} I^B$.

These subgroups are useful in medico-legal tests, increasing the chance of proving innocence in paternity cases, for example. They are also of interest anthropologically. In most populations studied, group A_1 is much more numerous than group A_2. In a typical study of Englishmen, the A_1 people outnumbered the A_2 people about 4:1. Some peoples seem to lack A_2 completely, e.g., Australian aborigines, Chinese, Japanese, American Indians, and inhabitants of Pacific islands (Boyd, 1950). In the peoples of Africa, like those of Europe, the subgroup is well represented. With so much diversity, the subgroups may contribute significantly to studies of human relationships.

Thus far, we have spoken of the group O phenotype as being characterized by *absence* of antigens A and B. This is correct; but does the genotype $I^O I^O$ have a more positive function in the form of producing an antigen of its own? There is evidence that group O people are characterized by having what is variously termed a "group O substance" or an "H substance" (the technical difference between the two need not concern us here). Because the methods of testing for it are not yet highly reliable, the substance has not found wide application in medico-legal and anthropological investigations.

Secretors

Antigens A and B are found not only in red blood cells but also in the cells of other tissues in the body. In some people the antigens are found in such secretions of the body as the saliva. It seems that all possessors of A or B have an alcohol-soluble form of these antigens but that some people have a water-soluble form as well. Such people are called **secretors**; persons who have the antigens only in their cells are called **nonsecretors**.

Genetic analysis leads to the conclusion that a single gene difference is involved, secretion of the antigens being dependent on a dominant gene, *Se*. Homozygotes for the recessive allele (*se se*) are nonsecretors. Although this conclusion is of interest in itself, the most meaningful question for our present consideration is: What evidence supports this conclusion? How would we go about determining whether or not it is correct?

One way of answering the question begins with determining the relative frequency, q, of the presumed recessive gene. Investigations of 1118 persons in Liverpool showed that 254 or 22.72 percent of them were nonsecretors (Race and Sanger, 1962).

From this, we obtain:

$$q^2 = 0.2272 \qquad q = \sqrt{0.2272} = 0.4767$$
$$\text{Therefore } p = 1 - 0.4767 = 0.5233$$

Table 9.5 presents data from an investigation of 185 families. Note that when both parents are nonsecretors, all the children are, too. This agrees with the hypothesis that nonsecretors are homozygous for a recessive gene.

The first line of the table presents the most numerous cases—105 families in which both parents are secretors. If our hypothesis that secretion depends on a dominant gene is correct, we have lumped together here three parental combinations: (a) both parents homozygous; (b) one parent homozygous, one heterozygous; (c) both parents heterozygous. From such grouped parentage what proportion of recessive (nonsecretor) children would be expected?

It was to answer such questions that we developed formula (2) in Chapter 7 (pp. 100–101). The proportion expected is

$$\left(\frac{q}{1 + q} \right)^2$$

Let us assume that the value of q given by the Liverpool data is typical of the gene pools to which these families belong. Then,

$$\left(\frac{q}{1 + q} \right)^2 = \left(\frac{0.4767}{1.4767} \right)^2 = (0.3228)^2 = 0.1042 = 10.42\%$$

Thus, 10.42 percent of the children would be expected to be nonsecretors. The total number of children in these families was 274 (Table 9.5); 10.42 percent of 274 is 28.6. Reference to the table shows that 33 nonsecretor children were actually found. Because 33 and 28.6 are not

TABLE 9.5   Inheritance of the secretor trait.

| | No. of | Children | | |
Parents	families	Secretor	Nonsecretor	Total
Secretor × Secretor	105	241	33	274
Secretor × Nonsecretor	62	103	67	170
Nonsecretor × Nonsecretor	18	0	42	42

From Wiener, A. S., *Blood Groups and Transfusion*, 3rd ed., 1943. Courtesy of the author and of Charles C Thomas, Publisher, Springfield, Illinois.

far apart, we are probably justified in concluding that the evidence supports the hypothesis of single gene-pair inheritance with the secretor gene dominant.

Perhaps, on the other hand, someone might object that the agreement is not close enough to support the hypothesis. Is there any way in which we can bolster our argument? We may ask: How frequently would one expect to find the observed deviation (between 33 and 28.6) arising just by chance? If we investigated a larger number of families, might not the discrepancy between observation and expectation disappear? These 105 families are just a sample of all families in which both parents are secretors. Perhaps the deviation observed arises from the fact that the 105 families are not completely typical of all families of this kind. In other words, perhaps an error of sampling is involved. How can we determine whether or not the observed deviation is probably a chance occurrence caused by a sampling error in our data?

Long ago, Karl Pearson invented a test to help in such a situation. It is called the **chi-square test**. Although it is by no means the only, or necessarily the best, means of testing statistical significance, it is one of the simplest and one of the most widely used tests. In Appendix C (pp. 403–405) the test is explained and applied to the present data. We find that with 274 children, obtaining 33 of one type when we expected 28.6 would occur by chance about 40 percent of the time. In other words, if we had a large number of investigations, each involving 274 children, 40 percent of the investigations would be expected to show as much deviation as this, just by random chance. Hence there is a good likelihood that chance alone is involved in the deviation between 33 and 28.6 and that this deviation is not significant (i.e., is not significant evidence against our hypothesis). In this manner, the chi-square test enables us to feel more confident of the validity of conclusions based on data that are limited in quantity, as they always are in human genetics.

We must not gain the impression that we have considered all the evidence supporting the conclusion that secretion of A and B in fluids such as saliva depends on a dominant gene. This example has been included to illustrate the type of thinking involved when geneticists approach a problem of this kind.

The alleles *Se* and *se* determine a pair of contrasting phenotypes that can be employed, along with the blood groups themselves, in investigations of families, populations, and racial or ethnic groups.

PROBLEMS

1. A widow belonging to blood group A had two children, of groups O and B, respectively. What must have been the genotype and phenotype of the father? Also give the genotypes of the widow and her children.

2. A sibship was composed of four children belonging, respectively, to groups A, B, O, and AB. Give the genotypes and phenotypes of the parents of the sibship.

3. To what blood groups may children from each of the following matings belong—A × O; B × O; A × A; AB × O; A × AB; B × B?

4. Give all the different matings that may give rise to a child belonging to group AB.

5. In the gene pool of a certain population the relative frequencies of the blood group genes are as follows: $p = 0.30$; $q = 0.06$; $r = 0.64$. In this population what percentage of the people belongs to each of the four groups?

6. If the multiple allele theory of ABO blood group inheritance is correct, how frequently should the combination of group O mother and group A child be encountered in a population? (Answer in terms of p and r, and then in terms of the gene frequencies given in problem No. 5.)

7. A baby belongs to blood type M, group O, and is a secretor. Which of the following pairs of parents could *not* have been the parents of this baby? Explain in each case.

      (1) M, A, nonsecretor   ×   M, B, secretor
      (2) M, AB, nonsecretor ×   M, O, secretor
      (3) M, O, secretor   ×   N, O, secretor
      (4) M, A, nonsecretor   ×   M, O, nonsecretor
      (5) M, A, secretor   ×   M, A, secretor

8. The baby in a paternity dispute was found to be A_2, MN. The mother was A_1, M. The accused man was A_1, N. What, if any, conclusions can be drawn?

In working the following problems, consult Appendix C (pp. 403–405).

9. From Table 9.5 we learn that an investigation of 62 families in which one parent was a secretor and the other a nonsecretor revealed that 103 of the children were secretors and 67 nonsecretors. If the nonsecretor trait depends on a recessive gene, how many of this total of 170 children would be expected to be secretors, how many nonsecretors? Apply the chi-square test to your findings. What is the probability that the observed deviation from expected numbers can be attributed to chance? Is the deviation significant evidence against the hypothesis that nonsecretors are homozygous for a recessive gene? What would you suggest as a next step in investigating the hypothesis?

10. In discussing inheritance of distal hyperextensibility of the thumb, we noted that of 108 children born to *dht* × *non-dht* parents 35.8 would be expected to be *dht* if the latter condition depends on a recessive gene (p. 104.) The actual data obtained by Glass and Kistler gave 37 *dht* children, 71 *non-dht* children. Use the chi-square test to determine the probability that the deviation from expectation is attributable to chance. Is the deviation significant evidence against the hypothesis?

11. If you worked problem No. 1 in Chapter 7 correctly (p. 109), you found that the population at equilibrium would have consisted of 147 *AA*, 126 *Aa*, 27 *aa*. The respective numbers actually observed were: 150 *AA*, 120 *Aa*, 30 *aa*. Use the chi-square test to determine whether or not the deviation is significant evidence against the hypothesis that the population is in equilibrium. What do you conclude and why?

12. Apply the chi-square test to the results you obtained in problem No. 4 of Chapter 7 (p. 109). What is the probability that the observed deviation from expected numbers is attributable to chance? Is the deviation significant evidence against the hypothesis that the population is in equilibrium?

REFERENCES

Bernstein, F., 1925. "Zusammenfassende Betrachtungen über die erblichen Blutstrukturen des Menschen," *Zeitschrift für induktive Abstammungs—und Vererbungslehre,* **37**:237–70.

Birdsell, J. B., 1950. "Some implications of the genetical concept of race in terms of spatial analysis," *Cold Spring Harbor Symposia on Quantitative Biology,* **15**:259–311.

Boyd, W. C., 1950. *Genetics and the Races of Man.* Boston: Little, Brown & Company.

Landsteiner, K., 1901. "Ueber Agglutinationserscheinungen normalen menschlichen Blutes," *Wiener klinische Wochenschrift,* **14**:1132–4.

Moody, P. A., 1962. *Introduction to Evolution,* 2nd ed. New York: Harper & Brothers.

Mourant, A. E., 1954. *The Distribution of the Human Blood Groups.* Springfield, Ill.: Charles C Thomas.

Race, R. R., and R. Sanger, 1962. *Blood Groups in Man,* 4th ed. Oxford: Blackwell Scientific Publications.

Snyder, L. H., and P. R. David, 1957. *The Principles of Heredity,* 5th ed. Boston: D. C. Heath & Company.

Stern, C., 1960. *Principles of Human Genetics,* 2nd ed. San Francisco: W. H. Freeman & Company.

von Dungern, E., and L. Hirschfeld, 1910. "Ueber Vererbung gruppenspezifischer Strukturen des Blutes. II." *Zeitschrift für Immunitätsforschung,* **6**:284–92.

Wiener, A. S., 1943–1962. *Blood Groups and Transfusion,* 3rd ed. Springfield, Ill.: Charles C Thomas. Reprinted—New York: Hafner Publishing Company.

10.

MULTIPLE ALLELES:
Rh AND OTHER ANTIGENS

Rh, the "Rhesus Factor"

Discovery of another red blood cell antigen was announced by Landsteiner and Wiener in 1940. These authors had inoculated rabbits and guinea pigs with suspensions of red blood cells from rhesus monkeys. The antibodies formed by the rabbits and guinea pigs agglutinated red blood cells of rhesus monkeys. These investigators then used the antiserums to test human red blood cells. They found that among 448 white inhabitants of New York City, 379 (84.6 percent) had cells that reacted with the antibodies, whereas 69 (15.4 percent) had cells that did not. People whose cells were agglutinated by the antibodies were called **Rh-positive**; those whose cells were not agglutinated were called **Rh-negative** ("Rh" refers to Rhesus).

Landsteiner and Wiener then investigated the inheritance of the new antigen, using methods of analysis much like those we have discussed in connection with the secretor gene investigations (see their paper of 1941). They demonstrated that the presence of the antigen Rh is determined by a dominant gene R. Thus Rh-positive people have the genotype RR or Rr, whereas Rh-negative people have the genotype rr.

Subsequent investigation by many people revealed that the genetic situation is much more complicated than the simple mode of inheritance just stated. Not all Rh-positive people are exactly alike in the antigens or "blood factors" they possess, and neither are all Rh-negative people. On the basis of extensive investigations, Wiener formulated the theory that a series of multiple alleles is involved, as in the ABO groups.

The whole subject has become complex. In a book such as this one, which emphasizes principles, there is no space for many of the details, and therefore, a simplified explanation must suffice. In our discussion of the MN types (pp. 56–57) and the ABO groups (pp. 127–128), we showed in each case how one's blood cells could be typed by the use of two antiserums, forming test fluids. To demonstrate the essentials of the Rh system, we need three antiserums. In Table 10.1, these three test fluids are called anti-**Rh**$_O$ or anti-D, anti-**rh'** or anti-C, anti-**rh''** or anti-E. The reason for the double designation in each case will be evident as we proceed. The original antiserums employed by Landsteiner and Wiener were of a specificity similar to anti-**Rh**$_O$ or anti-D. Hence people whose cells are clumped by this antiserum are "Rh positive," as that term is usually employed, and people whose cells do not react with this antiserum are "Rh negative."

Table 10.1 shows all the possible combinations of reactions between cells and these three antiserums. The first horizontal line, for example, represents a case in which the cells being tested do not react with any of the three antiserums. Possessors of such cells have a phenotype designated as rh. The second line of the table shows reaction with anti-**rh'** or anti-C but not with the other two antiserums. Persons who have such cells are said to be of the rh' phenotype.

TABLE 10.1   The eight Rh phenotypes demonstrable with three antiserums.

Reactions with antiserums			Phenotypes	
anti-**Rh**$_O$ or anti-D	anti-**rh'** or anti-C	anti-**rh''** or anti-E		
−	−	−	rh	Rh negative
−	+	−	rh'	
−	−	+	rh''	
−	+	+	rh$_y$	
+	−	−	Rh$_O$	Rh positive
+	+	−	Rh$_1$	
+	−	+	Rh$_2$	
+	+	+	Rh$_Z$	

$+$ = cells react with antiserum.
$-$ = cells do not react with antiserum.

What are the genotypes that produce the phenotypes given in the table? The eight phenotypes can be explained on the basis of various combinations of eight multiple alleles, designated as follows:

r or (dce)
r' or (dCe)
r'' or (dcE)
r^y or (dCE)
R^0 or (Dce)
R^1 or (DCe)
R^2 or (DcE)
R^Z or (DCE)

The designations on the left are those of Dr. Alexander S. Wiener who, as noted above, was one of the discoverers of Rh. The triplet symbols listed on the right are those used by exponents of the Fisher-Race linked-gene theory. We have used a parenthesis to represent a portion of a chromosome containing three genes (see Chap. 14). In this case, the genes are thought to be so close together that they stay together and behave as a unit in heredity.

Let us see how the system works. We note from Table 10.1 that people with the rh phenotype have red blood cells that do not react with any of the three antiserums (first horizontal row). Such people have the genotype rr or (dce) (dce).

People of the rh' phenotype (second row) may be homozygous $r'r'$ or heterozygous $r'r$; (dCe) (dCe) or (dCe) (dce). Note that in the linked-gene designation a capital (upper case) letter appears wherever a plus sign occurs in the table.

People who belong to rh'' maybe $r''r''$ or r'' r; (dcE) (dcE) or (dcE) (dce).

People of the rh$_y$ phenotype may have any one of five genotypes; three of them are: r^yr^y $[(dCE)$ $(dCE)]$, r^yr $[(dCE)$ $(dce)]$, $r'r''$ $[(dCe)$ $(dcE)]$. Readers can easily calculate the other possibilities, remembering that the phenotype will result from any combination of genes that produces cells that will react with anti-**rh'** and anti-**rh''** but will fail to react with anti-**Rh$_0$**.

All of the types mentioned so far are Rh negative. The last four rows of the table represent various Rh-positive phenotypes. In the first place, note that the cells of Rh-positive people always react with anti-**Rh$_0$** or anti-D, whereas the cells of Rh-negative people do not react with this antiserum. Among the Rh-positive people, those who belong to type Rh$_0$ have the genotype R^0R^0 or R^0r; (Dce) (Dce) or (Dce) (dce).

People with the Rh$_1$ phenotype may have the genotype R^1R^1 or R^1r; (DCe) (DCe) or (DCe) (dce). They may also have other genotypes such as R^0r'; (Dce) (dCe).

The Rh$_2$ phenotype may arise from the R^2R^2 or R^2r $[(DcE)$ (DcE) or (DcE) $(dce)]$ genotypes, but other pairs of genes may produce it [for example, R^0r'' (Dce) $(dcE)]$.

Similarly, a person belonging to type Rh$_Z$ may have the genotype R^ZR^Z or R^Zr $[(DCE)$ (DCE) or (DCE) $(dce)]$. He may also have the genotype R^ZR^0 $[(DCE)$ $(Dce)]$, R^1R^2 $[(DCe)$ $(DcE)]$, and so on. Dr. Wiener lists fourteen genotypes that Rh$_Z$ people may have.

Table 10.1 gives the results of tests with only three antiserums. Use of other antiserums reveals further complexity—phenotypes rh^W_y, Rh^W_1, and Rh^W_z, for example. However, the principle of multiple allele inheritance as it applies to Rh has been demonstrated sufficiently by the phenotypes based on various combinations of the eight multiple alleles we have discussed.

Let us turn to the problem presented by the two systems of designating genotypes. According to one idea there is, for example, a single gene r^y that produces one antigen with two "blood factors" (serological specificities), one which causes the antigen to react with anti-rh', another which causes the antigen to react with anti-rh". According to the other idea, instead of one gene there are three: (dCE) in this instance. Gene C produces an antigen that reacts with anti-C (anti-rh'); gene E produces an antigen that reacts with anti-E (anti-rh"). Thus the second theory pictures each gene as producing one antigen with one specificity, a simpler concept, in a way, than the idea that one gene may produce an antigen with two or more specificities. However, simplicity does not prove correctness.

The problem is: How can we determine whether there is a single gene or whether there are three genes so closely linked together that they behave like a single gene? As we will understand better when we have discussed the subject of linkage (Chap. 12), we cannot answer the question as long as the three genes stay together. However, if we could prove that the three have not stayed together but have recombined, then we should have evidence that we are dealing with three entities rather than one. Suppose a person with the genotype (DCE) (dce) marries a (dce) (dce) individual, and that they have a child with the genotype (dcE) (dce). This would show that crossing over (recombination) had occurred in the first parent, the E exchanging places with the e to form the chromosome (dcE), and would be evidence in support of the linked-gene theory. Such evidence can be obtained easily in experimental organisms, but it is extremely difficult to obtain in man.

For about twenty years there has been debate between proponents of the multiple-allele theory and proponents of the linked-gene theory. Interestingly enough, it seems likely that the controversy will be resolved by our changing concepts of what constitutes a gene.

The two theories are contrasted at the top of Figure 10.1. The chromosome is represented by a line. According to the multiple-allele theory, at some point on that chromosome a gene is located that determines Rh (we have shown the gene R^z, which as we have seen is thought to produce an antigen with three specificities). The line to the right, B, in Figure 10.1 shows the chromosome as conceived by proponents of the linked-gene theory, with genes D, C, and E close together, and combining to produce the same three antigenic effects ascribed to R^z.

As we noted in Chapter 4 (pp. 48–49), ideas of the nature of genes

A.   **B.**

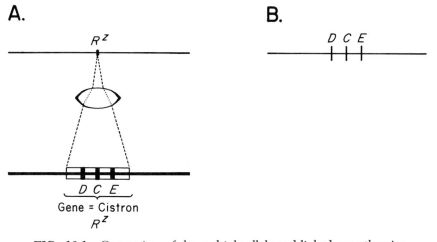

FIG. 10.1 Comparison of the multiple-allele and linked-gene theories of Rh inheritance. **A.** (Top). Gene R^z represented as a point in a chromosome. (Bottom). Gene R^z represented as a section of the DNA molecule including three subdivisions (mutons or recons), *D*, *C*, and *E*. **B.** *D*, *C*, and *E* represented as separate genes closely linked together. The question is: Are *D*, *C*, and *E* to be thought of as separate genes or as separate parts of one gene (cistron)?

have been changing rapidly. We no longer think of a gene as indivisible. We saw that a gene is a portion of a DNA molecule. How long a portion? The answer depends on how we define "gene." If we think of a gene in terms of function, we may, with Benzer, call it a "cistron" and think of it as incorporating many nucleotide pairs, hundreds perhaps. Such a sizable portion of a DNA molecule would contain much genetic information and so have a function of recognizable significance. Perhaps the gene R^z is such a cistron.

However, we noted in the earlier discussion that cistrons are subdivisible into mutons and recons, the smallest portions of the DNA molecule that can undergo mutation or recombination, respectively. Perhaps, then, *D*, *C*, and *E* are mutons or recons within the cistron R^z. We have attempted to convey this idea in Figure 10.1 by magnifying the gene R^z so that it becomes a bar, within which we can see subdivisions, the mutons or recons *D*, *C*, and *E*. (The simple lens shown in the figure is only symbolic; the magnification necessary far surpasses anything achievable by light microscopes and even exceeds the powers of the best electron microscopes available.) If we compare this arrangement with that shown at B in the figure, we see that we have very much the same result: three units in a row, call them three separate genes, or call them mutons or recons within one gene (cistron), as you wish. Race and Sanger (1962) stated that C and E seem to be in one cistron but that it has not been determined whether or not D is in the same cistron. In this way, by increasing knowledge of the finer structure of the gene, the controversy over the multiple-allele hypothesis versus the linked-gene hypothesis may be resolved.

Incompatibility

Rh Incompatibility   Rh-negative people lack certain antigens found in the red blood cells of Rh-positive people, but the serum of Rh-negative people normally does not contain antibodies against these antigens (isoantibodies). In this, Rh is like MN and unlike ABO.

However, Rh-negative people can be stimulated to form Rh antibodies—by blood transfusion, for example. If an Rh-negative person receives blood from an Rh-positive person, the introduced red blood cells may stimulate the Rh-negative recipient to form antibodies. These may do no damage at the time, but if, later on, the Rh-negative person receives a second transfusion of Rh-positive blood, the antibodies formed previously may clump and destroy the newly introduced Rh-positive cells, leading to a variety of undesirable and perhaps serious effects.

Soon after the discovery of Rh it was realized that Rh-negative women can be stimulated in another way to form antibodies. If such a woman marries an Rh-positive man, she may become pregnant with an Rh-positive fetus. (The marriage is either mother rr × father RR^* or mother rr × father Rr; if the father is homozygous, the baby is sure to be Rh-positive (Rr); if the father is heterozygous, the chance that the baby is Rh-positive is ½.) In some cases, but by no means in all, an Rh-positive fetus may stimulate its Rh-negative mother to form antibodies. In these instances the intact red blood cells of the fetus, with their Rh antigen(s), must find their way into the mother's blood stream and then stimulate her antibody-forming mechanisms. The circulatory systems of fetus and mother are separate. Maternal and fetal bloods come into contact in the placenta, but even there a thin membrane keeps them separate. It seems necessary to postulate that at times lesions (holes) must develop in this membrane, permitting fetal red blood cells to "leak" into the mother's blood stream. Richardson-Jones (Levine, 1958) actually demonstrated the presence of Rh-positive cells in the circulation of Rh-negative mothers during the last three months of pregnancy. He estimated a ratio of 1:2000–1:5000 fetal Rh-positive cells to maternal Rh-negative ones.

---

*For the sake of simplicity we use the initial R to represent any one of the "capital R genes" in Wiener's series of multiple alleles, r to represent any one of the "small r genes."

If the pregnancy is a first one, the antibodies may form slowly and not reach sufficient concentration to do any harm. However, if this first pregnancy is soon followed by a second one, involving a second Rh-positive fetus, unfortunate results may ensue. The antibodies already present from the first pregnancy may attack certain tissues in the new fetus, resulting in a variety of abnormalities and perhaps even death. The effects may not manifest themselves until after the baby is born, when a certain syndrome of symptoms known as *erythroblastosis fetalis* may ensue. (The name refers to the erythroblasts, the nucleated cells that form red blood cells.) Antibodies may destroy the red blood cells, resulting in severe anemia.

Sometimes the antibodies seem to be inhibited from their destructive work on red blood cells until a day or two after birth. It is for this reason that a complete exchange of a newborn infant's blood may save its life. The infant's own blood, containing Rh-positive cells, is replaced by Rh-negative blood. Then, when the Rh antibodies are "unleashed," they find no cells containing the Rh antigen to be attacked. The antibodies gradually disappear, so that by the time the introduced Rh-negative cells are replaced by Rh-positive cells formed by the baby himself the danger is past.

Because of these difficulties, marriages between Rh-negative women and Rh-positive men are called incompatible matings, a term that is perhaps ill-chosen. Such matings are not at all rare. In a population in which 85 percent of the men are Rh-positive, an Rh-negative woman is much more likely to marry an Rh-positive man than she is an Rh-negative man. Such marriages represent about 13 percent of all marriages in Caucasoid populations, and in most cases no difficulties are encountered. Why not?

The small size of human families is one reason. As we have noted, although a first Rh-positive child may stimulate his mother to form antibodies, he may suffer no ill effects himself. Many families consist of no more than one child.

Furthermore, if the father is heterozgyous (*Rr*), the first child may be Rh-negative and therefore fail to stimulate antibody formation. A second child, even if he is Rh-positive, will encounter no antibodies in his mother's blood. In fact, the second child may be Rh-negative, and so may a third or fourth child. (The chance of three successive Rh-negative children from an *Rr* × *rr* mating is $\frac{1}{2} \times \frac{1}{2} \times \frac{1}{2} = \frac{1}{8}$—not a small chance at all.) Even if the first child were Rh-positive and stimulated antibody production, if the second child is Rh-negative the antibodies will not act on it.

Thus there are genetic reasons why incompatible matings do not give rise to as many unhealthy infants as we might expect. There are other possible reasons, also. We have stated that it seems necessary to postulate that intact red blood cells must pass from the fetus, through lesions in the placenta, into the mother's blood stream. We do not yet know how common this occurrence is. Perhaps women differ as to whether or not such leakage occurs, although Levine (1958) stated that "it is assumed that this passage of fetal blood into the maternal circulation occurs in all pregnancies."

Again, women may well differ in their sensitivity to introduced Rh antigens. Wiener (1945) stated that "only 1 in 25 to 50 Rh-negative individuals respond to transfusions of Rh-positive blood, or to pregnancy with an Rh-positive fetus, by producing Rh antibodies." Hence one woman may form antibodies very readily, whereas another woman may form few, if any, antibodies under the same circumstances. This is comparable to the differences between people in their sensitivity to plant pollens— some people have symptoms of asthma or hay fever, others do not. In this case, there is evidence that genetic factors are concerned. Future research may well demonstrate that Rh-negative women have genetically determined differences in their sensitivity to Rh antigens introduced into their systems.

A few years ago, the newspapers carried a picture of a family of 14 children born to an Rh-negative woman and her Rh-positive husband. We find the adjective "incompatible" a bit inappropriate here! Every modern obstetrician, who knows that a woman under his care is Rh-negative and has an Rh-positive husband, determines from time to time whether or not antibodies are being formed, and he will take remedial measures if necessary, including blood transfusion of the newborn infant, if this is indicated. More often than not, however, such measures are not needed.

ABO Incompatibility   There is another reason why Rh incompatibility may not have as many untoward effects as we should expect. This reason is of interest both serologically and genetically.

As soon as the role of Rh incompatibility in causing erythroblastosis was known, investigators began to take a harder look at the ABO blood groups, hitherto regarded as a biological curiosity of no clinical importance, aside from problems concerned with blood transfusion. If a fetus containing Rh antigens can be damaged by anti-Rh antibodies in its mother's blood, might not a fetus containing antigen A be damaged by anti-A antibodies in its mother's blood? This situation may arise when, for example, the mother belongs to group O, the father to group A. We recall that in this case the anti-A antibodies are already present in the mother's blood. Perhaps the normal concentration is usually not great enough to cause difficulty, but in some cases the mother may be stimulated to form more, until a concentration is reached that will harm the fetus. Such antibodies might be particularly destructive to the group A fetus because the A antigen is present in tissue cells as well as in the red blood cells (whereas the Rh antigens are confined to red blood cells) (Levine, 1943). Hence anti-A antibodies in sufficient concentration might be widely destructive throughout the fetal body.

For these reasons, investigators look to ABO incompatibility to explain some of the previously mysterious early miscarriages and spontaneous abortions. Not infrequently, embryos are lost very early, often before the mother realizes that she is pregnant.

What evidence do we have that ABO incompatibility may play a role in such cases?

Long ago Hirschfeld, one of the pioneers in blood group research, noticed that in A × O marriages there are fewer group A children when the mother is O and the father A than there are when the mother is A and the father O (Levine, 1943). He attributed the difference to miscarriages and stillbirths when mother and fetus differed in blood group. This early clue was not pursued further until the discovery of the dramatic role of Rh in producing hemolytic disease in the newborn.

In investigations of this kind, we ask: What proportion of the children from A × O matings are expected to belong to group A? The answer depends on the gene frequencies in the population to which the families belong. We may apply the Hardy-Weinberg formula, as it relates to blood groups, to the problem (pp. 132–133).

Let us ask first concerning families in which the father is O, the mother A. Here the mother may be homozygous or heterozygous. We may write out the expected frequencies as we did previously:

Expected Frequency

Mother $I^A I^A$ × Father $I^O I^O$, $p^2 \times r^2 = p^2 r^2$ (all children A)
Mother $I^A I^O$ × Father $I^O I^O$, $2pr \times r^2 = 2pr^3$ (½ of children A)

Thus the expected frequencies of all children in these families are $p^2 r^2 + 2pr^3$. Among these, $p^2 r^2 + \dfrac{2pr^3}{2}$ are group A children. Hence the proportion of group A children is:

$$\frac{p^2 r^2 + pr^3}{p^2 r^2 + 2pr^3} = \frac{pr^2(p + r)}{pr^2(p + 2r)} = \frac{p + r}{p + 2r}$$

Therefore, if we know the values of p and r (frequencies of genes I^A and I^O, respectively), for a given population, we can calculate the proportion of the children of A mother and O father marriages that will be expected to belong to group A.

Now if incompatibility of blood group between mother and fetus did no harm, the same proportion should be found in families in which the mother belongs to group O, the father to group A.

Many investigations have indicated that this is contrary to fact, that when the mother is O, and the father A, there are fewer A children than expected. As an example, we may cite the investigation of Matsunaga (1955) on 2709 Japanese families, including 6360 children. He found that in families in which the mother was A and the father O, group A children occurred in the proportion expected with the gene frequencies characterizing Japanese people. On the other hand, when the mother was O and the father A, there were fewer A children than expected, the deficiency amounting to about 14 percent of all children. Similarly, a deficiency of about 10 percent was found in group B children produced from O mother × B father matings (as compared to B mother × O father matings).

Matsunaga found an added bit of evidence through study of miscarriages. The rate of miscarriage is significantly higher when the mother is O and the father A, than it is when the mother is A and the father O.

This study of Japanese families is particularly interesting because the findings are not complicated by Rh incompatibility. More than 99 percent of Japanese people are Rh-positive, so Rh incompatibility is extremely rare among them.

ABO incompatibility is said to occur whenever a mother lacks an antigen possessed by the father. In this sense, all the following matings are incompatible (the mother is given first in each case): O × A; O × B; O × AB; B × A; A × B; B × AB; A × AB. In our population, such matings constitute nearly 35 percent of all matings. Evidence from many investigations indicates that such incompatibility contributes to early spontaneous abortion and miscarriage but is by no means the only cause. Embryonic and early fetal deaths occur in compatible matings, also, and, conversely, they occur in only a small minority of pregnancies in incompatible matings.

Rh Incompatibility and ABO Incompatibility Combined   Our principal reason for discussing ABO incompatibility lies in the interesting relationship between it and Rh incompatibility. Conclusive evidence indicates that *ABO incompatibility may prevent the development of the harmful effects of Rh incompatibility.* This, then, is another reason why Rh-negative mothers married to Rh-positive fathers do not produce more erythroblastotic infants than they do.

As an example of how this protective action is believed to work, we may take the case of a group O, Rh-negative woman married to a group A, Rh-positive man. A zygote produced may inherit genes I^A and R from the father. This means that the embryonic red blood cells will contain antigens A and Rh. If these cells leak into the mother's circulation, they may be destroyed by the mother's anti-A antibodies, or, perhaps more probably, they may stimulate the mother to form more anti-A antibodies than she normally has, and these antibodies may then destroy the cells from the embryo (containing A and Rh). In any event, the reaction involving antigen A is pictured as destroying the cells before the Rh antigen can stimulate the mother to form anti-Rh antibodies. In severe cases, of course, the embryo is injured to such an extent that an early miscarriage occurs, but even when this does not happen, the fetal cells containing A and Rh are eliminated without stimulating the mother to form anti-Rh antibodies.

This is the theory proposed initially by Race; what sort of evidence indicates its correctness? If it is correct, an increased proportion of mothers who *do* form anti-Rh antibodies should be ABO-compatible with their husbands, as compared to the general population of wives. (Because they are ABO-compatible, the Rh-positive blood cells from the fetus are not destroyed, and so can stimulate the mother to form anti-Rh antibodies.) Investigators usually turn the statement around and say that among mothers who have formed anti-Rh antibodies there should be a *decreased* proportion of ABO-*incompatible* matings (if the theory is correct).

Many investigations demonstrate that such a decrease actually occurs. Typical of such studies is that of Reepmaker and his colleagues (1962) in Holland. These authors summarized the results of their predecessors, and added data from 1742 additional women who had developed anti-Rh antibodies; 18.5 percent of them were incompatibly mated with regard to ABO groups. Recall that, in general, about 35 percent of matings are ABO-incompatible.

Particularly striking was the complete absence of matings in which the mother was of group O, the father of group AB. Of 1742 matings, 25 would be expected, by chance, to be of this type. The fact that none were seems to indicate that since all the children of an O × AB mating inherit either A or B from their father, all of them fail to stimulate formation of Rh antibodies by their mothers. (Hence matings of this type were absent from the data based on 1742 mothers who *did* develop antibodies.)

Thus we see that an Rh-negative woman is more likely to develop anti-Rh antibodies as a result of fetal stimulation if her marriage is ABO-compatible than she is if the marriage is ABO-incompatible. However, a mother may develop anti-Rh antibodies even when the marriage is ABO-incompatible. Reepmaker *et al.* (1962) have suggested that this occurs only if the father is heterozygous; in this case, group O, Rh-positive fetuses can be produced and may stimulate the mother to form anti-Rh antibodies (whereas group A or B, Rh-positive fetuses, when produced, do not cause anti-Rh antibody formation).

The ramifications of this line of investigation far surpass the space we can devote to it. The paper by Reepmaker *et al.* (1962) provides a good discussion of accumulated data and of the factors involved in the protective action of ABO incompatibility. We might note in passing that there is evidence of interaction between ABO and Rh, such that when Rh-negative mothers do not form antibodies (although married to Rh-positive husbands), fetuses that are incompatible with their mothers in regard to both ABO and Rh seem to enjoy some advantage, compared to fetuses that are incompatible in one antigen only (Cohen and Glass, 1959; Cohen, 1960). For example, when the mother has the genotype $I^O I^O rr$, and the father the genotype $I^A I^O Rr$, a fetus that has the genotype $I^A I^O Rr$ seems to enjoy some advantage in terms of chances of survival, compared to a fetus with the genotype $I^O I^O Rr$ or to one with the genotype $I^A I^O rr$, if the mother does *not* form anti-Rh antibodies. Perhaps this is a special case of the general phenomenon of heterozygote superiority over homozygotes.

In Chapter 24 we shall mention other examples of heterozygote superiority and discuss their significance for human evolution. Here we may mention another apparent example from blood groups. We recall that group AB people are always heterozygous $I^A I^B$. In most of the world, the frequency of gene I^B is so low that relatively few people belong to group AB, and AB × AB marriages are proportionately rarer still. However, among Orientals (e.g., Japanese), AB people may constitute as much as 10 percent of the population, and marriages between people in this group are more common than they are in the rest of the world. Matsunaga (1959) reported 33 AB × AB matings, which produced 83 children. Children of such matings will be expected to form a 1:2:1 ratio—¼ A, ¾ AB, ¼ B. Thus half the children are expected to belong to group AB. Half of 83 is 42, in round numbers. Actually 54 of the 83 children were of group AB. The difference is highly significant, statistically, and seems to indicate that $I^A I^B$ zygotes (or the embryos and fetuses that develop from them) have some unknown advantage over $I^A I^A$ and $I^B I^B$ zygotes. The advantage presumably relates in some way to success in survival. Recall, by the way, that in a Japanese population Rh incompatibility is not present as a complicating factor.

In our discussion of Rh incompatibility, we have spoken in every case of Rh-negative mothers. The term refers to mothers who lack the blood factor **Rh$_0$** (or D). Sometimes Rh-positive mothers (possessing this factor) may nevertheless develop antibodies and have erythroblastotic children. When this occurs, the antigen that stimulates the antibody formation is likely to be **rh'** (or C). The fetus has it, and the mother, lacking it, forms antibodies against it. The antigen at fault, however, may be **Hr**, one of a group of antigens whose occurrence bears a sort of reciprocal relationship to the occurrence of the Rh antigens, and whose mention serves to remind us of the many facets of Rh for which there is no space in an introductory discussion (see Wiener, 1943–1962; Race and Sanger, 1962; Wiener and Wexler, 1958).

Blood Groups and Disease

We should mention briefly some interesting observations that must await further research before we can be sure of correct interpretations.

Investigations on various populations indicate the following correlations (Race and Sanger, 1962): People who belong to blood group O are about 40 percent more likely to have duodenal ulcers than are people belonging to the other groups. Nonsecretors are more likely to have duodenal ulcers than are secretors (pp. 140–142). There is also a correlation, although not so strong, between gastric ulcer and membership in group O. People who belong to group A are about 20 percent more likely to have cancer of the stomach than are members of groups O or B. Members of group A are about 25 percent more likely to have pernicious anemia than are members of group O or B, and members of group A seem somewhat more likely to have diabetes mellitus than are members of other groups.

Some other correlations of this sort are suspected or demonstrated by investigations involving small numbers of individuals. On the other hand, investigations sometimes fail to demonstrate any correlations at all. Thus susceptibilities to cancers of the colon, rectum, lung, or breast seem to display no correlation with blood groups.

When correlations do occur, what interpretation can be placed on them? Correlations do not of themselves prove that a cause-and-effect relationship exists. In a population, a strain might be present that has, for example, a high frequency of group O and a high susceptibility to duodenal ulcer, without any causal relationship existing between the two. However, it would be surprising if such a situation occurred in all the varied populations from different countries that have been investigated.

In an attempt to obtain evidence on the problem, Clarke (1959) investigated families in which some of the children were O, some A. He found no significant difference in susceptibility to duodenal ulcer between the group O sibs and the group A sibs in a given family. Similarly, in families in which some of the children were secretors, some nonsecretors: "an individual who is a non-secretor is not significantly more likely to have the ulcer than his secretor sib." Future research will doubtless shed light on the causes of these observed correlations.

There is also some evidence that epidemic diseases may differ in severity in persons of different blood groups. From an investigation of smallpox cases and pock-marked persons in India, Vogel (1961) concluded that the disease is more severe in groups A and AB patients than it is in people of groups O and B. If so, in the past before the advent of modern medicine, smallpox epidemics may have caused the death of more possessors of antigen A than of people not possessing that antigen. If this selective elimination occurred, it would form an example of natural selection, a subject we shall discuss in Chapter 24. The division of people into the different blood groups is an example of **polymorphism** (many-forms). It is one thing to discover that polymorphism is present, quite another to explain why it is present. As we shall see later, natural selection may well have been an important factor in the origin of this blood group polymorphism.

Other Red Blood Cell Antigens

In addition to the antigens we have discussed so far, the red blood cell is a veritable treasure trove of other antigens, some of them common, some rare. When inheritance is analyzed, we usually find that the genetics is of simple Mendelian variety, the presence of the antigen being dominant to its absence. In some cases there are interrelationships between the antigens or their genes. Thus, people who possess an antigen known as Le^a ("Lewis A") seem always to be nonsecretors. Space will not permit even a sample of the vast literature on these matters (see Race and Sanger, 1962; Wiener and Wexler, 1958).

In Chapter 5 we discussed the MN blood types. We noted that type M people (genotype, $L^M L^M$) have antigen M only, and that type N people ($L^N L^N$) have antigen N only. Type MN people (genotype, $L^M L^N$) have both antigens. Some twenty years after the discovery of the MN antigens, another pair of antigens or of antigenic factors, designated S and s, were discovered. These were associated with the MN antigens in such a way that they seem (a) to be caused by the same gene, or (b) to be caused by a gene very closely linked to the M and N genes. (Recall our discussion of the different points of view possible in the question of the genetic basis of Rh, p. 148). If we follow the first interpretation, we have here a series of four multiple alleles, which we may designate as follows:

Gene	Causing Production of Antigen or Antigenic Combining Group
M^S	M and S
M^s	M and s
N^S	N and S
N^s	N and s

Individuals may possess any two of the four alleles. Thus a person who has the genotype $M^S M^S$ will have red blood cells that react only with anti-M and anti-S antibodies, whereas the cells of a heterozygote of the constitution $M^S N^s$ will react with anti-M, anti-N, anti-S and anti-s antibodies.

Discovery of S and s has increased the usefulness of blood typing in medico-legal cases. For example, if the blood types of mother, child, and the man accused of paternity of the child are all M, then MN blood typing can be of no value in itself. However, if the mother is $M^s M^s$, the child $M^S M^s$, and the accused man $M^s M^s$, the latter's innocence is proved. The child must have received gene M^S from his father. The general principle is that an antigen cannot occur in a child unless it occurs in a parent.

PROBLEMS

1. A husband had the phenotype rh_y, his wife the phenotype rh. They had two children, one of rh' phenotype, the other of rh'' phenotype. Give the genotypes of the parents according to both systems of notation.

2. A husband was Rh negative, his wife Rh positive. Their first child was Rh_0, their second child Rh_2. Would it be possible for these parents to produce an Rh-negative child? Explain.

3. Four sisters had the phenotypes Rh_z, Rh_0, rh_y, and rh, respectively. Give the genotypes and phenotypes of their parents.

4. On page 147 we noted that persons having the phenotype Rh_z may have any one of fourteen genotypes. We listed four of them. What are the other ten?

5. In the gene pool of a certain population the relative frequencies of the ABO blood group genes are as follows: $p = 0.30$; $q = 0.06$; $r = 0.64$.
(a) In families of which the mother belongs to group A and the father to group O, what percentage of the children will be expected to belong to group A? (b) In families of which the mother belongs to group B and the father to group O, what percentage of the children will be expected to belong to group B?

6. In terms of gene frequencies, p, q and r; in families in which the mother is group AB and the father group A, what proportion of the children will be expected to belong to group B?

7. Which of the following matings is *least* likely to give rise to a child who will suffer erythroblastosis as a result of Rh-incompatibility?

Mother	Father
(a) Rh-negative, Group AB	Rh-positive, Group O
(b) Rh-negative, Group A	Rh-positive, Group O
(c) Rh-negative, Group B	Rh-positive, Group A
(d) Rh-negative, Group A	Rh-positive, Group A

8. We noted that among group O women in Holland who had developed anti-Rh antibodies, none were the wives of group AB husbands. In a population having the gene frequencies given in question No. 5, what percentage of marriages would be expected to occur between group O women and group AB men?

9. Three sibs had the following MNS constitutions: $M^S M^s$, $M^s N^S$, $M^s M^s$. Give the genotypes of the parents.

REFERENCES

Clarke, C. A., 1959. "Correlations of ABO blood groups with peptic ulcer, cancer, and other diseases," *American Journal of Human Genetics*, **11**:400–404.

Cohen, B. H., 1960. "ABO-Rh interaction in an Rh-incompatibly mated population," *American Journal of Human Genetics*, **12**:180–209.

Cohen, B. H., and B. Glass, 1959. "The relation of the ABO and Rh blood groups to differential reproduction," *American Journal of Human Genetics*, **11**:414–17.

Landsteiner, K., and A. S. Wiener, 1941. "Studies on an agglutinogen (Rh) in human blood reacting with anti-rhesus sera and with human isoantibodies," *Journal of Experimental Medicine*, **74**:309–20.

Levine, P., 1943. "Serological factors as possible causes in spontaneous abortions," *Journal of Heredity*, **34**:71–80.

Levine, P., 1958. "The influence of the ABO system on Rh hemolytic disease," *Human Biology*, **30**:14–28.

Matsunaga, E., 1955. "Intra-uterine selection by the ABO incompatibility of mother and foetus," *American Journal of Human Genetics*, **7**:66–75.

Matsunaga, E., 1959. "Selection in ABO polymorphism in Japanese populations," *American Journal of Human Genetics*, **11**:405–13.

Race, R. R., and R. Sanger, 1962. *Blood Groups in Man*, 4th ed. Oxford: Blackwell Scientific Publications.

Reepmaker, J., L. E. Nijenhuis, and J. J. Van Loghem, 1962. "The inhibiting effect of ABO incompatibility on Rh immunization in pregnancy: a statistical analysis of 1,742 families," *American Journal of Human Genetics*, **14**:185–98.

Vogel, F., 1961. "The theory of natural selection in the ABO blood group system." *Second International Congress of Human Genetics*. International Congress Series No. 32, p. E 28. New York: Excerpta Medica Foundation.

Wiener, A. S., 1943–1962. *Blood Groups and Transfusion*, 3rd ed. Springfield, Ill.: Charles C Thomas. Reprinted—New York: Hafner Publishing Company.

Wiener, A. S., 1945. "Competition of antigens in isoimmunization by pregnancy," *Proceedings of the Society for Experimental Biology and Medicine*, **58**:133–35.

Wiener, A. S., and I. B. Wexler, 1958. *Heredity of the Blood Groups*. New York: Grune & Stratton, Inc.

11.

POLYGENES:

MULTIPLE-GENE INHERITANCE

Thus far, we have been considering hereditary traits that depend mainly on the action of single genes, although, as we have noted, modifying genes may affect the phenotype produced by the main gene. Now we turn our attention to traits determined by the cumulative or additive action of several genes. Genes having such action are called **polygenes** or multiple genes,* and the traits they determine are of a quantitative nature (e.g., height, breadth, size, weight, degree of pigmentation).

Let us illustrate with a hypothetical but true-to-life example. Suppose that we have two varieties of a certain plant, one tall, the other dwarf. The tall variety has an average height of 32 inches, the dwarf variety an average height of 8 inches. When the experimenter crosses the two varieties, he finds that the F_1 hybrids have an average height of 20 inches. He then interbreeds the F_1 hybrids to produce an F_2 generation. These F_2 offspring show great variability, ranging in height all the way from 32 inches to 8 inches, but with an average of 20 inches. Moreover, they show an approximation to a normal distribution; a graph shows an approximation to the familiar, bell-shaped, normal frequency curve.

Here we note something quite unlike Mendel's experiments with tall and dwarf peas. The F_1 offspring in his experiment were all tall, and the F_2 generation showed a 3:1 ratio of tall to dwarf. Evidently in that case the difference in height between the tall and dwarf varieties depended on only a single pair of genes, with the gene for tallness dominant.

On the other hand, how can we explain our present example in which

---

*Note that multiple genes are to be distinguished clearly from multiple alleles, which were the subject of the preceding two chapters.

(a) the F_1 offspring are intermediate between the parents, and (b) F_2 offspring show wide variation with a tendency to a normal frequency distribution? We might note that in the early days of genetics this was called "blending inheritance" and was thought not to depend on pairs of genes at all. Investigators soon realized, however, that the results can be explained if we assume that the quantitative difference (e.g., in height) is dependent on two or more pairs of genes having cumulative effect.

Let us suppose that in our present example, *two* pairs of genes are involved, the tall variety having the genotype *AABB*, the dwarf variety the genotype *aabb*. Evidently, then, the *aabb* genotype produces the initial 8 inches of height, and the dominant alleles add to this. We may suppose that gene *A* and gene *B* have the same effect in increasing the height above the basic 8 inches. This need not be the case, but it forms a simplifying assumption for the present example. The difference in height between the two varieties is 24 inches. There are four "capital letter genes" in the genotype of the tall variety. These capital letter genes are preferably termed **effective alleles.** Evidently, then, each effective allele produces a height increase of 6 inches. A genotype of *aabb* gives a height of 8 inches; substituting an effective allele for the corresponding "small letter gene" increases the height by 6 inches. Thus a plant with the genotype *Aabb* is 8 + 6 or 14 inches high, a plant with the genotype *AAbb* is 8 + 12 or 20 inches high, and so on to the limiting genotype of *AABB*, which gives a plant 8 + 24 or 32 inches high. For the sake of simplicity, we speak of the contributions of the genes in terms of absolute units, inches in this case. Frequently, perhaps usually, the contribution may be a percentage increase, each effective allele causing the height to increase by a certain percentage.

In Figure 11.1 we present the results of the experiment in terms of two pairs of cumulative genes. All gametes produced by the 32-inch parent contain genes *A* and *B*; all gametes of the 8-inch parent contain *a* and *b*. Hence the F_1 hybrids have the genotype *AaBb* and are 20 inches tall (8 + 6 + 6). In accordance with the principle of independent assortment (pp. 37–38), the F_1 individuals produce four kinds of gametes in equal numbers. All combinations of the four kinds of ova and the four kinds of pollen grains are shown in the checkerboard diagram. In each square of this diagram we have placed the phenotype, in inches. Assembling these data, we find that $\frac{1}{16}$ of the F_2 offspring are 32 inches tall; $\frac{4}{16}$ are 26 inches; $\frac{6}{16}$ are 20 inches; $\frac{4}{16}$ are 14 inches; $\frac{1}{16}$ are 8 inches. When we plot these results at the bottom of the figure, we note their (rather rough) approximation to a normal frequency curve.

Thus we see that the observed facts of this type of inheritance are explained by assuming the existence of pairs of polygenes having additive effect. We readily understand that more than two pairs of genes may be involved in a quantitative difference. Three pairs might be involved in

PARENTAL GENERATION

Phenotypes:	32 inches		8 inches
Genotypes:	AABB	X	aabb
Gametes:	AB		ab

F₁ GENERATION

Phenotypes:	20 inches		20 inches
Genotypes:	AaBb	X	AaBb
Gametes:	AB, Ab, aB, ab		AB, Ab, aB, ab

Combinations of gametes producing an F₂ generation:

	AB	Ab	aB	ab
AB	AABB 32"	AABb 26"	AaBB 26"	AaBb 20"
Ab	AABb 26"	AAbb 20"	AaBb 20"	Aabb 14"
aB	AaBB 26"	AaBb 20"	aaBB 20"	aaBb 14"
ab	AaBb 20"	Aabb 14"	aaBb 14"	aabb 8"

F₂ GENERATION
Heights: 32"   26"   20"   14"   8"
Ratio: 1 : 4 : 6 : 4 : 1

GRAPH OF F₂ GENERATION
Length of columns represents the relative number of individuals having each of the heights listed along the base line.

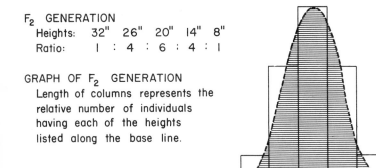

32"   26"   20"   14"   8"

FIG. 11.1 Polygenic inheritance of difference in height when two imaginary plant varieties are crossed. It is assumed that two pairs of effective alleles are concerned with producing the 24-inch difference in height, each A and B increasing the height by 6 inches.

our present example. In that case the 32-inch variety would have the genotype $AABBCC$, the 8-inch variety the genotype $aabbcc$. This would mean that each effective allele would produce $\frac{1}{6} \times 24 = 4$ inches of increase in height (over the basic 8 inches). The F_1 plants would have the genotype $AaBbCc$, and would produce eight kinds of gametes: $ABC, ABc, AbC, aBC, Abc, aBc, abC, abc$. A checkerboard diagram of eight squares on a side would be needed to compute the combinations. When we work this out, we find that the F_2 offspring occur as follows: $\frac{1}{64} = 32$ inches; $\frac{6}{64} = 28$ inches; $\frac{15}{64} = 24$ inches; $\frac{20}{64} = 20$ inches; $\frac{15}{64} = 16$ inches; $\frac{6}{64} = 12$ inches; $\frac{1}{64} = 8$ inches. These data are plotted in Figure 11.2. Note that there are seven phenotypic (size) classes, instead of the five present when we assume only two pairs of genes. The result is a closer approximation to a normal frequency curve than we obtained originally.

A still closer approximation would be obtained if we assumed that the difference in height depended on four pairs of polygenes, the tall variety having the genotype $AABBCCDD$. In this case, each effective allele would produce $\frac{1}{8} \times 24 = 3$ inches of increase in height (over the basic 8 inches). The F_1 hybrids would produce 16 kinds of gametes, and we should require a checkerboard diagram, 16 squares on a side, to compute the combinations. There would be 9 size classes (32 inches, 29 inches, 26 inches, 23 inches, 20 inches, 17 inches, 14 inches, 11 inches, 8 inches) in the F_2 offspring, and accordingly, a closer approximation to a normal frequency distribution.

We may wonder whether or not there is some way of telling, in a given instance, how many pairs of genes are involved. The simplest way is to raise large numbers of F_2 offspring and observe how frequently one extreme or the other appears. We note from Figure 11.1 that if two pairs of genes are involved, $\frac{1}{16}$ of the F_2 plants are expected to be 32 inches high (and $\frac{1}{16}$ to be 8 inches high). If, however, three pairs of genes are involved, only $\frac{1}{64}$ of the F_2 plants will be 32 inches high (and $\frac{1}{64}$ will be 8 inches high), as shown in Figure 11.2. If four pairs of genes are involved, only $\frac{1}{256}$ of the F_2 offspring will be expected to be 32 inches high (and $\frac{1}{256}$ to be 8 inches high). Therefore, if we raise large numbers of F_2 individuals and find that only 1 in 256 shows one extreme, or the other, we have evidence that the quantitative difference we are studying depends on four pairs of equal and cumulative alleles. Statistical methods of estimating the number of pairs of alleles are also available, and, of course, are particularly pertinent in human genetics, where experiments of the kind we have been discussing are impossible.

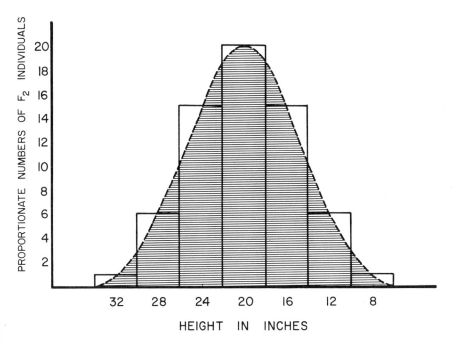

FIG. 11.2 Graph of the F_2 generation of the cross diagramed in Fig. 11.1 but assuming that the 24-inch difference in height depends on three pairs of effective alleles instead of two.

Human Skin Color

Probably the most famous investigation of polygenic inheritance in man is that of Dr. Charles B. Davenport on the heredity of skin color in Negro-white crosses (1913). Davenport and his co-workers carried on their investigation in Jamaica and Bermuda, where marriages of this type are more common than they are in the United States. The investigators employed a color top as a means of measuring skin pigments (Fig. 11.3). Colored paper disks were overlapped in such a way that varying proportions of each color were exposed. When the top was spun, the colors seemed to blend together. By varying the proportionate amounts of the colors black, yellow, red, and white, the investigators could match the skin color of the persons studied. In these days of photoelectric instruments employing spectral light (see below) this may seem a crude method of measuring color, yet it sufficed to reveal the fundamentals of skin-color inheritance in the families studied. Figure 11.4 shows the setting of

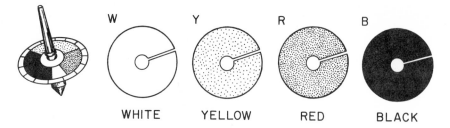

WHITE   YELLOW   RED   BLACK

FIG. 11.3   Color top of the type used in Davenport's investigation of human skin color, with the four discs employed. (Redrawn from Davenport, C. B., 1926. "The skin colors of the races of mankind," *Natural History*, **26**:44–49.)

the disks that resulted in a match to the skin color of a "white" person and of a Negro. Needless to say, both whites and Negroes showed variation from person to person—the Negroes more than the whites, the investigators found.

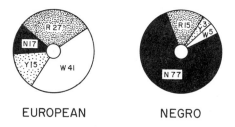

EUROPEAN   NEGRO

FIG. 11.4   Examples of color discs set to match the skin of a European and of a Negro. (Redrawn from Davenport, C. B., 1926. "The skin colors of the races of mankind," *Natural History*, **26**:44–49.)

At the present time we are interested in the inheritance of the black component measured by the investigators. This afforded a means of estimating the relative proportion of melanin in the skin (this is brown pigment, which may appear black when densely massed). With the exception of albinos, all persons possess melanin, but in varying amounts.

For comparison with the type of experimentation we have been discussing, we should like data on kindreds in which (a) Negroes marry whites, and (b) the offspring of such marriages (called mulattoes) marry each other:

Negro × White   Negro × White

Mulatto   ×   Mulatto

Offspring genetically comparable
to an F_2 generation

Davenport and his colleagues were able to obtain data on only six such families although they did obtain information on a larger number of first generation mulattoes (having one Negro and one white parent). The mulattoes were always intermediate between the parents in such cases. A typical example was a family in which the "black" reading for the father was 5 percent (5 percent of the black disk on the color top was exposed in the matching blend), and the comparable reading for the mother was 71 percent. The percentages for the seven children were 37, 35, 35, 43, 37, 35, and 35, respectively. These figures illustrate the fact that the readings for first generation mulattoes were fairly uniform, although if the Negro parent was lighter than the one in our example, the children also tended to be somewhat lighter (averaging around 26 percent).

In the matter of an intermediate and fairly uniform F_1 generation, then, the findings agree with expectation for polygenic inheritance. What about the "F_2" generation? Do the children of first-generation mulattoes show great variability (as in the F_2 of our experiment with height in plants)? The six families available to the investigators produced 32 children. Their "black" percentages ranged from 10 to 56. In Figure 11.5 we have indicated the distribution of the readings for the 32 individuals. Although the numbers are small, there is some resemblance to a normal frequency curve, a bit skewed to the left, perhaps.

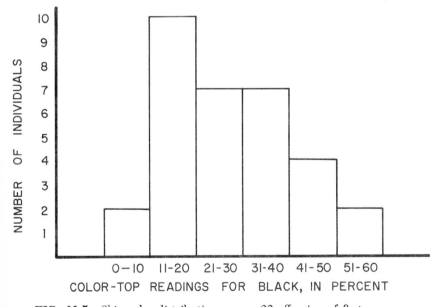

FIG. 11.5 Skin color distribution among 32 offspring of first generation mulattoes married to each other. (Based on the data of Davenport, C. B., 1913. "Heredity of skin color in Negro-white crosses," *Carnegie Institution of Washington*, Publication No. **188**, 1–106.)

Because Davenport found in his studies that many "white" persons showed a "black" reading of 10 percent or more, the two children having a reading of 10 percent were classified "white" (i.e., close to the skin color of the "ordinary brunet Caucasian") and thus represented one extreme of F_2 variability. Hence one extreme occurred twice in 32 times, or once in 16 times. We noted above that in the F_2 generation of experiments involving multiple genes, obtaining one extreme or the other $\frac{1}{16}$ of the time is evidence that two pairs of genes are involved. Davenport advanced the hypothesis that two pairs of genes, which he designated A and B, are involved in this difference in skin color.

From our discussion of the importance of basing conclusions on large numbers, we can see that Davenport based his hypothesis on numbers so small that we might well question the validity of the hypothesis. However, Davenport tested the hypothesis in many parental combinations, and demonstrated good agreement between actual findings concerning the offspring and expected findings based on the hypothesis.

He assigned the following ranges of percentage values of blackness to the genotypes:

Genotype	Percentage of Blackness	
aabb	0–11	white
Aabb or aaBb	12–25	light colored
AaBb, or AAbb, or aaBB	26–40	medium colored
AABb or AaBB	41–55	dark colored
AABB	56–78	black

He then analyzed various parental combinations to determine whether actual findings agreed with expectation. Suppose, for example, that one parent has the genotype *aabb,* the other the genotype *Aabb.* What types of offspring will be expected, and in what proportions will they be expected to occur?

Parents

	Phenotype	0–11%	12–25%
	Genotype	aabb	Aabb
	Gametes		

$$\left\{ \begin{matrix} ab \to Ab \\ \times \\ ab \to ab \end{matrix} \right\}$$

Offspring

	Genotypes	Aabb	aabb
	Phenotypes	12–25%	0–11%
	Ratio	1	:	1

Half the children will be expected to be white, half to be light colored. Davenport had data for 24 families of this kind, with a total of 99 children. Of the children, 42 were in the 0–11% category, 56 in the 12–25% category, 1 in the 26–40% category. Since the expectation was 49.5 in each of the first two categories mentioned and none in the third, it is evident that there was fairly good agreement between expectation and actual findings. Many other parental combinations were similarly analyzed; good agreement with expectation based on the hypothesis was usually demonstrated.

For sociological reasons, there is particular interest in families of which both parents are "white," or of which one or both are so light that they "pass for white." According to popular ideas, such people may have a "black" child. Davenport found three families in which both parents were in the 0–9% category. They had 9 children, none of whom graded higher than 9 percent. This is typical of other findings obtained since then. Students of the subject insist that no case has ever been proved of two "white" or very light parents having a "black" child. Proof in such a case would require removal of all doubt as to adoption or to the paternity of the child in question. It should be borne in mind that we refer only to the amount of pigment in the skin, not to other negroid physical characteristics.

As a general rule, in "mixed marriages" no child is darker than the darker parent. When darker children are produced, they are usually not much darker than the darker parent. For example, two light parents both having the genotype *Aabb* could have a child with the genotype *AAbb* who would probably be somewhat darker than either parent (but not "black").

This pioneer work by Davenport has stood the test of time in the sense that no one now questions the fact that skin color inheritance depends on multiple, cumulative genes. There is less agreement as to the actual number of pairs of these genes involved in the difference between Negro and white pigmentations. As we have seen, Davenport postulated two pairs, but with each resulting genotype represented by a considerable range of pigmentation. He recognized that superimposed on the effects of the genes were the effects of the environment. Exposure to the sun, for example, has a marked effect on skin pigmentation, as everyone knows. To minimize this effect on their results, the investigators matched, with their color tops, areas of skin normally covered by clothing—the upper arm, usually. Nevertheless, environmental effects were undoubtedly present. In addition, however, we should not be surprised to find that some of the variation was caused by genes other than the two pairs postulated by Davenport.

Thus, following a study of intermarriage between Negroes and whites in the United States, Gates (1949) suggested that three pairs of genes may be involved. Using a statistical approach and certain assumptions concerning the American Negro population, Stern (1953, 1954) has concluded that the range of variation in color exhibited by this group is best explained by postulating that the number of gene pairs is either four, five, or six, rather than fewer or more.

The simple color top of earlier investigators was replaced by a reflectance spectrophotometer in a study by Harrison and Owen (1964). This instrument measures the amount of light of different wave lengths reflected from a test surface: the skin in this case. Using it, the investigators measured the reflectance of the skin of the following residents of Liverpool: 105 Europeans; 106 people from various parts of West Africa; 94 "F_1 hybrids" (offspring of intermarriage between Europeans and West Africans); 30 "backcross European hybrids" (offspring of marriages between Europeans and F_1 hybrids); 26 "backcross African hybrids" (offspring of marriages between West Africans and F_1 hybrids); 14 "F_2 hybrids" (offspring of F_1 hybrids married to each other†).

The results are shown in Figure 11.6 (the number of F_2 hybrids was considered too small to warrant inclusion). Along the base line of the graph the shorter wave lengths (violet) are at the left, the longer wave lengths (red) at the right. We note that for all wave lengths the African

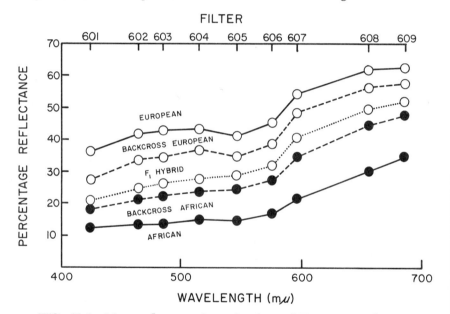

FIG. 11.6   Mean reflectance from the skins of Europeans, Africans, and various hybrid groups, as measured with a reflectance spectrophotometer. (Redrawn from Harrison, G. A., and J. J. T. Owen, 1964. "Studies on the inheritance of human skin color," *Annals of Human Genetics*, **28**:27–37.)

skin reflects much less light than does the European. The pigmentation of F_1 hybrids is intermediate, and the pigmentation of the respective backcross hybrids is intermediate between the pigmentations of the parental

_____

†This was not a literal F_2 generation as in animal experimentation, for these were not brother-sister matings.

groups concerned. Interestingly, the "backcross African" pigmentation is nearer that of the F_1 hybrid parent than it is the African parent. It is also interesting and perhaps significant that the curve for the F_1 hybrids is not precisely in the middle between the European and African curves. Toward the violet end of the spectrum the F_1 curve approaches the African more closely, and toward the red end the F_1 curve approaches the European more closely. This reminds us that skin color is complex, contributed to not only by the amount of melanin present but also by other factors, such as the color of the blood in the skin capillaries, which is more evident in lighter skins than in darker ones.

These more accurate measurements reinforce the interpretation of the polygenic nature of skin color inheritance. Statistical analysis led Harrison and Owen to conclude that the number of "effective factors" responsible for the difference in skin color between Europeans and Africans is "between 3 and 4."

Human Eye Color

Some readers may be surprised to find this subject included in a discussion of polygenic inheritance. If there is one thing the average person thinks he knows about human inheritance, it is that "brown eyes are dominant to blue." Traditionally this has been regarded as the best human example of Mendelian inheritance based on a single pair of genes, brown-eyed people having the genotypes *BB* or *Bb*, blue-eyed people the genotype *bb*. Such simplicity is appealing, yet a little thought will convince us that we should not really expect it to be true.

In the first place, people cannot really be classified so easily as brown-eyed, or blue-eyed. As we know from observation, eye colors come in all sorts of shades that are more or less intermediate between brown and blue—hazel, green, gray, light brown, dark brown, black. This range of variation in itself suggests polygenic inheritance.

When we examine the eye itself, we find that the color depends on the presence in the iris, near the front of the eye, of that same brown pigment that colors the skin: melanin. If no observable amount of melanin is present, the eye appears blue, not because of blue pigment but because of the same optical effect that causes the sky to appear blue on a clear day. The scattering of light by dust particles in the atmosphere causes blue light to be reflected back to the eye of an observer. Similarly, colorless cells in the more superficial layers of the iris (viewed against the dark background of the deeper layers) scatter the light so that blue is reflected back to the eye of an observer. A blue eye, then, is one in which the superficial layers of the iris have no observable amount of brown pigment.

At this point we may well mention that studies with a microscope indicate that no iris, save that of an albino, is completely without melanin. However, the amount may be so small and the individual particles so minute that an observer who does not use a microscope is unaware of their presence.

If, instead of a completely colorless iris, we have an iris with just a little pigment present, what color does the eye appear to the observer? That depends on the physical state of the small amount of pigment. If the pigment is massed together into small particles, the eye might appear blue flecked with brown. If the pigment is thinly dispersed, it might form a sort of yellow filter over the optical blue effect, the total result appearing green. A little more pigment combined with the blue optical effect would give a combined shade that an observer might classify as hazel.

With progressively larger amounts of pigment in the iris, hazel grades into dark brown and black (which in actuality is only the darkest brown of all). Sometimes a considerable amount of pigment may be present, but it is aggregated into masses, with clear blue areas between. Such eyes may appear blue when viewed in one light, and some shade of brown or hazel when viewed in another. The masses of pigment may be (a) irregularly placed, (b) arranged radially around the pupil like the spokes of a wheel, or (c) arranged in concentric circles around the pupil. All of which indicates that eye color is really a complex matter indeed, and suggests that we should hardly expect its inheritance to be simple.

Hence we see that when we classify people into the two categories, blue-eyed and brown-eyed, we are being arbitrary and are grouping together people who are quite unlike. In some cases, whether we call a person blue-eyed or brown-eyed depends on how closely we examine his eyes, and under what conditions of illumination.

Although other factors complicate the matter, the principal determinant of eye color is evidently the amount of melanin present in the surface layers of the iris. There is the possibility that a separate yellow pigment may also be present, but this yellow pigment may simply be melanin in a different physical (colloidal) state. We need more research on this point.

Focusing our attention on melanin, we note that it may vary in amount all the way from complete absence (for an observer not using a microscope, at least) to such a large amount that the eye appears black. This is the sort of continuous variation in a quantitative characteristic that is usually found to depend on multiple, cumulative genes. Do we have evidence of this in the inheritance of eye color?

Dr. Byron O. Hughes, working in the Laboratory of Vertebrate Biology of the University of Michigan, classified eye color into seven different grades (Hughes, 1944). To avoid subjective differences between observers, he made all the observations himself, and in good natural light. He did not use magnification or photoelectric devices for measuring color.

Recognizing that blue is an optical effect, and wishing to concentrate on the presence and absence of brown, he used the term "nonbrown" in place of "blue."

Hughes' seven eye-color grades were as follows: "1, no brown pigment observable; 2, a trace of brown; 3, one-fourth brown; 4, one-half brown; 5, three-fourths brown; 6, a trace of nonbrown; and 7, completely brown." He gathered data from 107 families with a total of 212 children, analyzing his results statistically. He classified the families by the eye-color grades of the parents: 1x1, 1x2, 1x3, and so on to 7x7 (actually he had no family that fitted this latter category). Although numbers were small in many categories, a general trend was indicated—the amount of pigment in the children's eyes increasing with increased amounts in the eyes of their parents. Of more interest was the fact that the greatest variation in eye color among the children was found in families in which the parents had the "middle" grades. For example, there were 9 families of which the parentage was "2x4" (one parent had a trace of brown, the other one-half brown). The children of these families were as follows: 4 of grade 1; 2 of grade 2; 3 of grade 3; 4 of grade 4; 3 of grade 5; 2 of grade 6; 1 of grade 7. Thus they ranged all the way from completely nonbrown (blue) to completely brown. Such a finding seems to indicate that the parents were heterozygous for several pairs of genes concerned with melanin production. There is nothing here, or elsewhere in the data, to suggest that dominance of brown over nonbrown is involved.

An interesting case is presented by the "1x1" matings, both parents having no observable brown in their eyes. If blue-eyedness depended on a recessive gene, then two blue-eyed parents could have only blue-eyed children. The idea that blue eyes *are* dependent on a recessive gene is so firmly implanted in popular thinking that when two persons regarded as blue-eyed do have a brown-eyed child there is sometimes embarrassment and the raising of eyebrows. Hughes studied 6 families in which both parents graded 1 in eye color; 17 of the children were of grade 1; 1 of grade 2; 1 of grade 3. Now we may surmise that a child graded 2 (trace of brown) would be regarded by friends and acquaintances as blue-eyed. The same might be true for a child of grade 3, who to Hughes' careful scrutiny appeared "one-fourth brown" (which we can equally well state as three fourths nonbrown, or blue). So perhaps all the parents and offspring in these families would be classified as blue-eyed by casual observers. The uncertainty emphasizes the artificiality of the popular classification into the two categories, blue-eyed and brown-eyed.

If, as seems likely, casual observers would call grade 2 people blue-eyed, then matings of "2x2" are matings of two blue-eyed people. Hughes' data included 15 such families; the children were as follows: 9 of grade 1; 17 of grade 2; 1 of grade 3; 1 of grade 4; 1 of grade 5. In the cases of grades 4 and 5, at least, there can be little doubt that everyone would notice the brown pigmentation. Hence these may be examples of brown-eyed children born to parents generally regarded as blue-eyed. Evidently these children inherit the genes for pigment from *both* parents and hence have darker eyes than does either parent. With polygenic inheritance, then, we should expect pairs of parents regarded as blue-eyed to occasionally have children with enough pigment to be regarded as brown-eyed.

Hughes concluded that inheritance of brown-versus-nonbrown eye color depends on multiple genes, but he did not attempt to estimate the number of pairs of these genes. Hughes investigated people of north European ancestry, and hence "nonbrown," and the smaller amounts of pigmentation predominated. It is interesting that the same general conclusion as to mode of eye color inheritance was reached by Davenport many years earlier (1913) from study of a very different group of people: the offspring of hybrids from Negro-white intermarriage. He classified eyes as "blue," "green," "hazel" (which to him meant "an eye that has brown pigment only in a narrow band around the pupil"), "light brown," "medium brown," "dark brown," and "yellow hazel." In this group of people the darker eyes were more abundant than the lighter, and, in fact, he had no record of a "blue × blue" mating. The diversity of eye colors in offspring of parents who had intermediate eye coloring, especially light brown and hazel, suggested multiple gene inheritance, and Davenport tentatively suggested two pairs of genes.

Brues (1946) in a study of 300 individuals by the sibling pair method classified eyes as "pure light," "near light," "yellow mixed," "light brown mixed," "medium brown mixed," "dark brown mixed," "near dark," and "pure dark." She also included study of the structure of the iris, variations in which affect the color seen by an observer. This more detailed analysis of iris pigmentation and structure resulted in phenotypic classes of greater complexity than had characterized earlier studies, and the greater phenotypic complexity suggested greater underlying genotypic complexity. Yet we may say, in general, that Brues found evidence of the operation of a series of genes interacting in various ways. The data suggested that some of the genes are sex-linked, a possibility also suggested by earlier investigators who noted that women tend to have darker eyes than do men. (No evidence of sex-linkage was found by Hughes, 1944.) It would be well to note at this point that there is no *a priori* reason why some genes in a series of polygenes may not be sex-linked. Polygenes are on various chromosomes, and the X chromosome may well be one of those included in any given series.

PARENTAL GENERATION
    Phenotypes: 32 inches   8 inches
    Genotypes: *AABB*   X   *aabb*
    Gametes: *AB*   *ab*

F_1 GENERATION
    Phenotypes: 20 inches   20 inches
    Genotypes: *AaBb*   X   *AaBb*
    Gametes: *AB, Ab, aB, ab*   *AB, Ab, aB, ab*

Combinations of gametes producing an F_2 generation:

	AB	*Ab*	*aB*	*ab*
AB	*AABB* 8+10+10+2 +2 = 32	*AABb* 8+10+10+2 = 30	*AaBB* 8+10+2+2 = 22	*AaBb* 8+10+2 = 20
Ab	*AABb* 8+10+10+2 = 30	*AAbb* 8+10+10 = 28	*AaBb* 8+10+2 = 20	*Aabb* 8+10 =18
aB	*AaBB* 8+10+2+2 = 22	*AaBb* 8+10+2 = 20	*aaBB* 8+2+2 = 12	*aaBb* 8+2 = 10
ab	*AaBb* 8+10+2 = 20	*Aabb* 8+10 = 18	*aaBb* 8+2 =10	*aabb* =8

F_2 GENERATION

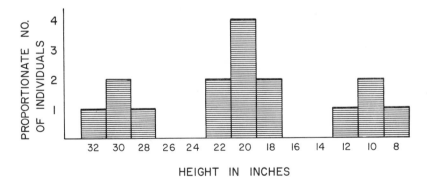

FIG. 11.7 Cross between two imaginary plant varieties differing in height by 24 inches (cf., Fig. 11.1). It is assumed that each *A* increases the height by 10 inches, each *B* increases it by 2 inches.

Polygenes and Modifying Genes

In discussing polygenes, we tend to visualize situations in which the various genes of a cumulative series contribute equally. Such an assumption makes for ease of computation, but in many, if not most, instances it may be an oversimplification. There is no reason why one gene of a series may not contribute more than does another one.

To illustrate such a difference in genetic effect, let us return to our example of height inheritance in a hypothetical plant variety (Fig. 11.1). In our earlier discussion we assumed that A and B contributed equal increments of increase in height (above the basic 8 inches). Now let us suppose that A contributes 10 inches, whereas B contributes 2 inches. How will such differential contribution affect the results?

The experiment is diagramed in Figure 11.7. Note that, as before, when 32-inch plants are crossed with 8-inch ones the F_1 offspring are intermediate, 20 inches tall. Then the mating together of the F_1 individuals is represented by the same 16-square, checkerboard diagram we used previously. The difference lies in the interpretation of this diagram. In each square, representing a zygote, we add, to the basic 8 inches, 10 inches for each A, 2 inches for each B.

The outcome, tabulated beneath the diagram, indicates that the F_2 will fall into three non-overlapping groups: (1) plants from 28 to 32 inches tall, (2) plants from 18 to 22 inches tall, and (3) plants from 8 to 12 inches tall. If we designate these as tall, medium, and short, respectively, we note that we have a 4:8:4, or 1:2:1 ratio.

Note the genotypes of these three groups. The tall individuals are all AA; the medium ones are Aa; the short ones are aa (neglecting the B's for the moment).

There are two, equally valid, ways of interpreting these results. According to the first interpretation, we may state, as we did at the outset, that A and B are multiple genes each contributing to increase in height but doing so unequally.

Or we may interpret the results as indicating that A is a *main* gene, and B is a *modifying* gene. According to this view, A is a gene for tallness, a its recessive allele for shortness, and dominance is lacking. Hence we obtain in the F_2 generation the ratio of ¼ AA (long) : ¾ Aa (medium) : ¼ aa (short).

Then, according to this view, the gene B modifies the action of the A genes. On the basis of the distribution of B's we find, for example, that ¼ of the AA plants will be 32 inches tall, ¾ of the AA plants will be 30 inches tall, ¼ of the AA plants will be 28 inches tall. The Aa and aa plants vary similarly (note that each group has a secondary 1:2:1 ratio determined by the distribution of the *B*'s).

This example illustrates the fact that there is no clear-cut distinction between polygenes and modifying genes. In general usage, the term "polygenes" would probably be employed in cases in which the relative contributions of the genes in the series were of more or less the same order of magnitude, the term "modifying genes" being reserved for cases in which one gene contributed much more than did the genes called modifiers. Where to draw the line is more or less a matter of taste on the part of the investigator.

Not all modifying genes are merely quantitative, adding "more of the same." Modifying genes that are comparable to polygenes do have this quantitative similarity, but in other cases modifying genes may modify the action of the main gene *qualitatively*. For example, in color production the main gene may produce yellow, and a modifier may cause the yellow to have an orangish shade. (A distinction between quantitative and qualitative is rather artificial. In this case, the modifier gene would presumably act by producing red pigment to mix with the yellow. If the distinction is between "red pigment present" versus "red pigment absent," then we should be inclined to say that the action of the modifier is qualitative. However, also involved may be a question of the *amount* of red pigment present—a small amount producing no visible effect on the shade of yellow, a larger amount producing an effect. In this case, the modifier is acting quantitatively, also.)

Other Polygenic Traits in Man

Thus far, our examples of human polygenic inheritance have involved differences in the amount of pigment produced. In point of fact, however, we may well suspect that this type of inheritance is the basis of all traits that vary quantitatively in a relatively continuous manner. Human stature is a familiar example. In view of the enormous volume of data on stature collected by anthropologists we may wonder that so little of a definite nature can be stated concerning its inheritance. In any given population of men (or women), stature varies quite continuously from shortest to tallest, with an average near the midpoint between the extremes. As a consequence, bell-shaped, normal frequency curves are commonly approximated whenever data on stature are graphed. This suggests that inheritance is based on multiple genes acting cumulatively. As a matter of fact, stature afforded the first example of continuous variation to be analyzed—by two pioneers in genetic research, Galton and Pearson.

Unfortunately for genetic analysis, stature is a complex human trait. It is the total of the lengths of body segments that do not always vary correspondingly: head, neck, trunk, legs. (For example, we recall among our acquaintances tall people who have tall "sitting height," and others who have fairly short "sitting height" but are of equal total stature due to the length of their legs.)

Stature is influenced by hormones. We see evidence of this in differences in height between men and women. The effects of secretions of endocrine glands are most striking in cases of extreme over- or undersecretion. One of the secretions of the pituitary gland is a growth-controlling hormone. Overproduction of this hormone during infancy and childhood results in giantism, whereas midgets are produced if the hormone is in short supply during these critical years. These giants and midgets, respectively, are of fairly normal proportions (other types of dwarfism have different causation). Presumably, variations in stature between these extremes are also connected with varying amounts of this hormone, acting during the years of growth. In fact, some of the genes controlling stature may well act by regulating the production of the hormone.

Genes do not act alone, however. Environment plays a significant role in determining how tall a person will become. Without doubt, the most important environmental factor is diet. Many statistics show (a) that people

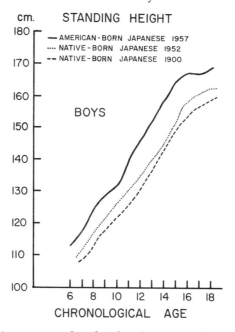

FIG. 11.8 Average standing height of American-born Japanese boys compared with that of boys in Japan, in 1900 and 1952. (Redrawn from Greulich, W. W., 1958. "Growth of children of the same race under different environmental conditions," *Science,* **127**:515–16.)

are becoming taller as the generations pass, and (b) that when people migrate to the United States their children, on an average, are taller than their contemporaries living in "the old country." Both of these trends are well illustrated for Japanese boys by Figure 11.8. Although other factors may contribute, the principal cause of the increase is probably improvement in diet.

In view of these and other complexities, we can readily see that although there is general agreement that multiple, cumulative genes are involved in the determination of stature, knowledge of the number and mode of action of these genes must await future research. In Chapter 21 we shall discuss evidence derived from study of twins concerning inheritance of stature (pp. 311–312).

Weight is also a quantitative characteristic that varies continuously between extremes. Variations in weight show the hallmarks of polygenic inheritance. Yet here, even more than with stature, differences in diet have such large effects that we readily understand the difficulties of genetic analysis. Evidence from experiments with lower animals (e.g., rabbits), with careful control of diet, confirms our suspicions that weight depends on multiple genes.

Every schoolchild knows that when grades or the results of intelligence tests are graphed, a bell-shaped curve is approximated. We may, then, predict that when the time comes that the genetic basis of intelligence is analyzed, the variations of this trait will be found to depend on multiple genes. At the present time we are a long way from such an analysis. A first requirement will be the development of an accurate means of measuring inherent intellectual ability—a means of measurement independent of cultural background and educational experience. Then with this perfected yardstick, we must measure large groups of people and especially successive generations in many kindreds. Since human generations are so long, this means a continuing program of research stretching over many years. Until this utopian day arrives, we must draw as many conclusions as possible from data obtained with less perfect measuring instruments. Evidence as to the inheritance of intelligence will be presented in connection with a discussion of twins (Chap. 21).

PROBLEMS

1. Referring to Fig. 11.1, what types of progeny and in what proportions will be expected from each of the following crosses: (a) *AaBb* × *aabb*; (b) *AaBB* × *aaBb*; (c) *AaBb* × *Aabb*?

2. Assume that the difference between a variety of oats yielding 4 grams per plant and a variety yielding 10 grams is caused by two equal and cumulative pairs of multiple genes. A 4-gram variety having the genotype *sstt* is crossed with a 10-gram variety having the genotype *SSTT*. Give the genotype and phenotype of the F₁ offspring. When these F₁ plants are mated together, what tyes of F₂ offspring will be expected, and in what proportions?

3. One variety of a certain species of plant is 48 inches high, another variety is 16 inches high. When the two varieties were crossed, the F₁ hybrids averaged 32 inches high and varied little in height. The F₁ plants were mated together to produce an F₂ generation. These F₂ offspring averaged 32 inches in height but varied widely. Of 2560 F₂ plants, 10 were 48 inches high, and 8 were 16 inches high. How many pairs of genes were probably involved in producing the difference in height between the two varieties? How much increase in height did each effective allele contribute?

4. In skin color inheritance, if the genotypes postulated by Davenport are correct (p. 168), what amounts of pigmentation will be expected in children produced by the following matings: (a) *AAbb* × *aaBB*; (b) *Aabb* × *Aabb*; (c) *AaBb* × *aabb*; (d) *Aabb* × *AaBb*?

5. Let us imagine that the amount of brown pigmentation of the eye is controlled by three pairs of polygenes (the number is almost certainly greater than this). Let us further imagine that there is an observational *threshold,* so that one effective allele by itself produces so little brown pigment that a microscope is needed to see it. People who have the genotype *aabbcc* are nonbrown-eyed (blue), and we may assume that people with the genotypes *Aabbcc, aaBbcc,* or *aabbCc* have so little pigment that their acquaintances regard them as blue-eyed. On the other hand, people with two effective alleles (*AAbbcc, aaBBcc, aabbCC, AaBbcc,* and so on) have enough iris pigmentation so that acquaintances regard them as brown-eyed. The greater the number of effective alleles above two, the darker the shade of brown.

   On the basis of this hypothesis, what eye colors would be expected from each of the following matings and in what proportions would the different colors be expected? In each case give the phenotypes of the parents as well as those of the children. (a) *Aabbcc* × *Aabbcc*; (b) *AaBbcc* × *Aabbcc*; (c) *AaBbcc* × *AaBbcc*; (d) *AaBbcc* × *AAbbcc*; (e) *aaBbcc* × *aabbCc*; (f) *AaBbCc* × *aabbcc*.

REFERENCES

Brues, A. M., 1946. "A genetic analysis of human eye color," *American Journal of Physical Anthropology*, New series 4:1–36.

Davenport, C. B., 1913. "Heredity of skin color in Negro-white crosses," *Carnegie Institution of Washington*, Publication No. 188, 1–106.

Gates, R. R., 1949. *Pedigrees of Negro Families*. Philadelphia: The Blakiston Company.

Greulich, W. W., 1958. "Growth of children of the same race under different environmental conditions," *Science*, 127:515–16.

Harrison, G. A., and J. J. T. Owen, 1964. "Studies on the inheritance of human skin color," *Annals of Human Genetics*, 28:27–37.

Hughes, B. O., 1944. "The inheritance of eye color in man—brown and non-brown," *Contributions from the Laboratory of Vertebrate Biology, University of Michigan*, No. 27:1–10.

Stern, C., 1953. "Model estimates of the frequency of white and near-white segregants in the American Negro," *Acta Genetica et Statistica Medica*, 4:281–98.

Stern, C., 1954. "The biology of the Negro," *Scientific American*, 191:81–85.

12.

SEX LINKAGE

Sex Chromosomes

In Chapter 3 we discussed the behavior of chromosomes during the process of meiosis. Males and females are alike with regard to the chromosomes discussed in that chapter (Fig. 3.1, p. 26). Such chromosomes are called **autosomes** to distinguish them from a pair of chromosomes with regard to which the sexes differ. Man, as mentioned previously, has 23 pairs of chromosomes; 22 of these are pairs of autosomes; one consists of a pair of **sex chromosomes.**

The sex chromosomes are of two kinds, called **X chromosomes** and **Y chromosomes.** Females have two X chromosomes and no Y chromosome. Males have one X chromosome and one Y chromosome. In man, the X chromosome is much larger than the Y chromosome, but despite the size difference, the fact that they synapse together in primary spermatocytes indicates that they constitute a homologous pair of chromosomes.

Figure 12.1 shows meiosis in a male, starting at the primary spermatocyte stage. The diagram is similar to Figure 3.5 (p. 32) except that in addition to the two pairs of autosomes in each spermatogonium, an X chromosome and a Y chromosome are also included. We note that these chromosomes, like the others, duplicate themselves, and pair in synapsis in the primary spermatocyte. When this cell divides to form two secondary spermatocytes, the X chromosome goes to one secondary spermatocyte, the Y chromosome to the other. When the spermatids are formed by division of the secondary spermatocytes, the chromatids separate. The outcome of meiosis is that two of the four spermatids, and hence sperm, developing from a primary spermatocyte contain X chromosomes and two

PRIMARY SPERMATOCYTE
Shown at metaphase.
Synapsis. Tetrads.

SECONDARY
SPERMATOCYTES

X chromosome

Y chromosome

SPERMATIDS

SPERM

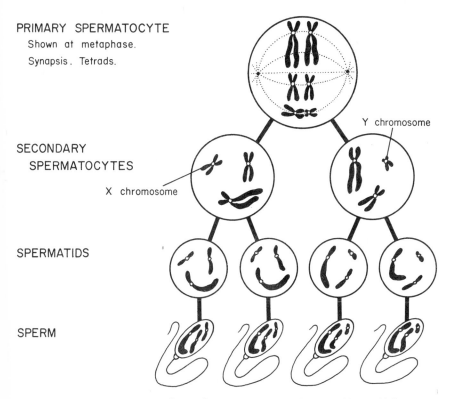

FIG. 12.1 Meiosis in the male (spermatogensis) as in Fig. 3.5 but with the addition of X and Y chromosomes. In the primary spermatocyte the X and Y chromosomes exhibit terminal (end-to-end) synapsis.

contain Y chromosomes. Thus males produce X-containing and Y-containing sperms in equal numbers.

Because females contain two X chromosomes, meiosis does not differ from meiosis of the autosomes (Fig. 3.8, p. 36). Each ovum produced contains one X chromosome.

In fertilization there are two possibilities: (1) An ovum, containing X, may be fertilized by a sperm containing X, in which case the zygote normally develops into a female. (2) An ovum, containing X, may be fertilized by a sperm containing Y, in which case a male is normally produced. Thus the sex of an individual is normally determined at the time of fertilization, although the sexual development of the individual may be modified subsequently by other influences. We shall discuss sex determination in Chapter 15.

Figure 12.2 shows the main regions in the X and Y chromosomes. Because the two pair together in synapsis (in primary spermatocytes), we infer that a certain portion of each is *homologous* to a corresponding portion of the other. In man the X and Y chromosomes synapse end to end instead of side by side, and therefore, the homologous portions are probably small. By homologous, in this case, we mean that they contain similar genetic material. Evidence from many sources indicates that in synapsis, genetic alleles pair with each other. Thus it would seem that there must be at least a few pairs of genes that are shared by the X and Y chromosomes. Such genes are called **incompletely or partially sex-linked** (see p. 200).

X Chromosome   Y Chromosome

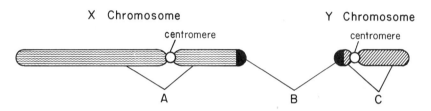

FIG. 12.2 Diagram of the regions of the X and Y chromosomes. A. Portion of the X chromosome not homologous to the Y chromosome. B. Portions of the X and Y chromosomes homologous to each other (where synapsing occurs). C. Portion of the Y chomosome not homologous to the X chromosome.

However, by far the greater portion of the X chromosome is not homologous with the Y chromosome. The genes in this portion of the X chromosome have no alleles in the Y chromosome. Such genes are called completely **X-linked.**

Similarly, a portion of the Y chromosome is not homologous to the X chromosome. Genes present in this portion of the Y chromosome are said to be completely **Y-linked**, or holandric.

X-Linked Inheritance

Of the completely X-linked human genes, the best known is that for red-green color blindness (**Daltonism**). This is the commonest form of partial color blindness. At the outset it will not be necessary to subdivide the trait further. Suffice it to say that people having X-linked color blindness may differ in the nature of the visual defect, and that these phenotypic differences reflect genotypic differences as yet only partially analyzed (see, however, p. 206).

In addition to these X-linked forms of partial color blindness, there is also the trait of complete color blindness. Genetically, however, that is another story; therefore, when we refer to color blindness in the present discussion we shall mean X-linked partial color blindness.

If a woman inherits a gene for color blindness from one parent and a gene for normal vision from the other, she will have normal color vision. This fact demonstrates that the gene for color blindness is recessive. We may represent it by the initial c, its normal allele by C.

We have implied that this pair of alleles is carried in the nonhomologous portion of the X chromosome (Fig. 12.2). The evidence for this is circumstantial: the trait behaves as if the genes were carried in this portion of the X chromosome. Let us look at some of the evidence.

1. *If a woman is color-blind, all her sons are color-blind, but none of her daughters are* (unless her husband is color-blind). If the gene is in the X chromosome, this would work out as follows (using initials **X** and **Y** to represent the chromosomes):

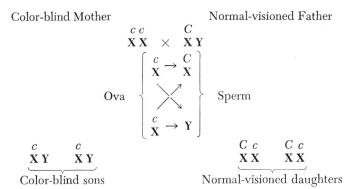

Color-blind Mother   Normal-visioned Father

Ova   Sperm

Color-blind sons   Normal-visioned daughters

Note that the mother must be homozygous if she shows the trait, since c is recessive.

Note also that the father, having the gene C in his X chromosome, has no allele for it in the Y chromosome. He is said to be **hemizygous**—he has only one allele of a pair (hence he cannot be either homozygous or heterozygous for X-linked genes).

2. *A woman cannot be color-blind unless her father is* (and unless her mother also has the gene).

Heterozygous Mother   Color-blind Father

Ova   Sperm

C X Y — Normal son

c X Y — Color-blind son

C c X X — Normal daughter

c c X X — Color-blind daughter

Note that every daughter receives one X chromosome from her father. Unless this X chromosome contains the gene c (in which case the father himself is color-blind), she will not be color-blind.

Color-blind daughters can only arise when a color-blind man happens to marry a woman who is heterozygous (or herself color-blind). Color-blind women are quite rare, therefore, in comparison to the number of color-blind men. During my years as a teacher of human genetics, only one girl in my classes has confessed to being color-blind. She had a sister who was color-blind and a brother who was *not* color-blind—an unusual combination. She gave me the facts with regard to her family; Figure 12.3 presents these data, although the order of birth of the children in some of the sibships may not be shown correctly.

The girl herself (the propositus) is III-1, with her brother and sister as mentioned. Her father, II-1, was color-blind, as he must necessarily have been to have color-blind daughters. As we have indicated on p. 185, the mother, II-2, must have been heterozygous to have had color-blind daughters, but in this case her heterozygosity is also indicated by the fact that her father, I-2, was color-blind. I-2 had six daughters; all

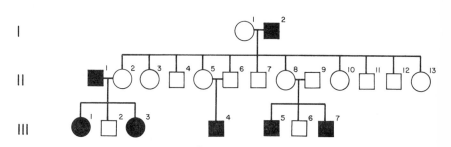

FIG. 12.3   Red-green color blindness. A kindred including a family composed of two color-blind daughters and one noncolor-blind son. Solid squares and circles represent color-blind individuals.

of them must have been heterozygous; two of them proved that they were by producing color-blind sons.

We have stated that a family consisting of two color-blind daughters and a noncolor-blind son is an unusual combination. How often would such a sibship of three be expected when a color-blind man married a heterozygous woman (II-1 × II-2)? The genotypes are given in the preceding diagram, which indicates that ¼ of the children are expected to be noncolor-blind sons, ¼ color-blind sons, ¼ noncolor-blind daughters, and ¼ color-blind daughters.

Following the practice set forth in Chapter 5, we may let

$$c = \text{chance for a color-blind daughter} = \tfrac{1}{4}$$
$$d = \text{chance for a noncolor-blind son} = \tfrac{1}{4}$$

Then sibships of three are represented by the expression

$$(c + d)^3 = c^3 + 3c^2d + 3cd^2 + d^3$$

In this equation the "$3c^2d$" item represents families consisting of two color-blind daughters and one noncolor-blind son. The chance of such a family occurring is: $3 \times (\frac{1}{4})^2 \times \frac{1}{4} = \frac{3}{64}$ or about 1 in 21. This is not such a very small chance after all.

3. *Half of the sons of heterozygous mothers are expected to be color-blind*, regardless of the genotype of the fathers. This is illustrated in the diagram just given. The father contributes a Y chromosome to all his sons. Of course, as with all Mendelian expectations, the 1:1 ratio of color-blind to normal sons is most closely approximated when data regarding sons of many heterozygous (carrier) mothers are pooled.

4. *Fathers do not pass on the gene for color blindness to their sons, but only to their daughters.* This follows from the fact that fathers transmit a Y chromosome, not an X, to all their sons (see diagram on p. 185). X-linked inheritance is sometimes called "crisscross inheritance" because males transmit the gene to female offspring, and it is, in turn, the male offspring of the latter who exhibit the trait.

Types of Inheritance that May Be Confused with X-Linkage   As indicated above, men show the phenotype of a recessive X-linked gene when they inherit the gene from only one parent (the mother), whereas women show the phenotype only if they inherit the gene from both parents. This difference explains in large measure why X-linked traits are shown much more commonly by men than by women. Indeed, unlike Figure 12.3, many pedigrees of X-linked traits show only males exhibiting the phenotype. (In such kindreds no affected male happened to marry a heterozygous female, or if such a marriage did occur it did not produce homozygous female offspring.) However, we must beware of the temptation to jump to a conclusion here. If we assemble a pedigree and find only males exhibiting a trait, that finding does not in itself constitute proof that the trait depends on a recessive X-linked gene. What other genetic situations might result in only males showing a certain phenotype?

1. The trait might depend on *autosomal* genes but be **sex-limited**. This means that females may have the genes but for some reason do not show the phenotype. Secondary sex characteristics are an example; in this case the male and female sex hormones are important in determining which characteristics shall appear in the individual. To take an example from cattle, bulls may have the genetic constitution for high milk production, but obviously they do not produce large quantities of milk; milk production is sex-limited to females. Among human beings, production of a heavy beard is normally limited to males, although there is no reason to doubt

that females may transmit the genes concerned.

Note that with regard to sex-limited traits, males and females may be genotypically alike. Both may be *aa,* for example (recall that the genes are in the autosomes), but for some reason, hormonal or otherwise, the genotype *aa* produces a phenotypic effect in only one sex.

2. The trait might depend on *autosomal* genes that are **sex-influenced** or **sex-controlled.** This means that in one sex the gene produces its phenotypic effect only in homozygotes. Horns in sheep are an example of this.

If the gene for the development of horns is designated by the initial *H* and the gene for hornlessness by *h,* three genotypes are possible: *HH, Hh, hh.* Individuals *of both sexes* having the genotype *hh* are hornless. On the other hand, males having the genotype *Hh* are horned, whereas females having the genotype *Hh* are hornless. (It is as if in females the *h* becomes dominant to the *H.* We sometimes say that sex-influenced genes, e.g., *H,* are dominant in males and recessive in females.)

Although we need more research on the subject, there is some evidence that "pattern baldness" in human beings depends on a sex-influenced gene, *B.* Women having the genotype *BB* are bald, but women having the genotype *Bb* are not bald, whereas men of both genotypes *BB* and *Bb* are bald.

Note that both sex-limited and sex-influenced genes, being autosomal, may be passed on from fathers to sons, as well as to daughters. In this respect they differ from X-linked genes.

The phenotypic expression of both sex-limited and sex-influenced genes is restricted in some way by the sex of the individual. Sex hormones are probably involved in the examples we have given. On the other hand, sex in itself really has no effect on the expression of X-linked genes. A man is not color-blind because he is a male, but merely because he has the gene *c* in his X chromosome, with no allele to "cover it up" in the Y chromosome. A woman's sex hormones have no influence on whether she is color-blind or not; if she has the genotype *cc,* she is color-blind; if her genotype is *CC* or *Cc,* she is not. These genes in the X chromosome, then, really have nothing to do with sex. Judging from studies of lower animals where our knowledge is more complete than it is in man, the varied and miscellaneous assemblage of genes in the X chromosome seems to be there by historical accident. If we had knowledge of the evolution of chromosomes, we should be in a position to understand why some genes happen to be in X chromosomes, others in autosomes.

In summary, the genetic phenomena of sex-limitation and sex-influence result in pedigrees in which phenotypic expression of autosomal genes occurs predominantly in one sex. Predominant expression of the trait in the male sex is most easily confused with X-linked inheritance, of course. Perhaps the most easily applied means of distinguishing X-linkage from sex-limitation and sex-influence is the fact that fathers do not transmit X-linked genes to sons, whereas inheritance from father to son does occur in the other cases. Nevertheless, in the absence of ability to arrange matings, distinguishing between the three types of inheritance is sometimes difficult when we encounter a "new" trait whose genetics is as yet unknown.

3. Finally, we should mention that pedigrees in which persons showing the phenotype in question are all males may occur just by *chance* (no X-linkage, sex-limitation, or sex-influence being involved). This is particularly likely to happen if the pedigree includes small numbers of individuals showing the phenotype. For example, suppose that in a certain pedigree 5 people show the phenotype in which we are interested. If the phenotype depends on a simple autosomal gene, uninfluenced by sex in any way, what are the chances that all 5 of the people will be males? In our general population the ratio of male births to female births is about 105:100. This is so near 1:1 that for present purposes we may say that the chance for a male birth is ½, the chance for a female birth is ½. The chance that all 5 of the people showing the phenotype will be males is $(½)^5$ or $\frac{1}{32}$. This is not really a small chance. Of course, if there are 10 people showing the phenotype and all are males, the likelihood of this happening just by chance is only $(½)^{10}$ or $\frac{1}{1024}$. Nonetheless, it *could* happen. Human geneticists are well aware of the danger of placing undue emphasis on isolated pedigrees that happen to "look good"—pedigrees that come to an investigator's attention because of their "curiosity value." Here again we can see the importance of including large numbers of individuals whenever possible, and of analyzying as many different kindreds as possible.

X-Linkage and the Hardy-Weinberg Formula   In employing the Hardy-Weinberg formula we use the initial p to represent the relative frequency of a dominant gene, the initial q to represent the frequency of its recessive allele. We then square the algebraic sum of these: $(p + q)^2$. Why do we square this binomial? Because two parents are involved in the production of zygotes, and hence of the offspring that develop from them.

This same principle applies to X-linked inheritance and the production of female offspring. Each female has two X chromosomes, one received from the mother, one from the father. Returning to our example of color blindness, we may let p represent the frequency of gene C, and q the frequency of c.

Then, *among females*, $p^2 + 2pq + q^2$ represents the expected frequency of (a) homozygous noncolor-blind individuals (p^2), (b) heterozygous noncolor-blind individuals $(2pq)$, and (c) color-blind individuals (q^2). If, for example, $p = 0.95$ and $q = 0.05$, then $q^2 = 0.0025$. This means that we will expect to find that 0.25 percent of all women in this population are color-blind. Incidentally, a much larger proportion will be carriers (heterozygous): $2pq = 2 \times (0.95) \times (0.05) = 0.095 = 9.5$ percent.

What proportion of *males* will be color-blind? A male inherits the gene for color blindness from only one parent, his mother. His father contributes neither C nor c, as we have seen. Thus every male who develops from an ovum containing C is noncolor-blind, and every male who develops from an ovum containing c is color-blind. What are the relative frequencies of these two kinds of ova? The frequency of C-containing ova is p, the frequency of c-containing ova is q. Hence it follows that the frequency of noncolor-blind men is p, the frequency of color-blind men is q (not q^2 as in women, who receive genes concerned with color vision from *both* parents).

Because every man who receives the gene c is color-blind, we need only count the number of color-blind men in a population to determine the value of q. If, as sometimes happens, we find that 5 percent of the men are color-blind, we then know that q is 0.05 in the gene pool of that population.

Here we find mathematical expression of the fact mentioned previously that color-blind men are much more numerous than color-blind women. If q is 0.05, we expect 5 percent of the men to be color-blind, but only 0.25 percent of the women to be $[q^2 = (0.05)^2 = 0.0025]$. In other words, the number of color-blind women is expected to be the square of the number of color-blind men. Actual data indicate that this relationship is approximated. Sources of error include the fact, mentioned previously, that there is more than one type of X-linked partial color blindness, and the fact that some heterozygous women have poor enough color discrimination so that they may be classified as color-blind (in other words, dominance of C over c is not always complete; recall our discussion of partial penetrance, pp. 78–79).

The Xg[a] Blood Groups

In our discussion of color blindness we listed several criteria for distinguishing X-linked inheritance from autosomal inheritance in pedigree study. Application of the Hardy-Weinberg formula adds another means of obtaining evidence as to whether or not a trait is X-linked. We may ask such questions as this: If the trait is X-linked, what proportion of the sons and of the daughters, born in families of which the father shows the trait but the mother does not, will be expected to show the trait? Or again, in families in which neither parent shows the trait, what proportion of the sons will be expected to show it? What proportion of the daughters will be expected to do so? The answers to the questions will depend on the frequency of the gene in the population, as well as on the dominance or recessiveness of that gene. Then, having determined the expectation, we can see how closely actual findings agree with expectation, and thereby support our hypothesis concerning the mode of inheritance.

A particularly instructive example of this means of attacking the problem is furnished by the initial investigation of the **Xg^a blood groups**, first called to the attention of the scientific world in 1962 (Mann *et al.*, 1962). A certain "Mr. And.," a patient who had received many blood transfusions, was found to possess in his serum an antibody against a previously unknown antigen. The red blood cells of some people reacted with this antibody [they were called Xg(a+)], whereas the cells of other people did not [they were called Xg(a−)]. The antigen possessed by cells that did react was named **Xg^a**, and the corresponding antibody in Mr. And.'s serum was called anti-**Xg^a**. The gene for the presence of the antigen was designated as *Xg^a*, and the gene for its absence was called *Xg*.

At the outset, tests with Mr. And.'s serum were made on the cells of 342 Caucasians selected at random, with the following results:

	Male	Female
Xg (a+)	95	167
Xg (a−)	59	21

Thus nearly 89 percent of the females tested were Xg(a+), whereas only about 62 percent of the males were Xg(a+); the difference was highly significant statistically. This difference between the sexes suggested the possibility of sex-linkage, with gene *Xg^a* being dominant to gene *Xg*. This hypothesis was then investigated qualitatively and quantitatively.

The qualitative portion of the investigation consisted of studying as many family groups as possible: 50 families with a total of 104 children in the initial investigation. These are represented in Figure 12.4, classified by the type of mating.

Most numerous were the Xg(a+) × Xg(a+) matings. If *Xg^a* is an X-linked, dominant gene, all daughters from such matings must be Xg(a+) because they receive at least the one *Xg^a* gene from their fathers. Sons may be either Xg(a+) or Xg(a−) because some of the mothers are heterozygous (*Xg^a Xg*). Figure 12.4 shows that all offspring in these families agreed with these principles.

There were 3 families in which the father was Xg(a+) and the mother Xg(a−). If *Xg^a* is an X-linked, dominant gene, this mating is *Xg^a Y* × *Xg Xg*. In such a mating all sons must be Xg(a−) and all daughters Xg(a+). Although the numbers were small, the offspring conformed to this rule. Shortly after the original investigation, the number of families in this category was increased to 10, with continued conformity to the rule (Race and Sanger, 1962).

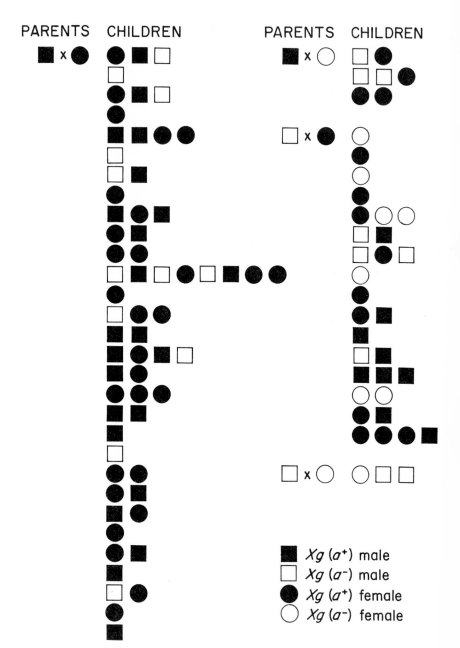

FIG. 12.4 The Xg^a blood groups. Fifty sibships classified by nature of the parents. (Redrawn from Mann, J. D. *et al.*, 1962. "A sex-linked blood group," *Lancet*, 1:8–10.)

In 16 families the father was Xg(a−) and the mother Xg(a+). As the mother could be heterozygous, this mating could be $Xg\,Y \times Xg^a\,Xg$ and could give rise to both Xg(a+) and Xg(a−) sons, and Xg(a+) and Xg(a−) daughters. We note that all four possibilities were in fact realized.

Finally there was one family in which both parents were Xg(a−). All three of the children were Xg(a−). This tells us nothing about X-linkage but is a bit of evidence that gene Xg is recessive.

The authors (Mann *et al.*, 1962) called attention to two correlated rules of X-linked dominant inheritance, which these data exemplify. Mothers and daughters of Xg(a+) men must be Xg(a+). Fathers and sons of Xg(a−) women must be Xg(a−). The data conform to these principles.

Turning to the quantitative aspect of the investigation, we recall that about 62 percent (actually 61.69 percent) of the men in the original random sample were Xg(a+). If the gene is X-linked, this means that the frequency, p, of the gene Xg^a is 0.6169, and the frequency, q, of the recessive allele is 0.3831 (see pp. 189–190).

Using the Hardy-Weinberg formula we can then calculate the expected frequencies of the *women*, as follows:

Xg(a+) homozygotes $(Xg^a\,Xg^a) = p^2 = (0.6169)^2 = 0.3806$
Xg(a+) heterozygotes $(Xg^a\,Xg) = 2pq = 2 \times 0.6169 \times 0.3831 = 0.4726$
Xg(a−) homozygotes $(Xg\,Xg) = q^2 = (0.3831)^2 = 0.1468$

We have already noted that the frequency of Xg(a+) men is 0.6169 and that of Xg(a−) men is 0.3831.

Using these data we can now calculate the proportions of the different types of children to be expected from each of the different types of mating. These expectations are given in Table 12.1. It is important that we understand the reasoning on which the expectations given in the table are based. It will suffice to illustrate the reasoning for one type of mating, that in which both parents are Xg(a+) (first row of the table). The frequency of this type of mating is found by multiplying the frequency of Xg(a+) women by the frequency of Xg(a+) men. We have noted that the frequency of homozygous Xg(a+) women is 0.3806, that of heterozygous women is 0.4726. Hence the total frequency of Xg(a+) women is the sum = 0.8532. The frequency of Xg(a+) men is 0.6169. Therefore, the frequency of Xg(a+) × Xg(a+) matings is 0.8532 × 0.6169 = 0.5263.

Half of the offspring are expected to be females, half males. Of the female offspring, all are expected to be Xg(a+) as we noted previously (p. 191). Hence, 0.5 of the children are expected to be Xg(a+) females; none are expected to be Xg(a−) females (Table 12.1).

Similarly, 0.5 of the children are expected to be males. How many of them are expected to be Xg(a+), how many Xg(a−)? In answering this question we can neglect the fathers, for with X-linked inheritance the

TABLE 12.1. Expected distribution of the Xg^a groups in Caucasian parents and offspring.

Matings			Proportion of children from each mating			
Type		Frequency	Male	Male	Female	Female
Father	Mother		Xg(a+)	Xg(a−)	Xg(a+)	Xg(a−)
Xg(a+) × Xg(a+)		0.5263	0.3615	0.1385	0.5000	0
Xg(a+) × Xg(a−)		0.0906	0	0.5000	0.5000	0
Xg(a−) × Xg(a+)		0.3269	0.3615	0.1385	0.3615	0.1385
Xg(a−) × Xg(a−)		0.0562	0	0.5000	0	0.5000

From Mann, J. D. *et al.*, 1962. "A sex-linked blood group," *Lancet*, 1:8–10.

nature of a son is determined by the genes received from the mother. Of these mothers, 0.3806 are homozygous ($Xg^a\,Xg^a$), and all of their sons are Xg(a+). Of the mothers, 0.4726 are heterozygous ($Xg^a\,Xg$); half of their sons are Xg(a+) and half are Xg(a−). So we may summarize the expectation as follows:

Mothers	Frequency	Sons Xg(a+)	Xg(a−)	Total
($Xg^a\,Xg^a$)	0.3806	0.3806	0	0.3806
($Xg^a\,Xg$)	0.4726	0.2363	0.2363	0.4726
		0.6169	0.2363	0.8532

Thus $\frac{0.6169}{0.8532}$ of the sons are expected to be Xg(a+). This is 0.7230, but since the sons constitute 50 percent of the children, we halve it = 0.3615 (Table 12.1). The remaining sons (0.5000 − 0.3615 = 0.1385) are Xg(a−).

By similar calculations the expectations given in the remainder of Table 12.1 were obtained. In Table 12.2 these expectations are translated into actual numbers for the 104 children in the 50 families originally investigated. The expected numbers of each type of offspring are given in parentheses, the actually observed numbers being entered above them. We note that agreement is remarkably good considering the small number of children involved.

Subsequent investigations have added further evidence in support of the theory that gene Xg^a is in fact an X-linked dominant gene. Its possible utility as a genetic marker will be discussed in Chapter 13. We have gone into some detail concerning the Xg^a blood groups because the investigation affords a particularly clear case history of the manner in which a "new" trait is tested, qualitatively and quantitatively, to determine the mode of inheritance.

TABLE 12.2. The Xg^a groups of 50 Caucasian families and their 104 children.

Matings					Children[*]			
Type		Number			Male	Male	Female	Eemale
Father	Mother	Observed	Expected	Total	Xg(a+)	Xg(a—)	Xg(a+)	Xg(a—)
Xg(a+) × Xg(a+)		30	26.3	64	23 (23.1)	12 (8.9)	29 (32.0)	0 (0)
Xg(a+) × Xg(a—)		3	4.5	7	0 (0)	3 (3.5)	4 (3.5)	0 (0)
Xg(a—) × Xg(a+)		16	16.4	30	9 (10.8)	4 (4.2)	10 (10.8)	7 (4.2)
Xg(a—) × Xg(a—)		1	2.8	3	0 (0)	2 (1.5)	0 (0)	1 (1.5)

From Mann, J. D. *et al.*, 1962. "A sex-linked blood group," *Lancet*, 1:8–10.
[*]Number of children *expected* is shown in parentheses.

Hemophilia

Another well-known X-linked trait in man is hemophilia ("bleeder's disease"). The clotting of human blood is the result of a complex chain reaction involving several organic compounds. One of these is fibrinogen; we have already discussed afibrinogenemia, the hereditary lack of this substance (pp. 117–118). On the other hand, the blood of hemophiliacs fails to clot because of lack of some other substance necessary for clotting.

Hemophilia A In the commonest form of hemophilia, hemophilia A, the deficiency is in a serum substance known as **antihemophilic globulin**. The presence of the substance depends on the gene H, its absence on the recessive allele h.

Because the genes are X-linked, women with the genotypes HH and Hh are not hemophilic, whereas women with the genotype hh are hemophilic. Men, necessarily hemizygous, who have the gene H are nonhemophilic; men having the gene h are hemophilic.

At one time it was thought that a woman could not be a hemophiliac, and that the genotype hh might be lethal. More recently, however, investigators have found women who are hemophilic. One reason that they are so rare lies in the fact that they can be produced only when a husband is hemophilic and his wife is heterozygous $\overset{h}{X} Y \times \overset{H}{X} \overset{h}{X}$. Hemophilia is such a disabling condition that until recently most hemophilic boys died young, or, at any rate, did not marry and become fathers. Not only do hemophiliacs bleed seriously from the slightest wound, but the simplest surgical operation, even the extraction of a tooth, precipitates a major crisis. Moreover, they suffer from internal bleeding and hemorrhages in the tissues even when no wounds have occurred. Recently medical science has come to their rescue. Transfusions of blood containing the missing antihemophilic globulin will alleviate symptoms temporarily, as will extracts of the globulin prepared from blood plasma. Additional means of treatment will doubtless be found; thus in the future we may expect more hemophilic boys to live to maturity, marry, and produce children. If the wives happen to be carriers, we may expect an increased number of hemophilic daughters among these children.

Even if hemophilic boys had a normal life expectancy, marriages between them and carrier women would still be rare. The frequency of hemophilic males is about 1 in 25,000 (Snyder and David, 1957). Thus $q = 0.00004$, and $p = 1 - q = 0.99996$. The frequency of heterozygous females is $2pq = 0.00008$. Marriages of hemophilic males with heterozygous females are represented by $q \times 2pq = 0.00004 \times 0.00008 = 0.0000000032$. This tiny fraction represents one marriage in 312,500,000, and only half the daughters from these marriages would be expected to be hemophilic. Under the circumstances, it is amazing that a hemophilic woman was ever discovered.

Another difficulty, which we might not anticipate, lies in establishing the diagnosis beyond reasonable doubt. Various conditions other than hemophilia prevent normal clotting of the blood (e.g., afibrinogenemia). Consequently an investigation must demonstrate that a woman thought to be a hemophiliac has exactly the same deficiency as that possessed by male hemophiliacs. Fortunately a whole battery of tests is now available for determining whether or not a person, male or female, actually has hemophilia rather than some other condition in which blood clotting is abnormal. Application of these tests has revealed at least three women who seem to have true hemophilia, and more will doubtless be found in the future.

As we might expect from earlier discussions, consanguinity increases the likelihood that a hemophilic man will marry a heterozygous woman. Such a marriage is shown in Figure 12.5; III-5 was a hemophilic man who married his first cousin (III-2), daughter of his mother's sister. Evidently both mothers (II-4 and II-6) were heterozygous and transmitted the gene h to III-2 and III-5, respectively.

Of the daughters in generation IV, Dr. Merskey (1951) tested IV-4 and IV-11 intensively to demonstrate that they actually had true hemophilia. The daughters IV-1 and IV-9 had symptoms similar to those of their more intensively analyzed sisters. IV-7 had many of the symptoms; she is especially interesting because she had four sons, all hemophiliacs. All the sons of a homozygous hemophilic woman would be expected to be hemophilic.

As would be expected, none of the sixth generation have inherited hemo-

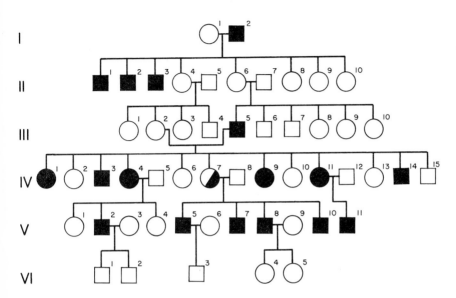

FIG. 12.5 Inheritance of hemophilia in a kindred including affected females. Black squares and circles represent affected individuals. IV-7 may have been hemophilic; she had some of the symptoms. (Abbreviated and redrawn from Merskey, C., 1951 "The occurrence of haemophilia in the human female," *Quarterly Journal of Medicine,* **20**:299–312.)

philia from their hemophilic fathers (although VI-4 and VI-5 must be carriers).

Note that I-2 is indicated as having been hemophilic. There seems to be some doubt about this. He lived long ago, and the investigators were dependent on family hearsay. Even if he were, we may be sure that II-1, II-2, and II-3 were hemophilic, not because of that fact but because their mother, I-1, was a carrier.

Hemophilia has received much attention because of its occurrence in European royalty. Queen Victoria must have been heterozygous for the gene because among her large family were a son with hemophilia and two daughters who had hemophilic sons. From the two carrier daughters the gene found its way into the royal families of Russia and Spain, respectively. Fortunately, it is absent from the present royal family in Great Britain. Prince Philip is not hemophilic, and Queen Elizabeth's inheritance from Queen Victoria comes through a line of nonhemophilic males: Edward VII, George V, and George VI.

How did Queen Victoria acquire the *h* gene? Because there is no clear record of "bleeders" in her ancestry, it is possible, and perhaps probable, that the gene originated as a new mutation in the sperm or ovum that combined to form the zygote from which she developed. Further discussion of this historically interesting example is found in Iltis, 1948, and McKusick, 1965.

Hemophilia B   Within the last few years a second type of hemophilia has been discovered. It is called hemophilia B (or "Christmas disease," a title having no reference to December 25, but derived from the surname of one of the families in which it was first recognized) to distinguish it from the hemophilia we have been discussing, hemophilia A. The deficiency present in hemophilia B is not in antihemophilic globulin, as it is in A, but in a blood constituent known as "plasma thromboplastin component." Hemoglobin B is also X-linked.

In Chapter 13 we shall utilize these and other X-linked genes as we discuss the problem of mapping the X chromosome.

Y-Linked Inheritance

Any genes that may be found in the nonhomologous or differential part of the Y chromosome (Fig. 12.2) will be passed directly from a father to *all* his sons but to *none* of his daughters. This means that all the sons of a father who shows the trait will also show the trait. (Males are hemizygous for the genes because the X chromosome does not contain alleles for them.)

Women, never normally possessing a Y chromosome, will not show the trait or possess the gene for it. Hence they cannot pass the gene on to any of their sons (or daughters).

Direct inheritance through males (grandfathers to fathers to sons, and so on) but never through females characterizes Y-linked inheritance. The criteria, therefore, are clear-cut. Can we find human examples of this type of inheritance? A time-honored example has been that of the so-called porcupine men, whose skin developed rough scales and bristle-like protrusions suggesting a porcupine's quills. Earlier accounts indicated that the trait was passed on from fathers to all their sons, and never to daughters, for seven generations in one English family. Penrose and Stern (1957–1958) reexamined all available evidence and concluded that much of the information concerning details was uncertain. Probably not all the sons of an affected man showed the trait, and it seems likely that some of the daughters did show it. Hence the authors concluded that the trait behaved as if it were caused by a rare autosomal dominant gene, chance determining that most of the affected individuals were males (recall our discussion on p. 189).

Stern (1957) reviewed seventeen human traits that have been proposed at one time or another as possible examples of Y-linked inheritance. In some cases the evidence indicated clearly that Y-linkage was not the basis of inheritance; in other cases the data conformed to expectation for Y-linked inheritance but could equally well be examples of inheritance through a dominant autosomal gene whose expression was sex-limited to males. Recalling our discussion of sex-limited traits (pp. 187–188), we can understand the difficulty of distinguishing between Y-linked inheritance and sex-limitation of the expression of an autosomal gene. Perhaps the best means of distinguishing between the two is on the basis of transmission through females. A Y-linked gene is not transmitted by females to their sons. On the other hand, an autosomal gene, even one whose phenotype is expressed only in males, is freely transmitted by females to their sons. This is a good test but, unfortunately, many of the proposed pedigrees are too fragmentary to permit definite decisions by its use.

The most probable example of Y-linked inheritance available at present is that of hypertrichosis or hairiness of the pinna of the ear. The trait refers to a growth of prominent hairs on the surface of the pinna and along the rim of the ear (Fig. 12.6). Originally described in an Italian

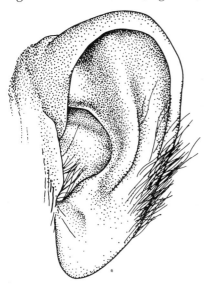

FIG. 12.6 Hypertrichosis of the pinna of the ear. (Drawn from a photograph in Dronamraju, K. R., 1960. "Hypertrichosis of the pinna of the human ear, Y-linked pedigrees," *Journal of Genetics*, **57**:230–43.)

kindred, the trait has recently been investigated in kindreds in India (Gates, 1960; Sarkar *et al.*, 1961; Dronamraju, 1960; Gates *et al.*, 1962; Stern *et al.*, 1964).

Many family studies of the trait have been made (see references above). On the whole, the two criteria are met: (1) All sons of an affected male show the trait. (2) Females do not show the trait or transmit the gene. The trait is variable in the amount of hair developed, some males developing only three or four hairs on the pinna of the ear. The fact that occasionally the son of an affected male does not develop the trait may be an example of lack of penetrance (pp. 78–79). In some families the hair does not develop until the men are between 20 and 30 years of age, and hence younger men cannot be classified accurately. In the case of an occasional woman who seems to transmit the trait, Gates *et al.* (1962) have suggested that crossing over (in the father of the woman) may have transferred the gene from the Y to the X chromosome. If such transference is possible, the gene should not be classified as completely Y-linked at all, but as incompletely sex-linked (see below). Moreover, once the gene had been transferred to an X chromosome, it should thenceforth be readily transmitted by both females and males. As a result, female transmission of the gene should be more common than it is observed to be.

It seems wisest to suspend judgment at the present time. The trait *may* be Y-linked, yet the possibility of autosomal inheritance has not been excluded "beyond the shadow of a doubt." The case is instructive as an example of the great difficulty frequently encountered in determining how human traits are inherited.

Examples of Y-linked inheritance have been found in fishes and in insects but, so far, not in mammals, even in such genetically well-known ones as mice and guinea pigs. Hence, if hypertrichosis of the pinna of the ear does depend on a Y-linked gene, it will form the first well-established example among mammals.

We may note that the human Y chromosome is very small (Fig. 16.6, p. 254. Accordingly, we might not expect it to contain many genes. As we shall see in our discussion of sex determination (Chap. 15), the mammalian Y chromosome has important male-determining properties, presumably dependent on the genes that it contains.

Partial or Incompletely Sex-Linked Inheritance

Referring back to Figure 12.2, we note that incompletely sex-linked genes are genes located in the homologous portions of the X and Y chromosomes. Because the Y chromosome, as well as the X chromosome, carries the gene, sons can inherit it from their fathers. We note that this is in direct contrast to X-linked inheritance. Sons also inherit genes on autosomes from both fathers and mothers, so that the problem is to distinguish incomplete sex-linkage from ordinary autosomal inheritance.

This problem, although interesting, is not of sufficient importance to warrant a large portion of an elementary textbook. Models are frequently useful for bringing subjects into sharp focus; in the present instance a simple model will enable us to sample the sort of evidence that indicates the presence of incomplete sex-linkage.

In my teaching I find useful an imaginary human trait: "forked eyelashes." The term is self-explanatory, and because it is a nonexistent trait, we can imagine anything we desire about its genetic basis.

Let us suppose in the first place that forked eyelashes depends on a dominant *autosomal* gene, F. What offspring will be expected when a heterozygous man marries a woman with unforked eyelashes?

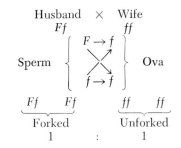

Husband × Wife
Ff ff

Sperm { $F \to f$ / $f \to f$ } Ova

Ff Ff	ff ff
Forked	Unforked

Ratio   1   :   1

We note that this is comparable to a back-cross (p. 17) and that half the offspring *of both sexes* are expected to have forked eyelashes, half unforked ones.

Now let us imagine that forked eyelashes depends on a dominant *incompletely sex-linked* gene. What will be the expectation when a heterozygous man marries a woman with unforked eyelashes? Here we have two possibilities:

(1) The gene F may be in the husband's X chromosome. If so:

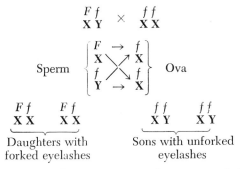

$\begin{matrix} F\,f \\ X\,Y \end{matrix}$ × $\begin{matrix} f\,f \\ X\,X \end{matrix}$

Sperm { $\begin{matrix} F & \to & f \\ X & \diagdown\diagup & X \\ f & \diagup\diagdown & f \\ Y & \to & X \end{matrix}$ } Ova

$\begin{matrix} F\,f \\ X\,X \end{matrix}$ $\begin{matrix} F\,f \\ X\,X \end{matrix}$	$\begin{matrix} f\,f \\ X\,Y \end{matrix}$ $\begin{matrix} f\,f \\ X\,Y \end{matrix}$
Daughters with forked eyelashes	Sons with unforked eyelashes

Thus, in contrast to the situation with autosomal inheritance, the diagram indicates that all the daughters will be expected to have forked eyelashes, all the sons unforked ones. This is not quite correct. We recall that when chromosomes pair in synapsis, portions of them can be exchanged—recombination through crossing over. If the section of the X chromosome containing F is exchanged with the corresponding section of the Y chromosome containing f, occasional Y chromosomes containing F will be formed. If a sperm with an F-containing Y chromosome fertilizes an ovum, a son with forked eyelashes will result. If the X chromosome that received the f gene is in a sperm that fertilizes an ovum, a daughter with unforked eyelashes will be produced.

Because such recombination is likely to be relatively rare, we can state: When F is in the husband's X chromosome, *most* of the daughters will have forked eyelashes and *most* of the sons will have unforked eyelashes. (With autosomal inheritance *half* of the daughters will be expected to have forked eyelashes, *half* of them unforked ones, and the same expectation will hold for the sons.)

(2) The gene F may be in the husband's Y chromosome. If so:

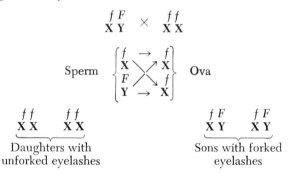

In this case *most* of the daughters will have unforked eyelashes and *most* of the sons will have forked eyelashes. As before, recombination (crossing over) will occur, resulting in this case in an occasional daughter with forked eyelashes and an occasional son with unforked ones.

What has this model demonstrated? If we examine a series of families in which the father is heterozygous for a dominant, incompletely sex-linked gene, the families will divide into two classes: (1) those in which most of the daughters will show the trait and most of the sons will not; and (2) those in which most of the sons will show the trait and most of the daughters will not. (As we saw, with autosomal inheritance we expect to find in *all* the families that sons and daughters showing the trait and those not showing it will occur in equal numbers.)

Haldane (1936) carried the comparison back to the preceding generation, the grandparents. In our class (1) above, the daughter receives the gene in an X chromosome from her father; the father received it from his mother (who must have shown the trait because the gene is dominant). In our class (2), the son receives the gene in a Y chromosome from his father, and the father had received it from his father. Thus, with a dominant, incompletely sex-linked trait, among the offspring of affected males most of the children who show the trait will be of the same sex as the affected grandparent.

If the gene in which we are interested is recessive rather than dominant, calculations are somewhat more complicated. The manner of reasoning, however, is much the same.

Our model has indicated some of the criteria for which we should look in attempting to find an example of an incompletely X-linked gene. In practice, application of the criteria is beset with difficulties. The small size of human families (so that not all types of children possible to any mating are actually produced) and the ever-present possibility of recombination through crossing over are two of the sources of error. (If crossing over is frequent, daughters and sons may have nearly a 50–50 chance of showing or not showing the trait, as they would have with ordinary autosomal inheritance.)

By analogy with our knowledge of genetics of lower organisms, we may feel confident that, despite the difficulties, incompletely sex-linked genes will be discovered in man. Some genes have already been suggested as possible, perhaps even probable, examples. More extensive discussions will be found in Neel and Schull (1954) and in Stern (1960). In view of present uncertainties, however, we are hardly justified in devoting more space to the subject. We can do no better than to quote Dr. Stern's concluding sentence concerning the matter: "All this does not exclude the possibility that partial sex linkage in man may exist, but proof that it does—or does not—lies in the future."

PROBLEMS

1. A color-blind man marries a woman with normal vision whose father was color-blind. (a) What is the chance that their first child will be a color-blind son? a color-blind daughter? (b) If they have four children, what is the chance that two will be color-blind sons, two will be noncolor-blind daughters?

2. A sibship consists of a color-blind son, a noncolor-blind daughter, and a color-blind daughter. Give the phenotypes and genotypes of the parents.

3. If one male in 120 shows a defect dependent on a recessive, X-linked gene, what proportion of the females will be expected to exhibit the defect? What proportion of the females will be expected to be normal but heterozygous?

4. If 36 percent of men show a *dominant* X-linked trait, what percentage of the women will be expected to show the trait?

5. In the accompanying pedigree chart, I-1, and III-1 have hemophilia. All other individuals are nonhemophilic. What are the chances that IV-1, yet unborn, will be hemophilic?

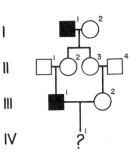

6. In the accompanying pedigree chart, solid squares and circles represent persons who show a certain trait.

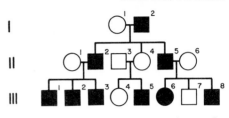

(a) Could the trait depend on a recessive autosomal gene?

(b) Could the trait depend on a recessive X-linked gene?

Give the genotypes all individuals would have if this were the mode of inheritance.

(c) Could the trait depend on a Y-linked gene? Give as many reasons as possible for your answer.

(d) Could the trait depend on an autosomal gene having expression limited to males?

(e) Could the trait depend on a sex-influenced autosomal gene (dominant in males, recessive in females)? Give the genotypes all individuals would have if this were the mode of inheritance.

7. In a certain family neither husband nor wife was bald but their three sons developed pattern baldness. Give the genotypes of the parents.

8. A sibship consisted of two daughters, one Xg(a+), the other Xg(a−). Give the genotypes and phenotypes of the parents.

9. If an Xg(a+) man marries an Xg(a+) woman whose father was Xg(a−), what types of sons and daughters will be expected and in what proportions?

10. Ability to taste phenylthiocarbamide (PTC) depends on a dominant autosomal gene, T, inability to taste the chemical on its recessive allele, t. An Xg(a+) man who is a taster but whose mother was a nontaster marries an Xg(a−) woman who is a nontaster. Give expectations with regard to their children.

11. Table 12.1 shows that from matings in which the father is Xg(a−) and the mother is Xg(a+), 36.15 percent of the daughters are expected to be Xg(a+), 13.85 percent to be Xg(a−). Explain, giving the derivation of these percentages.

12. About one man in 25,000 is hemophilic. If a hemophilic man marries his first cousin, the daughter of his father's sister, what is the chance that their first child will be hemophilic?

13. In a certain population 20 percent of the men show a phenotype dependent on a recessive X-linked gene; i.e., they are "affected." In pooled data from the marriages of unaffected women to unaffected men, what percentage of the children will be expected to be (a) unaffected sons, (b) affected sons, (c) unaffected daughters, (d) affected daughters?

14. Suppose that the imaginary trait "forked eyelashes" depends on a partially sex-linked gene (F). (a) What will be the expectation concerning the sons produced by the following marriage:

$$\frac{F\,f}{X\,Y} \times \frac{F\,f}{X\,X}\,?$$

How can sons homozygous for forked eyelashes arise in this family? (b) A sibship consisted of five sons with unforked eyelashes, four daughters with forked eyelashes, and one daughter with unforked eyelashes. Give the most probable genotypes for the parents.

REFERENCES

Dronamraju, K. R., 1960. "Hypertrichosis of the pinna of the human ear, Y-linked pedigrees," *Journal of Genetics,* **57**:230–43.

Gates, R. R., 1960. "Y-chromosome inheritance of hairy ears," *Science,* **132**:145.

Gates, R. R., M. R. Chakravartti, and D. R. Mukherjee, 1962. "Final pedigrees of Y chromosome inheritance," *American Journal of Human Genetics,* **14**:363–75.

Haldane, J. B. S., 1936. "A search for incomplete sex-linkage in man," *Annals of Eugenics,* **7**:28–57.

Iltis, H., 1948. "Hemophilia, 'The Royal Disease'," *Journal of Heredity,* **39**:113–16.

Mann, J. D., A. Cahan, A. G. Gelb, N. Fisher, J. Hamper, P. Tippett, R. Sanger, and R. R. Race, 1962. "A sex-linked blood group," *Lancet,* **1**:8–10.

McKusick, V. A., 1965. "The royal hemophilia," *Scientific American,* **213**:88–95.

Merskey, C., 1951. "The occurrence of haemophilia in the human female," *Quarterly Journal of Medicine,* **20**:299–312.

Neel, J. V., and W. J. Schull, 1954. *Human Heredity.* Chicago: The University of Chicago Press.

Penrose, L. S., and C. Stern, 1957–1958. "Reconsideration of the Lambert pedigree (Ichthyosis hystrix gravior)," *Annals of Human Genetics,* **22**:258–83.

Race, R. R., and R. Sanger, 1962. *Blood Groups in Man,* 4th ed. Oxford: Blackwell Scientific Publications.

Sarkar, S. S., A. R. Banerjee, P. Bhattacharjee, and C. Stern, 1961. "A contribution to the genetics of hypertrichosis of the ear rims," *American Journal of Human Genetics,* **13**:214–23.

Snyder, L. H., and P. R. David, 1957. *The Principles of Heredity,* 5th ed. Boston: D. C. Heath & Company.

Stern, C., 1957. "The problem of complete Y-linkage in man," *American Journal of Human Genetics,* **9**:147–69.

Stern, C., 1960. *Principles of Human Genetics,* 2nd ed. San Francisco: W. H. Freeman & Company.

Stern, C., W. R. Centerwall, and S. S. Sarkar, 1964. "New data on the problem of Y-linkage of hairy pinnae," *American Journal of Human Genetics,* **16**:455–71.

13.

MAPPING
THE X CHROMOSOME

When we say that a gene is sex-linked we mean that the gene is in one of the sex chromosomes, as we saw in the preceding chapter. When we say that two genes are linked to each other, on the other hand, we mean that they are in the same chromosome. This may or may not be a sex chromosome.

Obviously, if the gene for color blindness and the gene for hemophilia are both sex-linked, as discussed in Chapter 12, they must also be linked to each other. Somewhere in the nonhomologous (differential) part of the X chromosome there is a gene locus that may be occupied by the color blindness gene or its normal allele, and somewhere in the same chromosome there is a locus that may be occupied by the hemophilia gene or its normal allele.

In the interest of exactitude we must now recognize that there are two common kinds of partial color blindness and two kinds of hemophilia. The two kinds of color blindness are: (a) **deuteranopia**, in which there is confusion in distinguishing red, yellow, and green, and (b) **protanopia**, in which difficulty in distinguishing red predominates. The genes concerned have sometimes been regarded as alleles of each other (i.e., as occupying, alternatively, the same locus in the X chromosome). However, recent evidence casts doubt on this assumption, as we shall see.

Similarly, as noted in the preceding chapter, there are two types of hemophilia: hemophilia A and hemophilia B or "Christmas disease." It had been suggested that the genes concerned might be the alleles of each other, but recent investigation renders this conclusion unlikely (Whittaker *et al.,* 1962). Accordingly, if our discussion of gene loci is to be meaningful, we must designate in each instance the type of color blindness and the type of hemophilia.

It will seldom happen, of course, that the genes for color blindness and for hemophilia will be found in the same family. Nevertheless, a considerable number of families are known in which both traits are present. Let us look at the various possible genotypes, considering males first and taking for example deuteranopia and hemophilia A. Most men have neither deutan color blindness nor hemophilia A. This means that the two loci just mentioned are occupied by the normal, dominant alleles. We may represent the deuteranopia gene by d, the hemophilia A gene by h^A, using the corresponding capital letters to represent the dominant alleles. It is convenient to indicate a chromosome by a parenthesis and to write the genotype of such normal men as $(D\,H^A)Y$ (the Y standing for the Y chromosome).

Similarly, men who are color-blind but not hemophilic have the genotype $(d\,H^A)Y$. Men who have normal color vision but who are hemophilic have the genotype $(D\,h^A)Y$, and those who are color-blind and hemophilic have the genotype $(d\,h^A)Y$.

Turning to the women, we note that most women do not possess either of the two recessive genes; this means that their *two* X chromosomes contain the dominant alleles and may be represented as $(D\,H^A)(D\,H^A)$. Suppose that such a woman is married to a color-blind, hemophilic man. We may represent the mating as follows:

$$(D\,H^A)(D\,H^A) \quad \times \quad (d\,h^A)Y$$

Ova $\left\{ \begin{array}{l} (D\,H^A) \to (d\,h^A) \\ (D\,H^A) \to Y \end{array} \right.$ Sperm

Offspring: $\underbrace{(D\,H^A)(d\,h^A) \quad (D\,H^A)(d\,h^A)}_{\text{Daughters}} \quad \underbrace{(D\,H^A)Y \quad (D\,H^A)Y}_{\text{Sons}}$

All the children will be normal, but all the daughters will be heterozygous for *both* pairs of genes. What types of offspring will be expected when such a doubly heterozygous daughter marries a man normal in both traits?

$$(D\,H^A)(d\,h^A) \quad \times \quad (D\,H^A)Y$$

Ova $\left\{ \begin{array}{l} (D\,H^A) \to (D\,H^A) \\ (d\,h^A) \to Y \end{array} \right.$ Sperm

Offspring: $\underbrace{(D\,H^A)(D\,H^A) \quad (D\,H^A)(d\,h^A)}_{} \quad (D\,H^A)Y \quad (d\,h^A)Y$

Phenotypes: Normal daughters   Normal   Color-blind
             son   hemophilic son

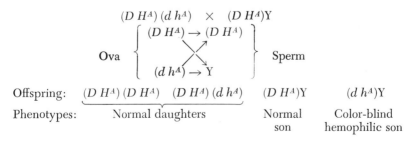

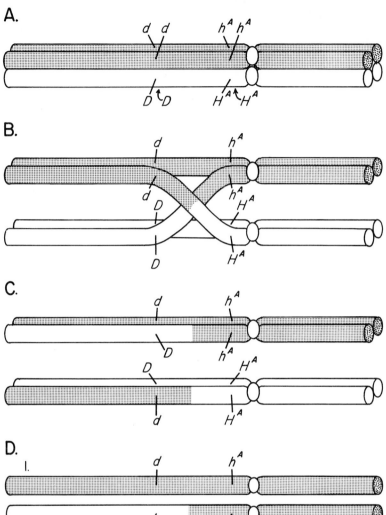

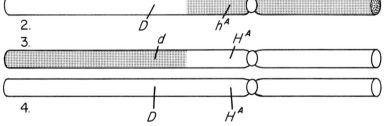

FIG. 13.1 Chromosomal basis of recombination of X-linked genes, using the genes for deuteranopia and hemophilia A as examples. The genes are represented as being located in the long arm of the X chromosome. Location in this arm is probable but has not been established with certainty (cf., Fig. 3.6, p. 33).

Notice the sons especially; their phenotypes (for X-linked traits) are determined by the genes received from the mother. Half the sons will be expected to have normal color vision and normal blood clotting, half to be color-blind and hemophilic (deuteranopia and hemophilia A). This is what actually occurs for the most part. Occasionally, however, a son will be found to have normal color vision but be hemophilic, and occasionally a son will have the converse combination: color blindness but no hemophilia. How can such occasional occurrences be explained? Evidently the son with normal color vision and hemophilia has an X chromosome of the constitution $(D\ h^A)$ and the other son has a chromosome of the constitution $(d\ H^A)$. Both came from the mother. How can a mother with $(D\ H^A)\ (d\ h^A)$ chromosomes produce $(D\ h^A)$ and $(d\ H^A)$ chromosomes? **Recombination** must have occurred.

The mechanism of this recombination is the *crossing over* mentioned in Chapter 3 in our discussion of meiosis. At A in Figure 13.1 we represent a tetrad composed of two duplicated X chromosomes in synapsis in a primary oöcyte (cf., Fig. 3.6, p. 33). This is represented as occurring in a woman with the $(D\ H^A)\ (d\ h^A)$ constitution. At this time the chromatids frequently twist around each other. We have represented a single twist involving two of the chromatids. The twist is shown between the loci of the genes in which we are interested. If, instead of untwisting, these chromatids break and recombine, crossing over will have occurred, as indicated at B and C.

At D in Figure 13.1 we see the four kinds of X chromosomes formed when the pairs of chromatids separate. Every ovum receives one of these X chromosomes. Ova that receive chromosome No. 1 or chromosome No. 4 have the same constitution they would have had if no crossing over had occurred, but ova that receive chromosome No. 2 or No. 3 have the recombinations. Ovum No. 2, if fertilized with a Y-containing sperm cell, will give rise to a noncolor-blind but hemophilic male, $(D\ h^A)Y$, ovum No. 3 to a color-blind, nonhemophilic male, $(d\ H^A)Y$.

This is an appropriate place to call attention to the fact that linkage may be of two types. Dominant gene may be linked to dominant gene, and recessive gene to recessive gene. $(D\ H^A)$ and $(d\ h^A)$ are examples. This is called **coupling linkage** (or sometimes the *cis* phase). On the other hand, the dominant gene of one pair may be linked to the recessive gene of the other, and vice versa, e.g., $(D\ h^A)$ and $(d\ H^A)$. This is called **repulsion linkage** (or the *trans* phase).

The doubly heterozygous woman whose offspring we have been discussing exhibited coupling linkage: $(D\ H^A)\ (d\ h^A)$. Some other doubly heterozygous woman might have the same genes but have them in repulsion linkage. In her case what would we expect concerning her offspring?

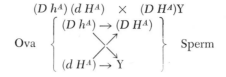

Offspring:

$$(D\ h^A)\ (D\ H^A) \quad (d\ H^A)\ (D\ H^A) \qquad (D\ h^A)Y \qquad\qquad (d\ H^A)Y$$

Phenotypes: Normal daughters   Noncolor-blind,   Color-blind,
                                                   hemophilic son   nonhemophilic son

Concentrating on the sons again, we note that most of them would be expected to have normal color vision and be hemophilic, *or* to be color-blind and not be hemophilic. These are the phenotypes arising when recombination does not occur. Occasional crossing over, with resulting recombination, would give rise to sons who are noncolor-blind and non-hemophilic, $(D\ H^A)$Y, or color-blind and hemophilic, $(d\ h^A)$Y. When crossing over occurs in a $(D\ h^A)\ (d\ H^A)$ female, the recombinant chromosomes are $(D\ H^A)$ and $(d\ h^A)$, respectively.

In sum, when a mother is $(D\ H^A)\ (d\ h^A)$ most of her sons are $(D\ H^A)$Y and $(d\ h^A)$Y, but when a mother is $(D\ h^A)\ (d\ H^A)$ most of her sons are $(D\ h^A)$Y or $(d\ H^A)$Y. Or to put it another way, the rare combinations (resulting from crossing over) in the offspring of a mother with coupling linkage are the frequent combinations (arising in the absence of crossing over) in the offspring of a mother with repulsion linkage. Because there is no reason why coupling-phase mothers should be more common than repulsion-phase mothers in a population, there is no reason why coupling-phase sons, $(D\ H^A)$Y and $(d\ h^A)$Y, should be more abundant than repulsion-phase sons, $(D\ h^A)$Y and $(d\ H^A)$Y, in that population.

We mention this matter to dispel a widespread misunderstanding of linkage. When we say that deuteranopia and hemophilia A are linked, many people gain the impression that if this is true most color-blind people should be hemophilic, or vice versa. Now we see why this idea is incorrect. In linkage, the dominant allele of one pair may be found combined with the dominant allele of the other pair or with the recessive allele of that other pair. In individual families more definite associations are likely to be found. For example, when the mother is $(D\ H^A)\ (d\ h^A)$, a color-blind son is much more likely to be hemophilic than he is to be nonhemophilic (he can be the latter only if crossing over has occurred). On the other hand, when the mother is $(D\ h^A)\ (d\ H^A)$, a color-blind son is much more likely to be nonhemophilic than he is to be hemophilic.

Let us be a little more specific: *How much* more likely is occurrence of a son not involving recombination than is occurrence of a son whose genotype arose as a result of recombination? Or, conversely, how frequently does crossing over occur between the loci of these two genes? A recent study of one large kindred indicates that recombination between deutan color blindness and hemophilia A occurs about 6 percent of the time (Whittaker *et al.*, 1962). Assuming that this finding has general applicability, this means that when mothers have the genotype $(D\ H^A)\ (d\ h^A)$, 94 percent of their sons will either have normal color vision and normal blood clotting or have deutan color blindness and hemophilia A, whereas 6 percent of their sons will either have normal color vision and be hemophilic or have deutan color blindness and normal blood clotting. Similarly, if the mothers have the genes in repulsion linkage, $(D\ h^A)\ (d\ H^A)$, 94 percent of the sons will either have normal color vision and be hemophilic or be color-blind but not be hemophilic, whereas 6 percent of the sons will either have both normal traits or both abnormal ones.

We may well point out that some matings are informative in determination of recombination frequencies but that some are not. Only if the mother is heterozygous for *both* pairs of genes can the constitution of her sons give us information about the amount of crossing over between her X chromosomes. If, for example, a mother has the genotype $(d\ H^A)\ (d\ h^A)$, *all* of her sons will be color-blind regardless of whether or not crossing over has occurred between the loci of the two gene pairs. This necessity for double heterozygosity considerably reduces the number of informative matings available to investigators.

The figure of 6 percent is of the same order of magnitude as a figure of 10 percent reached previously as the percentage of recombination between color blindness and hemophilia (Haldane and Smith, 1947). However, in these earlier studies the type of color blindness was not always specified, and the studies were made before the distinction between hemophilia A and hemophilia B had been recognized. Because hemophilia A is about four times as common as hemophilia B, it is probable that the earlier studies dealt principally with hemophilia A.

Chromosome Mapping

What use can be made of data concerning percentage of recombination? Percentage of crossing over is thought to be at least approximately proportional to the distances between the gene loci concerned (see pp. 220–222).

In the present instance, we interpret the information that recombination between the loci of deutan color blindness and hemophilia A occurs only 6 percent of the time to indicate that these gene loci are relatively close together in the X chromosome. The same investigation (Whittaker *et al.*, 1962) indicated that protan color blindness and hemophilia B recombine about 50 percent of the time. We interpret this to mean that these gene loci are far apart in the chromosome.

We may consider that we have started to "map" the X chromosome by recognizing that the gene loci for deuteranopia and hemophilia A are close together in that chromosome. (A word is in order about the naming of gene loci. They are named in terms of the unusual or abnormal allele of the pair. Thus we call it the "deuteranopia locus" even though in noncolor-blind people the locus is occupied by the normal allele of the "deuteranopia gene.")

Another locus near the deuteranopia locus is the "G6PD locus." The symbol **G6PD** stands for *glucose-6-phosphate dehydrogenase deficiency.* Glucose-6-phosphate dehydrogenase is an enzyme which most people possess. Persons who are deficient in the enzyme develop hemolysis (destruction of red blood cells, causing anemia) when they take antimalarial drugs such as primaquine, or when they eat the fava bean. Recombination between the loci for deuteranopia and G6PD occurs only about 4 or 5 percent of the time (McKusick, 1964; Siniscalco *et al.*, 1964).

The loci for G6PD, deuteranopia, and hemophilia A are evidently close together in the X chromosome. Some investigations have indicated that the locus of the gene for the Xg^a blood groups is at a measurable distance from the three loci just mentioned. Recent investigations have failed to confirm the earlier findings, however, so at the time this book goes to press it seems wisest to state that the distance of the Xg locus from the other loci has yet to be determined (Adam *et al.*, 1966).

A tentative map representing the relationships just mentioned might be as follows (cf. Davies *et al.*, 1963; Jackson *et al.*, 1964; McKusick, 1964):

Xg	G6PD	deutan	hem. A

Of the genes for partial color blindness only the gene for deuteranopia is included on the map. The genes for both types of color blindness seem to be close to the G6PD locus. Are they closer to this locus than they are to each other? Siniscalco, Filippi, and Latte (1964) concluded that such is the case; they suggested the following sequence:

Xg	deutan	G6PD	protan

(Their investigation did not include hemophilia A.) Note that the maps agree in some respects, disagree in others. Undoubtedly neither is entirely correct. Knowledge is being acquired so rapidly in this field that we shall not have long to wait for resolution of points of difference. Furthermore, new loci will be added to the map continually. Where, for example, is the gene for hemophilia B? We have indicated above that it seems to be far from the protan gene. It also seems to be far from the Xg locus (Davies *et al.*, 1963). What is it *near?* The question is merely suggestive of many that will be answered by future research.

Readers familiar with the elaborate and detailed chromosome maps that have been worked out for lower animals and plants, notably *Drosophila* and corn, may feel that the attempts to map a fragment of the human X chromosome represent small achievement indeed. Yet it is cause for considerable satisfaction in view of the difficulties presented by an organism in which no genetic experimentation is possible and in which individual families are small. Other X-linked traits are known but the few we have discussed illustrate sufficiently the principles of chromosome mapping. Interested readers will find in McKusick (1964) a catalog of X-linked traits and a summary of linkage investigations involving them.

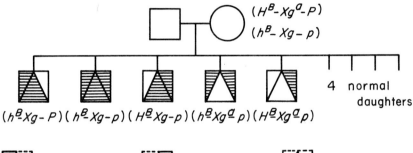

FIG. 13.2   Double crossing over. Five sons of a mother heterozygous for three pairs of genes. A suggested sequence of the genes is indicated, but we do not know whether or not the *Xg* locus is between the other two loci. In the mother, the gene *Xg^a* may have been in the chromosome with the other two dominant genes, or it may have been in the chromosome with the genes for hemophilia B and protanopia. In either case, double crossing over occurred. (After Graham, J. B., H. L. Tarleton, R. R. Race, and R. Sanger, 1962. "A human double cross-over," *Nature*, **195**:834.)

We have mentioned the fact that informative families in studies of this kind consist of those in which the mother is heterozygous with regard to the two gene pairs being studied. The more sons she has the better. Figure 13.2 shows five sons born to a mother who was heterozygous for *three* of the known X-linked genes (Whittaker *et al.*, 1962; Graham *et al.*, 1962). This triple heterozygosity was evidenced by the fact that (a) some sons had hemophilia B, some did not; (b) some sons had protan color blindness, some did not; and (c) some sons were Xg(a+), whereas some were Xg(a−). The various ways in which the traits were combined in the five sons are represented in the figure.

The most interesting aspect of this family lies in the fact that it presents the first clear case of *double* recombination (crossing over) known in man. In double crossing over, chromosomes in synapsis break and recombine at *two* points (instead of only one as in Fig. 13.1). This phenomenon is well known in plants and lower animals and there was no reason to doubt its occurrence in man. Still, the actual demonstration of an example is of interest. Triple heterozygosity, as in the present family is essential for such a demonstration.

The mother was normal in vision and blood clotting, and belonged to the Xg(a+) blood group. Study of her ancestry seemed to indicate that the genes for color blindness and hemophilia were both inherited from her mother. This would suggest coupling linkage. It is not known whether the Xg gene came from her father or her mother, but the principles illustrated will be the same in either case, so let us assume that this recessive allele also came from her mother. The genotype of the mother of the five sons can then be represented as follows: $(H^B - Xg^a - P)$ $(h^B - Xg - p)$. Here h^B is the gene for hemophilia B; p is the gene for protanopia (H^B and P, respectively, are their normal alleles); Xg^a and Xg are the Xg^a blood group alleles. At the present time the arrangement of the genes with Xg in the middle is purely arbitrary; future research will doubtless establish the true arrangement.

Assuming that the linkage and the arrangement are as indicated, how was the X chromosome of each of the sons produced? The chromosome possessed by the first son, $(h^B - Xg - P)$, must have arisen through crossing over between the Xg locus and the p locus. The chromosome of the second son, $(h^B - Xg - p)$, was inherited intact, without crossing over. The chromosome of the third son, $(H^B - Xg - p)$, arose through crossing over between the h^B locus and the Xg locus.

The chromosome of the fourth son, $(h^B - Xg^a - p)$, arose by crossing over at *two* points: (a) between the h^B locus and the Xg locus, and (b) between the Xg locus and the p locus. This, then, would be the double crossover mentioned above. It is represented diagrammatically in Figure 13.3. Finally, the chromosome of the fifth son, $(H^B - Xg^a - p)$, arose by crossing over between the Xg locus and the p locus. Notice that in a sense it is the reciprocal of the chromosome possessed by the first son.

We should emphasize that our designation of the fourth son as the double-crossover individual rests on two assumptions: (a) that the linkage in the mother is coupling, for all three pairs; and (b) that the Xg locus is in the middle. If the p locus is in the middle, both the first and fifth sons are double crossovers and the third and fourth sons are single crossovers. Because double crossing over is a rare event, the law of parsimony might bid us to regard the postulated occurrence of two double crossovers in five individuals as evidence against the hypothesis that the p locus is in the middle. However, we need more substantial evidence than this for the mapping of the three loci.

If, on the other hand, the Xg locus is in the middle but the mother had the linkage relationships $(H^B - Xg - P)$ $(h^B - Xg^a - p)$, then the second son's chromosome arose through double crossing over, and the fourth son's

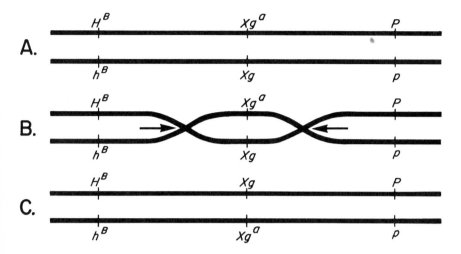

FIG. 13.3 Portions of two chromatids in synapsis, with double crossing over and consequent double recombination of genes (as in Fig. 13.2). The chromatids that do not cross over are omitted (cf., Fig. 13.1). A. Chromatids as originally constituted. B. Chiasma formation. The chromatids break and recombine at the points marked by the arrows. C. Chromatids resulting from the double crossover.

chromosome was inherited intact, without crossing over. The point is that this interesting family presents such variety that, whatever the assumptions made, double crossing over must have occurred in at least one instance.

Genetic Markers

Some reader may ask: What of it? Why are investigations of this kind important? Increased understanding of our own genetic mechanisms is the greatest justification of such studies. In addition, there are possible practical applications in the fields of preventive medicine and genetic counseling. Geneticists are eager to discover as many genes as possible that may serve as **marker genes.** Ideally a good marker gene should produce a trait that is clearly defined, not harmful, and present at birth. Such a gene would afford evidence that a certain chromosome is present, with its genetic contents (insofar as crossing over does not scramble these genetic contents). To be of maximum utility the marker gene should be located near a gene having harmful effects, so near that crossing over would seldom occur. Then the marker would serve as warning that the harmful gene is present, even though the latter might not produce its harmful effects until long after birth.

As our knowledge of the genetic contents of the X chromosome expands, Xg^a blood group genes may well prove to be such useful markers. Suppose that eventually a harmful gene is discovered, having it locus close to the Xg locus. Suppose also that this gene produces a severe crippling effect, either physical or mental, in people of middle age, but has no effect in earlier years. We may assume that the gene is recessive and designate it by c (for "crippling").

Let us suppose that a normal woman who is Xg(a+) is heterozygous for the hypothetical crippling gene, with linkage as follows: $(Xg^a\,c)\,(Xg\,C)$. We can readily see that, granted close linkage, any son of hers who is Xg(a+) will be almost certain to have the harmful gene c, and (unless preventive measures are possible) will suffer its ill effects as he grows older. This knowledge may present a difficult human problem. Is it good for a son to know that he faces such a prospect? The knowledge might be catastrophic to his morale and even to his mental balance *if* nothing can be done to prevent the ultimate crippling. The hope is, however, that this may be an instance in which preventive medicine *can* do something to prevent the expected calamity. Most disabilities that have a hereditary component also have an environmental component, against which preventive measures are effective. We recall the example of phenylketonuria (pp. 2;380), a hereditary trait the dire effects of which can now be prevented by control of diet in early infancy. We may hope that medical science, forewarned by the presence of the marker gene in the $(Xg^a\,c)$Y son, may be able to apply measures that will prevent the crippling. If it is not possible to do so in this case, the son had perhaps best not be told what awaits him.

The picture has a brighter side as well. Any son of an $(Xg^a\,c)\,(Xg\,C)$ mother who is Xg(a−) may be almost certain that he will not have the crippling later in life. This knowledge can be an immense comfort to him, knowing, as he is likely to, that the crippling is in his ancestry. He may be reasonably sure that he and his descendants will be free of it.

We have mentioned genetic counseling as well as preventive medicine. We shall discuss this subject further in Chapter 25, but here we simply raise the question of whether a woman of the hypothetical genotype given above should have children. In the first place, how might she know, prior to marrying and having sons, that she has the genotype? Let us suppose that her father was Xg(a+) and developed the crippling as he advanced in years. If there are no known preventive measures, the genetic counselor can simply advise her of the statistical probability that half of any sons she produces will be cripples (in middle age) and half of her daughters will, like herself, be carriers. The value judgment then must be made by the woman herself. How serious is the crippling? Should she take the chance?

If preventive measures are possible, then the problem is less acute. All her sons will be normal if she sees to it that the Xg(a+) sons receive the preventive treatment. Her children will be normal, but having them will increase the "genetic load" of future generations (see pp. 279–281). However, few people probably would be deterred by this consideration if medical measures to prevent the actual crippling were available.

PROBLEMS

1. In a certain sibship half the children *of both sexes* had deuteranopia and hemophilia A; half were not color-blind or hemophilic. Give the genotypes of the children and their parents, assuming that crossing over is not involved.

2. A woman of normal phenotype whose father had normal color vision and had hemophilia A married a man who had deuteranopia and hemophilia A. They had two sons and two daughters. One son had normal color vision and hemophilia A; the other son had deuteranopia and was not hemophilic. The daughters married and produced several sons apiece (grandsons of the original couple). What proportion of these grandsons would be expected to have *both* deuteranopia and hemophilia A? Give the genotypes of all individuals. (Assume that crossing over had not occurred in the grandmother.)

3. Let us suppose that the imaginary trait "forked eyelashes" depends on a recessive X-linked gene, *f*.

    A normal woman whose father had deuteranopia and forked eyelashes married a normal man. They had seven sons. Three sons had deuteranopia and forked eyelashes; three were not color-blind and had unforked eyelashes; one was not color-blind and had forked eyelashes.

    Another woman had unforked eyelashes and was Xg(a+). Her father was Xg(a+) and had forked eyelashes; her mother's brother had unforked eyelashes and was Xg(a−). This woman's husband had unforked eyelashes and was Xg(a+). They had eight sons. Two sons had forked eyelashes and were Xg(a−); two had forked eyelashes and were Xg(a+); three had unforked eyelashes and were Xg(a−); one had unforked eyelashes and was Xg(a+).

    Give the genotypes of both pairs of parents and of their sons. Insofar as conclusions can be drawn from so few data, approximately where is the "*f* locus" on the X-chromosome map (p. 212)?

4. Suppose that in the case of the family diagramed in Fig. 13.2 the *p* locus were in the middle, and that the mother had the linkage relationships: $(H^B - p - Xg^a) (h^B - P - Xg)$. Then which son or sons would have represented the occurrence of double crossing over? Which ones single crossing over? Which ones no crossing over?

REFERENCES

Adam, A., C. Sheba, R. Sanger, and R. R. Race, 1966. "The linkage relation of G6PD to Xg," *American Journal of Human Genetics,* 18:110.

Davies, S. H., J. Gavin, K. L. G. Goldsmith, J. B. Graham, J. Hamper, R. M. Hardisty, J. B. Harris, C. A. Holman, G. I. C. Ingram, T. G. Jones, L. A. McAfee, V. A. McKusick, J. R. O'Brien, R. R. Race, R. Sanger, and P. Tippett, 1963. "The linkage relations of hemophilia A and hemophilia B (Christmas disease) to the Xg blood group system," *American Journal of Human Genetics,* 15:481–92.

Graham, J. B., H. L. Tarleton, R. R. Race, and R. Sanger, 1962. "A human double cross-over," *Nature,* 195:834.

Haldane, J. B. S., and C. A. B. Smith, 1947. "A new estimate of the linkage between the genes for colour-blindness and haemophilia in man," *Annals of Eugenics,* 14:10–31.

Jackson, C. E., W. E. Symon, and J. D. Mann, 1964. "X chromosome mapping of genes for red-green colorblindness and Xg," *American Journal of Human Genetics,* 16:403–9.

McKusick, V. A., 1964. *On the X Chromosome of Man.* Washington, D. C.: American Institute of Biological Sciences.

Siniscalco, M., G. Filippi, and B. Latte, 1964. "Recombination between protan and deutan genes; data on their relative positions in respect to the G6PD locus," *Nature,* 204:1062–64.

Whittaker, D. L., D. L. Copeland, and J. B. Graham, 1962. "Linkage of color blindness to Hemophilias A and B," *American Journal of Human Genetics,* 14:149–58.

14.

AUTOSOMAL LINKAGE
AND CHROMOSOME
MAPPING

Investigations of linkage in the X chromosome have a great advantage over investigations of autosomal linkage. Because males are hemizygous, the genetic contributions of their mothers are clearly revealed, without regard to dominance. The Y chromosome from the father does not obscure the genetic contribution from the mother. Hence linkage and recombination in the mother are clearly revealed by the phenotypes of her sons. It was no accident that in the fruit fly, *Drosophila,* mapping of the X chromosome proceeded more rapidly than did mapping of the autosomes. Nevertheless, with suitably planned experiments, mapping of autosomes is also perfectly feasible.

As background for our discussion of autosomal linkage in man, we shall describe the method of studying autosomal linkage in the fruit fly.

Method of Studying Autosomal Linkage in Drosophila

Normal or "wild-type" fruit flies have red eyes and long wings. One mutant gene is known that changes the color of the eyes to purple. Because this gene is recessive, we may represent it by the initial *p* and its normal allele by the initial *P*. Another mutant gene results in the wings being short, functionless stubs. This recessive gene, called vestigial, we may represent by *v*, its normal allele by *V*.

219

We are interested in determining whether or not these genes are linked to each other (they are not sex-linked). One way of starting is to produce two homozygous stocks, one stock homozygous for the wild-type traits—red eyes and long wings, and the other stock homozygous for purple eyes and vestigial wings. Then we interbreed the two stocks to produce double heterozygotes:

$$PPVV \quad \times \quad ppvv$$

Germ Cells	PV	pv
Zygotes		$PpVv$

Because of dominance, these hybrids have red eyes and long wings.

As the simplest means of investigating linkage in the hybrid females, we mate them, *not* to hybrid males but to purple-eyed, vestigial-winged males: $PpVv$ females $\times$ $ppvv$ males. In this way we gain the advantage that nature provides in the case of the X chromosome: genetic phenomena of linkage and recombination in the female parent are not obscured by the genetic constitution of the male (for he contributes only recessive genes). This is a back cross or test cross (p. 17). What types of offspring will occur and in what proportions will they occur?

First let us answer the question *on the assumption that the genes are not linked.*

$$PpVv \quad \times \quad ppvv$$

$$\text{Ova} \left\{ \begin{array}{l} PV \rightarrow pv \\ Pv \rightarrow pv \\ pV \rightarrow pv \\ pv \rightarrow pv \end{array} \right\} \text{Sperm}$$

Genotypes:	$PpVv$	$Ppvv$	$ppVv$	$ppvv$
Phenotypes:	red, long	red, vestigial	purple, long	purple, vestigial
Proportions:	25%	25%	25%	25%

Thus we see that, in the absence of linkage, independent assortment of genes (pp. 37–38) will occur in the formation of ova so that all four possible phenotypic combinations will be present in equal proportions.

On the other hand, if the genes *are* linked, what shall we expect? We shall expect to find the same four types of offspring, but *in very unequal proportions.* Specifically, we shall expect that the offspring having phenotypes like their grandparents (the mother's parents) will far outnumber those having phenotypes that represent recombination of the grandparental characteristics.

We recall that the original stocks were homozygous $PPVV$ and $ppvv$. Hence, *if* the genes were linked, this must have been coupling linkage: $(PV)(PV)$ and $(pv)(pv)$, respectively. Their hybrid daughters, $PpVv$, would have the same coupling linkage: $(PV)(pv)$. The back cross would then be as follows:

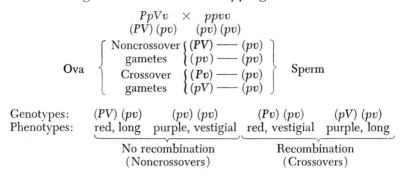

Genotypes: $(PV)(pv)$ $(pv)(pv)$ $(Pv)(pv)$ $(pV)(pv)$
Phenotypes: red, long   purple, vestigial   red, vestigial   purple, long

No recombination   Recombination
(Noncrossovers)   (Crossovers)

Data on actual experiments of this type were summarized by Dr. Calvin B. Bridges and Dr. Thomas Hunt Morgan, two of the pioneers in *Drosophila* genetics (Bridges and Morgan, 1919). Combining results of several investigations by three geneticists, they found that of a total of 13,601 back-cross offspring, 88.2 percent showed no recombination, whereas 11.8 percent did show recombination, divided almost equally between the two crossover types.

As we have seen, if there were no linkage the four types would have been expected in equal numbers; the results obtained were therefore interpreted to mean that the genes are linked, by being in the same autosome, and that crossing over between the loci of the genes occurs 11.8 percent of the time. This percentage was interpreted to mean that the loci are 11.8 "map units" from each other in the chromosome.

In the above experiment we deliberately started with genes in coupling linkage. We could just as easily have started with genes in repulsion linkage: $(Pv)(pV)$. If we had done that, the results would have been the same, except that what in our experiment were the noncrossover types would have been the crossover types, and vice versa.

Let us carry our experimentation one step further. Another recessive mutant gene in *Drosophila* causes the body to be black instead of the normal gray. We may represent the genes by b and B, respectively. Are these genes linked to the other two pairs we have been discussing? For variety we will plan our experiment so that the genes, if they are linked, will be in repulsion phase. In other words, we begin by producing homozygous gray-bodied, purple-eyed flies and homozygous black-bodied, red-eyed flies:

$$BBpp \quad \times \quad bbPP$$
$$(Bp)(Bp) \quad\quad (bP)(bP)$$

Germ Cells (Bp) (bP)
Zygotes $(Bp)(bP)$

The doubly heterozygous females are then mated to black-bodied, purple-eyed males:

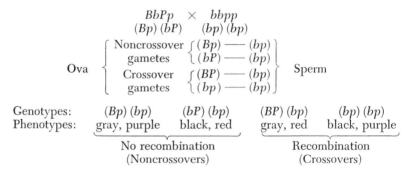

Again, if the genes for body color and eye color are *not* linked, the four types of back-cross offspring will be expected to occur in equal numbers. If they *are* linked, the two "grandparental types" (gray-bodied, purple-eyed, and black-bodied, red-eyed) should predominate. When the experiments of this type were performed, 48,931 offspring were raised (Bridges and Morgan, 1919). Of these offspring, only 6.2 percent were of the two recombination types. This is interpreted to indicate that the genes are indeed linked—with 6.2 percent crossing over. The further interpretation is that the loci of the genes for body color and eye color are 6.2 "map units" apart.

Now we can begin to map this autosome. In doing so we designate the loci by the mutant genes (always remembering that on occasion each locus may be occupied by the corresponding "wild-type" allele). The first experiment showed us that p and v are 11.8 units apart. Now we find that p and b are 6.2 units apart.

Representing the chromosome by a line, we may map these relationships in two ways:

$$
\begin{array}{ccc}
b & p & v \\
\underbrace{\qquad}_{6.2} & \underbrace{\qquad}_{11.8} &
\end{array}
$$

$$
\text{or} \qquad
\begin{array}{ccc}
 & \overbrace{\qquad}^{6.2} & \\
p & b & v \\
\underbrace{\qquad\qquad}_{11.8} &
\end{array}
$$

As far as present data indicate, either arrangement is equally likely. How can we decide which is correct? By determining the amount of crossing over between b and v. If the first arrangement is correct, the amount of crossing over between them should be about the sum of 6.2 plus 11.8, or about 18 percent. If the second arrangement is correct, the amount of crossing over between b and v should be 11.8 minus 6.2, or about 5.6 percent.

When the experiments were performed, over 20,000 back-cross offspring were produced; of these, 17.8 percent were crossover types (Bridges and Morgan, 1919). Therefore, we see that the first arrangement shown is the correct mapping of the three loci b, p, and v.

This gives a taste of the means by which autosomes were mapped in the early days of chromosome mapping. Many experiments, carefully planned, added one gene after another to the maps until the detailed maps of the *Drosophila* chromosomes found in all genetics textbooks were built up. More complex experiments than the ones we have described add data more rapidly. For instance, a "three-point test," using females simultaneously heterozygous for black-body, purple-eye, and vestigial-wing, would enable us in one experiment to do what we required three experiments to accomplish: show the sequence and distances between the loci b, p, and v. Such experiments are commonplace in *Drosophila* genetics, but they are far beyond anything attainable as yet in human genetics.

Autosomal Linkage in Man

We have seen that study of autosomal linkage in experimental organisms involves carefully planned breeding experiments and the raising of progeny in large numbers. In human genetics neither of these procedures is available. How then is it possible to learn anything about human autosomal linkage? Here, as elsewhere in human genetics, instead of experimentation we must substitute mathematical analysis of such data as are available. In fact, the study of autosomal linkage in man is so completely the province of the biometricians (mathematical biologists) that I hesitate to discuss it in a book of this kind. Yet mathematics, in this context, is a tool, and one can understand something of the work for which a tool is intended without understanding much about the tool, or without being able to wield it.

In our discussion of linkage in the X chromosome, we noted that because of the two types of linkage (coupling and repulsion), linked genes are not more likely to be found together in a population than they are to be found separated. If A and B are linked genes, their respective alleles being a and b, individuals with the chromosome (AB) are not more likely to be found than are individuals with the chromosome (Ab) or (aB). This statement is not completely accurate, but it is correct in emphasizing that there is nothing about linkage itself that would cause one type to be more common than another. The actual proportions of the different types depend on the *gene frequencies*, not on linkage itself. We could show mathematically that a population at equilibrium will have the frequencies of different genotypes (*AABB*, *AaBB*, *AaBb*, and so on) determined by the gene frequencies, whether or not there is linkage. When the A's and a's are in one pair of chromosomes, the *B*'s and *b*'s in another pair, they assort independently according to the second Mendelian law. When the *A*'s (or *a*'s) and *B*'s (or *b*'s) are in one pair of chromosomes they do not assort independently in this way, but eventually crossing over will result in their being as thoroughly mixed and recombined as if they *had* undergone independent assortment.

Thus, we cannot detect genetic linkage by noting what characteristics seem to occur together *in a population*. However, as we suggested with linkage in the X chromosome, we *can* gain some clue as to linkage by noting what characteristics seem to occur together *in individual families*. This fact forms the basis of the different methods of attacking the problem. Several methods have been devised, and each has its own advantages. The method most easily discussed without recourse to the mathematics is the sib-pair method of Penrose.

The Sib-Pair Method   To illustrate the principles of the method, we shall employ a model utilizing again the imaginary trait of forked eyelashes. This time, we shall imagine that the trait depends on a dominant gene, *F*, and "unforked eyelashes" on its recessive allele, *f*. We shall state at the outset that the locus of this allelic pair is in the same chromosome as the locus (or loci) of the Rh gene (or genes). Now the problem is how would someone who did not know that linkage is present determine it from the data of the model?

Our model starts with ten pairs of parents. To keep things as simple as possible, we shall imagine that one parent of each pair is Rh-positive and has forked eyelashes, but is heterozygous for both traits, and that the other parent is Rh-negative and has unforked eyelashes. Thus all ten matings are of the type: *FfRr* × *ffrr*. (We recognize that this is exactly the "back cross" mating that experimental geneticists use in investigating linkage.)

Now *if there were no linkage*, what offspring would we expect from these matings?

$$FfRr \quad \times \quad ffrr$$

$$\text{Germ Cells} \quad \left\{ \begin{array}{l} FR \longrightarrow fr \\ Fr \longrightarrow fr \\ fR \longrightarrow fr \\ fr \longrightarrow fr \end{array} \right\} \quad \text{Germ Cells}$$

Offspring: ¼ *FfRr* = Forked eyelashes, Rh-positive
           ¼ *Ffrr* = Forked eyelashes, Rh-negative
           ¼ *ffRr* = Unforked eyelashes, Rh-positive
           ¼ *ffrr* = Unforked eyelashes, Rh-negative

We would expect the four possible combinations in equal numbers. That, in fact, is what we find in our "population" of ten families. Each pair of parents has four children, and when we pool the latter we discover:

> 10 children: Forked eyelashes, Rh-positive
> 10 children: Forked eyelashes, Rh-negative
> 10 children: Unforked eyelashes, Rh-positive
> 10 children: Unforked eyelashes, Rh-negative

There is nothing about these data to suggest linkage! However, we have just stated that we should not expect linkage to be revealed by such pooled data. What we need to do is to analyze the data, family by family. Table 14.1 presents the data in this way. The families (sibships) are designated by letters of the alphabet, and the four children in each family are designated by Roman numerals across the top of the table.

TABLE 14.1   The sib-pair method of testing for autosomal linkage, applied to an imaginary model.

	I		II		III		IV	
Sibship	Lashes	Rh	Lashes	Rh	Lashes	Rh	Lashes	Rh
A	Forked	+	Unforked	−	Forked	+	Forked	+
B	Forked	−	Forked	−	Unforked	+	Unforked	+
C	Forked	+	Forked	+	Forked	+	Unforked	−
D	Unforked	−	Unforked	−	Unforked	−	Forked	+
E	Forked	−	Forked	−	Forked	−	Forked	+
F	Unforked	+	Forked	−	Unforked	+	Unforked	+
G	Forked	+	Unforked	−	Unforked	−	Forked	−
H	Unforked	−	Unforked	−	Forked	+	Unforked	−
I	Unforked	+	Forked	+	Unforked	+	Unforked	+
J	Unforked	+	Forked	−	Forked	−	Forked	−

The name **sib-pair method** suggests that we analyze the data by pairing the children within each family. The children in a sibship of four may be paired arbitrarily in six different ways: I with II, I with III, I with IV, II with III, II with IV, and III with IV. Let us apply this to Sibship A:

> I with II: sibs are unlike with regard to eyelashes and unlike with regard to Rh.
> I with III: sibs are alike with regard to eyelashes and alike with regard to Rh.
> I with IV: sibs are alike in both traits.
> II with III: sibs are unlike in both traits.
> II with IV: sibs are unlike in both traits.
> III with IV: sibs are alike in both traits.

We can conveniently tabulate our data in a "fourfold table":

Eyelashes

		Alike	Unlike
Rh	Alike	XXX 30 pairs	2 pairs
	Unlike	4 pairs	XXX 24 pairs

The "X's" in the table represent tabulations of the sib-pair comparisons we have just made for Sibship A. In three pairs the sibs were alike with regard to both traits, in three pairings they were unlike with regard to both traits. As far as they go, these data suggest linkage, with the four children having the genotypes: I, *(FR) (fr)*; II, *(fr) (fr)*; III, *(FR) (fr)*; IV, *(FR) (fr)*. (Recall the fact that the parents are *FfRr × ffrr*. The data suggest that their genes are linked: *(FR) (fr) × (fr) (fr)*.)

If we now analyze the other nine sibships in the same way, we obtain the total tabulation indicated above in the fourfold table: in 30 pairings both sibs alike with regard to both traits; in 24 pairings both sibs unlike with regard to both traits; in 6 pairings the sibs alike with regard to one trait but unlike with regard to the other one. The fact that within each family there is such great regularity in sib-pairs' agreeing or disagreeing in *both* traits strongly suggests that linkage is present.

The six pairings showing exceptions to this regularity involve child IV of Family E and child IV of Family G. The first three children of Family E evidently have the genotype *(Fr) (fr)*. In contrast to Family A, repulsion linkage is apparently present here, the parents having the genotypes *(Fr) (fR) × (fr) (fr)*. If this is correct, child IV, with the genotype *(FR) (fr)*, must be the product of recombination through crossing over. Similarly, in Family G (where coupling linkage is present) child IV would be a crossover individual.

The data of the model suggest that crossing over is infrequent and hence that the loci for eyelash traits and for Rh are close together in an autosome.

This model has taken us about as far as we can go into the sib-pair method without mathematics (for a good introduction to the mathematics of the method, see Li, 1961, pp. 131–141). Perhaps our greatest oversimplification was in starting with only *FfRr × ffrr* families. In practice, an investigator would often be unable to tell whether an Rh-positive parent with forked eyelashes was *FfRr*, or *FFRr*, or *FfRR*. A moment's reflection will indicate that an *FfRR × ffrr* mating will give the same offspring whether linkage is or is not present. In either case all offspring will be Rh-positive and half of them will have forked eyelashes, half will have unforked ones. In other words, crossing over does not lead to recombination in such an individual.

Thus many matings that an investigator may include in his analysis do not yield data of significance. However, because other matings do yield significant data, the method works despite lack of the precise regularity shown by our model.

Maximum-Likelihood Methods   The sib-pair method has the advantage that it can be applied even when knowledge concerning some sibs in a sibship is unavailable. We note that it utilizes data concerning only one generation. Evidently there would be an advantage in including parents as well as offspring in the analysis. This is done in other methods of studying autosomal linkage. Oversimplifying, we may say that other methods attempt in one way or another to answer this question: Is it more *probable* that the observed parent-child relationships would arise if linkage is present or if linkage is not present? On the basis of the relative mathematical probabilities we may reach conclusions as to the likelihood that linkage is present. Although this may seem a far cry from the definiteness possible with experimental plants and animals, the task is eminently worth doing, and methods will no doubt become more precise in the future.

Human Linkage Groups

A series of genes linked together constitutes a linkage group. In organisms like *Drosophila*, which have been subjected to thorough genetic analysis, there are found to be as many linkage groups as there are pairs of chromosomes. This is exactly what we would expect if each linkage group is indeed the assemblage of genes contained in one chromosome.

For man with his 22 pairs of autosomes we expect eventually to demonstrate that there are 22 linkage groups (plus the linkage group of X-linked genes, and probably a short group of Y-linked genes). Because of the evident difficulties, we are far from our goal in this respect. At the time this is written three pairs of linked genes have been clearly demonstrated (Renwick, 1961). Each pair constitutes the beginning of a linkage group, each representing an autosome. Thus we may say that we have begun to map 3 of the 22 pairs of autosomes. The three well-established cases are the following:

1. The Secretor gene (pp. 140–142) is linked to the gene for a red blood cell antigen known as Lutheran [Lu(a)]. (The name is a surname and does not refer to the Lutheran Church.) The recombination frequency is about 7.5 percent (Renwick, 1961). Hence we may conclude that the two loci are about 7.5 units apart in some one of the 22 pairs of autosomes.

2. The Rh gene (or genes) is linked to a gene that causes the red blood cells to be elliptical in shape (instead of circular); the condition is called *elliptocytosis*. Two genes at different loci have been found to produce elliptical red blood cells; one of the two is linked to the Rh gene or genes with a recombination frequency of about 3 percent.

3. A gene causing the *nail-patella syndrome* is linked to the locus of the ABO blood group genes, with a recombination frequency of about 10 percent. This rare syndrome is identified by abnormalities of the finger-

nails, but the gene also produces skeletal abnormalities, especially of the ilium (one of the bones of the pelvic girdle) and of the patella (kneecap).

Usefulness of Linkage Studies

In the face of so much difficulty why do human geneticists persist in the study of autosomal linkage? The best reason is the desire for knowledge. The dream of an eventual 22 maps of human autosomes would be attractive even if such maps had no practical use.

In the preceding chapter we discussed the value, in preventive medicine and in genetic counseling, of marker genes in the X chromosome. Marker genes in autosomes may be similarly useful. The situation is a bit more complicated, in that the genetic contribution of fathers to their sons, as well as to their daughters, must be taken into account, as it need not be in X-linked traits. Yet the same principles of potential usefulness apply. For example, some seriously disabling traits do not develop until the reproductive period is past. A young person who knows the trait is "in his family" wonders if he will develop the symptoms later in life, and what the chances are that if he has children they will inherit the trait. Huntington's chorea (pp. 73–75) is a case in point. The son of a choreic parent wonders if he has the dominant gene concerned. Telling him that his chances of having it are 50 percent does not convey much help or comfort. If he has the gene, he may not know it until he is 40 years old. If, however, there were a blood group gene (let us call it Bd) closely linked to the H gene (for Huntington's chorea), blood tests early in life might enable the son to know whether or not he had the H gene.

The mother might have the genotype $(Bd\,H)\,(bd\,h)$, the father the genotype $(bd\,h)\,(bd\,h)$. If the son inherited the gene Bd, he would be very likely to inherit the gene H. We must say "very likely to" rather than "sure to," for there is always the possibility that crossing over will result in recombination. However, if linkage is close, the chance of recombination will be small, and the son possessing the red cell antigen produced by Bd would be almost certain to develop Huntington's chorea eventually. He could expect that half of his children would develop it, too. On the other hand, a son who did not inherit Bd would be very unlikely to become choreic or to transmit the gene for chorea.

The value of linkage in this connection will be lessened if means are eventually developed for the direct detection of the H gene in childhood. We shall discuss this later in connection with a means of detecting genetic carriers (pp. 381–382).

There are certain recessive genes that are harmless in heterozygotes but harmful, even lethal, in homozygotes. In order to avoid producing abnormal children, it would be desirable that two such heterozygotes not marry each other. However, because the genes are recessive and heterozygotes are normal, it is frequently difficult to tell who the heterozygotes are.

Suppose that we could demonstrate that in a certain kindred a dominant gene for a red blood cell antigen (we shall use *Bd* again) is closely linked to such a recessive gene, *a* (for "abnormality"). Then heterozygotes in that kindred would have the genotype (*Bd a*) (*bd A*), and two people whose blood tested positive for the *Bd*-determined antigen could be warned of the danger of marrying each other, or, if they did marry each other, of having children. In Chapter 8 we found that if a heterozygote marries his first cousin, the chance is ⅛ that he will be marrying another heterozygote. With the imagined knowledge of linkage we could change this ⅛ to a very high degree of probability.

Recall that although in one kindred *Bd* may be linked to *a*, in some other kindred *Bd* may be linked to *A* (the normal gene). Hence we would not expect that in a population as a whole all possessors of *Bd* would be carriers of the harmful gene.

Trait Association Versus Linkage   This last statement reminds us of the fact stressed previously that traits dependent on linked genes are not found associated together *in a population* more frequently than they are found to be separated. In this connection it might be of value to turn the matter around and ask: What *are* some of the genetic reasons that traits are found associated together?

(1) In the first place, a gene may have more than one effect. More complete knowledge may demonstrate that this is true of all genes, but at present we call genes that demonstrably have more than one effect **pleiotropic genes**. For example, the gene for white eye color in *Drosophila* not only removes the pigment from the eye (leaving it white) but also changes the color of the testicular membrane, changes the shape of the spermatheca, and affects the length of life. Hence these traits are found to be associated because they all result from the action of one gene.

(2) Sex limitation (pp. 187–188), frequently dependent on sex hormones, which in turn reflect genetic constitution, affords another familiar example. Beards are associated with bass voices more frequently than they are with soprano voices.

(3) Another cause of observed association of characters results from the nature of the gene pool. Over much of the earth, brown skin, brown hair, and brown eyes occur together. This does not mean that they are all the effect of one gene, or that the genes are linked. It simply means that the gene pools of these people have the genes in high proportion, with correspondingly low frequencies of the genes producing blue eyes

or red hair, for example. This is sometimes called **stratification.** Sometimes the gene pool of an isolated group or of a caste or clan may have an unusual constitution, resulting in an unusual association of characteristics. Stratification is not to be confused with genetic linkage.

PROBLEMS

1. In addition to the recessive genes for black body, purple eyes, and vestigial wings in *Drosophila*, another recessive gene, *c*, causes the wings to be curved instead of straight.

   Black-bodied, curved-winged flies were mated to homozygous gray-bodied, straight-winged flies, and the F_1 females were back-crossed to black-bodied, curved-winged males. Progeny produced totalled 62,679; of these 14,237 (22.7 percent) were recombination types, the result of crossing over. What were the genotypes and phenotypes of the two recombination types?

   On the chromosome map (p. 222) how far from the locus of gene *b* is the locus of gene *c*? Is gene *c* to the "left" of gene *b* or to the "right" of it? In attempting to answer this last question, the experimenters produced females heterozygous for straight wing and long wing $(C\,V)\,(c\,v)$, and mated them to curved-winged, vestigial-winged males. Of 1720 progeny, 141 (8.2 percent) were recombination types. With this added bit of information, place gene *c* on the chromosome map. (NOTE: The total map distance obtained by adding short intermediate distances is greater than the *apparent* map distance indicated by an experiment in which only the amount of crossing over between the genes at the extremes of a series of genes is measured. When genes are far apart, some of the crossing over between them is double crossing over, Fig. 13.3, p. 215. As the figure indicates, double crossing over leaves the genes at the ends unchanged in their linkage relationships and so reduces the *apparent* amount of crossing over that has occurred.)

2. About what percentage of crossing over would you expect to observe if you mated purple-eyed, curved-winged flies to homozygous red-eyed, straight-winged ones, and then back-crossed the F_1 females to purple-eyed, curved-winged males? Diagram the experiment, giving genotypes and phenotypes of all individuals, and indicating linkage correctly.

3. Another imaginary human trait is "eyebrowlessness." The accompanying table presents data concerning five families of three children each. In these

Family	Child I		Child II		Child III	
	Eyebrows	Eyelashes	Eyebrows	Eyelashes	Eyebrows	Eyelashes
A	present	forked	absent	unforked	present	forked
B	absent	forked	present	unforked	present	unforked
C	absent	unforked	absent	forked	absent	unforked
D	present	forked	present	forked	absent	unforked
E	present	unforked	absent	forked	present	unforked

families the following traits are being studied: eyebrows present versus eyebrows absent; eyelashes forked versus eyelashes unforked. Apply the sib-pair method to the data in the table to determine whether they form evidence for *or* against the hypothesis that the two loci are linked.

4. The nail-patella syndrome arises through the action of a dominant gene, which we may designate as *N*.

(a) A certain woman has the syndrome and belongs to blood group B. Her father lacked the syndrome and belonged to group O. If she marries a man of group O who lacks the syndrome, which two of the following types of offspring will be expected to be the more numerous, which two the less numerous? (1) Group B, with syndrome. (2) Group B, without syndrome. (3) Group O, with syndrome. (4) Group O, without syndrome. Diagram the mating, giving the genotypes of all individuals and indicating linkage correctly.

(b) A certain man has the nail-patella syndrome and belongs to group A. His mother had the syndrome and belonged to group O; his father lacked the syndrome and belonged to group A. If this man marries a woman of group O who lacks the syndrome, what types of offspring will be expected and with what relative frequencies? Diagram the mating, giving genotypes and phenotypes of all individuals, and indicating linkage correctly.

5. In our general population, why do not most people with the nail-patella syndrome belong to the same blood group?

REFERENCES

Bridges, C. B., and T. H. Morgan, 1919. "Contributions to the genetics of *Drosophila melanogaster*. Part II. The second-chromosome group of mutant characters," *Carnegie Institution of Washington,* Publication No. **278**:125–304.

Li, C. C., 1961. *Human Genetics.* New York: McGraw-Hill Book Company, Inc.

Renwick, J. H., 1961. "Elucidation of gene order." In L. S. Penrose (ed.). *Recent Advances in Human Genetics.* Boston: Little, Brown & Company. Pp. 120–38.

15.

SEX DETERMINATION
AND CHANGES IN NUMBER
OF SEX CHROMOSOMES

In our discussion of sex chromosomes (Chap. 12), we noted that females normally have two X chromosomes, and that males have one X chromosome and one Y chromosome. Does the distribution of the chromosomes determine the sex of the individual? What is the role of the sex chromosomes in determining sex?

At the outset we should note that if the sex chromosomes determine sex, the determination will occur at the time of fertilization and will depend on whether an X-bearing sperm or a Y-bearing sperm fertilizes the ovum. Direct evidence on this point is not available, but indirect evidence indicates that sex is determined very early in the embryonic life of the individual. In some animals the fertilized ovum gives rise to an embryonic mass, which then divides to form several or many individual offspring. In this case, all the offspring come from the same ovum, and all are of the same sex. This indicates that sex was determined in the ovum stage, or at least before the subdivision of the embryonic mass. Armadillos afford a mammalian example. Normally four armadillos are born at a time and all four are of the same sex. Investigations of the embryology have demonstrated that the four come from one ovum (that is, they are monozygotic). A similar situation is found in human "identical" twins, who are always of the same sex, having come from a single ovum. Here, however, we must beware of circular reasoning, for twins would not be classified as identical (monozygotic) in the first place unless they *were* of the same sex. In every case, the conclusion that a pair of twins arose from a single ovum is only

232

an inference, not a matter of direct observation. Problems concerned with classifying twins will be discussed in Chapter 20.

As frequently happens, abnormalities give us valuable clues about normal functions. What happens when individuals have an abnormal number of X and Y chromosomes? If such abnormalities interfere with normal sex determination, then we may reach some conclusions concerning the roles of these chromosomes. First, however, we may well inquire into the means by which abnormal numbers of X and Y chromosomes arise.

Nondisjunction

In our discussion of meiosis (Fig. 3.5, p. 32; Fig. 12.1, p. 183), we stressed the normal separations of chromosomes as the process proceeds. In the primary spermatocyte, for example, each tetrad consists of a pair of chromosomes that have duplicated themselves to form two chromatids held together by a centromere. When the primary spermatocyte divides to form the two secondary spermatocytes, each of the latter receives one pair of chromatids from each tetrad. This normal separation of chromosomes is called **disjunction**. The failure of the chromosomes to separate is called **nondisjunction**.

Figure 15.1 shows nondisjunction of the X chromosomes in the first meiotic division of a female. For simplicity, only 2, instead of 22, pairs of autosomes are shown in the primary oöcyte in addition to the X chromosomes. The autosomes are shown undergoing normal disjunction, but the X chromosomes fail to separate, both entering the first polar body. Thus the ovum is left with autosomes only.

Suppose that such an ovum is fertilized by a sperm cell containing an X chromosome. The zygote will then contain, in addition to the 44 autosomes, only one X chromosome. It will be of the XO type. What will be the sex of the resulting individual? Will one X chromosome by itself be sufficient to cause the individual to be female? The answer is: *partially*. Human XO individuals are characterized by a combination of traits known as **Turner's syndrome**, or **gonadal dysgenesis**. The sexual organs are those of the female, but the ovaries are absent or are so abnormal that they fail to produce ova. Secondary sex characteristics do not develop normally but remain in a juvenile state. There are other characteristics, too, such as "webbing" (folds of flesh) at the sides of the neck, short stature, and skeletal abnormalities. Evidently the lack of a second X chromosome has very important effects.

Interestingly, the fact that a single X chromosome is present has its effect on the occurrence of sex-linked recessive traits. Thus, in Turner's

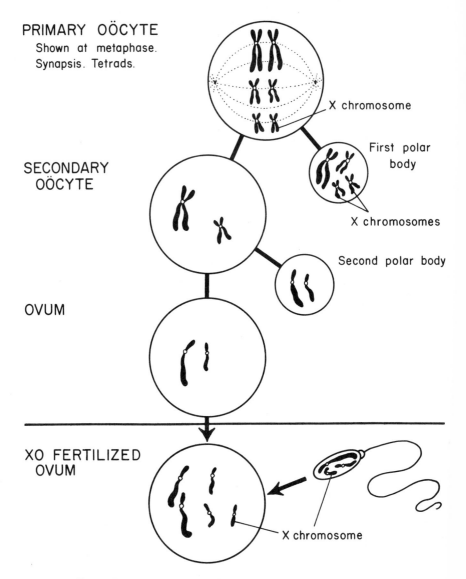

PRIMARY OÖCYTE
Shown at metaphase.
Synapsis. Tetrads.

X chromosome

First polar body

SECONDARY OÖCYTE

X chromosomes

Second polar body

OVUM

XO FERTILIZED OVUM

X chromosome

FIG. 15.1 Above the line: Nondisjunction of X chromosomes in the first meiotic division, producing an ovum containing the normal haploid number of autosomes but no X chromosome. Below the line: Fertilization of such an ovum by a sperm cell containing an X chromosome, to produce an XO zygote.

syndrome, color blindness occurs relatively as frequently as it does in *men,* instead of appearing as rarely as it does in normal women (pp. 185–187; Polani *et al.,* 1956).

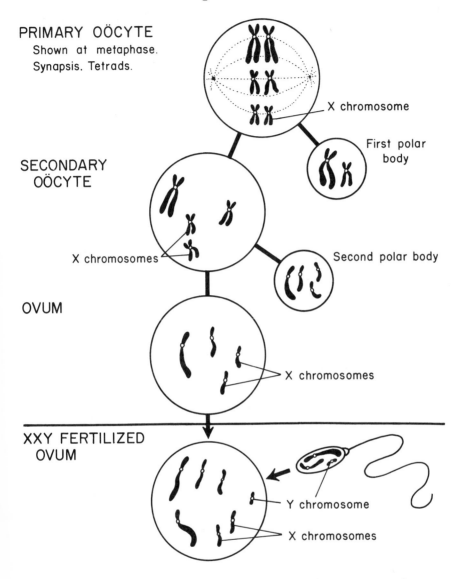

PRIMARY OÖCYTE
Shown at metaphase.
Synapsis. Tetrads.

X chromosome

First polar body

SECONDARY OÖCYTE

Second polar body

X chromosomes

OVUM

X chromosomes

XXY FERTILIZED OVUM

Y chromosome

X chromosomes

FIG. 15.2 Above the line: Nondisjunction of X chromosomes in the first meiotic division, producing an ovum containing the normal haploid number of autosomes but two X chromosomes. Below the line: Fertilization of such an ovum by a sperm containing a Y chromosome, to produce an XXY zygote.

Turning from man to mouse, we might note that XO mice are *fertile* females. Evidently in mice a single X chromosome has greater female-determining potency than it does in humans.

If the ovum lacking an X chromosome were fertilized by a sperm cell containing a Y chromosome, there would be no X chromosome at all in the zygote. The evidence is that a YO zygote could not survive, that an individual cannot live without at least one X chromosome.

Suppose, on the other hand, that nondisjunction had occurred as in Figure 15.2; the ovum has received two X chromosomes and the first polar body, none. Then let us suppose that this ovum were fertilized by a sperm cell containing a Y chromosome. The result would be an XXY individual. Would the two X chromosomes cause such an individual to be a female? What would be the influence of the Y chromosome?

Actually a human XXY individual has the sex organs of a male but is usually sterile, lacking functional testes. He is likely to have feminine breast development. The condition is known as **Klinefelter's syndrome**, or **seminiferous tubule dysgenesis**. The fact that he is a male, albeit an abnormal one, indicates that the Y chromosome contains potent male-determining properties capable of outweighing the effects of two X chromosomes, although not completely.

Figure 15.3 shows the chromosomes of a person who has Klinefelter's syndrome. This type of diagram is called a **karyotype** (or sometimes

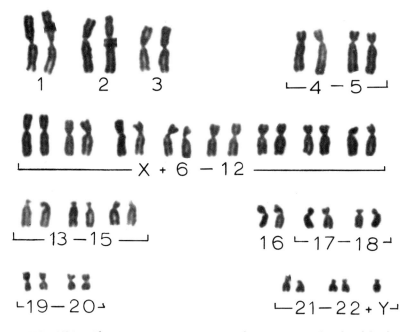

FIG. 15.3 Chromosomes (Karyotype) of a person with Klinefelter's syndrome: 47 chromosomes, including two X chromosomes and one Y chromosome. (Courtesy of Dr. Victor A. McKusick.)

idiogram). The chromosomes are arranged in matching pairs according to size and other characteristics, and are identified by number in a manner that will be described more fully in Chapter 16. Here we note that the group consisting of "medium-sized" chromosomes is composed of the X chromosomes and the autosomes numbered 6 through 12, inclusive, eight pairs in all. Thus this individual has two X chromosomes and one Y chromosome (lower right-hand corner, Fig. 15.3).

It is interesting to note that the Y chromosome is not always of the same importance in determining maleness. In the fruit fly, *Drosophila*, for example, an XXY individual is a *female*. Evidently the Y chromosome does not contain important male-determining genes for fruit flies. Further evidence is afforded by XO flies, which are *males* despite the absence of a Y chromosome (contrast the situation in human beings and in mice). XO males are sterile, however; apparently the Y chromosome contains genes for male fertility. Experimentation in *Drosophila* indicates that the X chromosome contains female-determining factors or genes and that the *autosomes* contain the male-determining genes. The female-determining genes of two X chromosomes outweigh the effect of the male-determining genes in a normal set of autosomes, but the female-determining "strength" of one X chromosome is unable to do this.

Returning to Figure 15.2, we may ask: What will be the result if an ovum containing two X chromosomes is fertilized by a sperm cell containing an X chromosome? We might anticipate that such an XXX individual would be a "super female," and indeed that term is sometimes used. However, such women are usually abnormal, physically or mentally, or both. They are also likely to be infertile although one mentally defective XXX woman, was the mother of four children (Stewart and Sanderson, 1960).

Thus far we have confined our attention to nondisjunction occurring in females in the production of ova. Nondisjunction may also occur in males in the production of sperm. Figure 15.4, A, shows an example in which nondisjunction of the sex chromosomes in the first meiotic division leads eventually to the production of two kinds of sperm cells: those containing *both* an X and a Y chromosome, and those containing no sex chromosomes at all. If a sperm of the first type fertilizes a normal ovum, with its one X, an XXY individual will result (Klinefelter's syndrome). If a sperm of the second type fertilizes a normal ovum, an XO individual will be produced (Turner's syndrome).

If nondisjunction occurs in the second meiotic division rather than in the first one, three types of sperm are produced: those containing two X chromosomes, those containing two Y chromosomes, and those containing no sex chromosomes (Fig. 15.4, B). Offspring that result from fertilization of normal ova will be, respectively, XXX, XYY, and XO. One XYY individual has been discovered. (Hauschka *et al.*, 1962). He was a normal

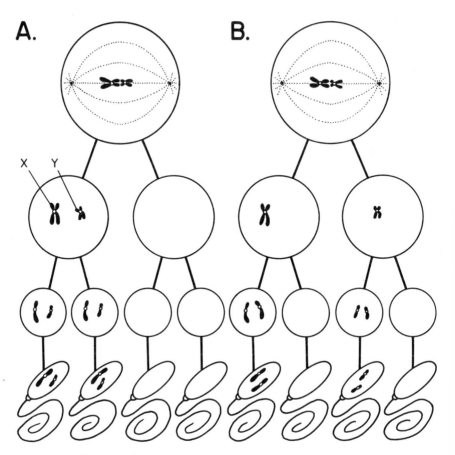

FIG. 15.4 Nondisjunction of sex chromosomes in meiosis in the male. Autosomes are omitted although they are present in all cells. Both A and B start with a primary spermatocyte having the sex chromosomes in terminal synapsis (cf., Fig. 12.1, p. 183, in which the stages are named). A. Nondisjunction in the first meiotic division. Resulting sperm contain either (1) both an X and a Y chromosome or (2) no sex chromosomes. B. Nondisjunction in the second meiotic division. Resulting sperm contain either (1) two X chromosomes, or (2) two Y chromosomes, or (3) no sex chromosomes. In this portion of the diagram, both secondary spermatocytes are shown undergoing nondisjunction simultaneously; this need not occur.

man who came to the investigators' attention because he had a mongoloid daughter (see below). This, coupled with some other abnormalities in his children, suggested that he might be transmitting a hereditary tendency to nondisjunction.

This is only a beginning. Nondisjunction may occur in *both* first and second meiotic divisions, or the effects of nondisjunction in one generation may have added to them the effects of nondisjunction in a subsequent generation, "secondary nondisjunction." In this way ova may be produced that have three or four X chromosomes, and sperm with two X chromosomes and one or two Y chromosomes, and so on, in almost any combination imaginable. As a consequence, people are known who have such genotypes as XXXY, XXXXY, XXYY, XXXX (see McKusick, 1964, especially Table 7). It would serve no good purpose in our present discussion to catalog them in detail. Suffice it to say that the possessors of large numbers of sex chromosomes are usually very abnormal, and many of them are mentally defective. This appears to be a case of "too much of a good thing"; X chromosomes are good, but having too many of them upsets delicate balances that must be maintained if an embryo is to develop into a normal individual.

Sex Chromatin or Barr Bodies

An interesting and useful discovery of relatively recent date is recognition of the fact that nuclei of cells that are not undergoing mitosis usually reveal the sex of the individual from which the cells were derived. Suppose, for example, that we scrape a few cells from the lining of the cheek of a woman (using a wooden tongue depressor, perhaps). We spread the cells on a microscope slide and stain them, preparing what is called a *buccal smear*. We will find a deeply stained particle or mass attached to the inside of the nuclear membrane of many of the cells (Fig. 15.5, A). This particle is called a **sex chromatin body** or **Barr body**, from its discoverer Dr. Murray L. Barr of the University of Western Ontario (Barr, 1959). A similar buccal smear from the mouth of a man is devoid of such Barr bodies. Here is a means of distinguishing male tissue from female tissue even when chromosomes as such are not visible. The mucous membrane of the mouth was taken merely as an example; in general, tissues of all kinds from a female possess Barr bodies in cell nuclei, whereas nuclei of male tissues lack such bodies.

Although a Barr body is not visible in all cells from female tissue, according to McKusick (1964): "Probably essentially all cells of the female have a Barr body. That it cannot be identified in many cells is probably because it is not in profile, because it is not in its characteristic position subjacent to the nuclear membrane, or because of other technical factors."

Of what is the Barr body composed? Various suggestions have been advanced, but the present consensus is that the body consists of *one* of the two X chromosomes that female cells contain. According to this idea, when a cell is not undergoing mitosis, the substance of one X chromosome,

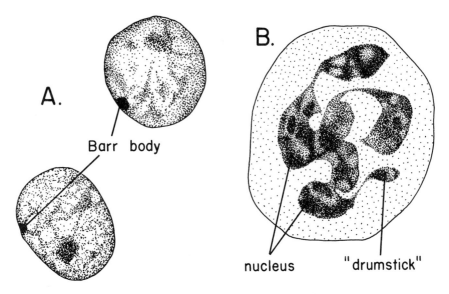

FIG. 15.5 A. Nuclei of skin cells from a normal female, showing sex chromatin bodies (Barr bodies). B. Leucocyte (white blood cell) from a normal female. Note the irregular nucleus with the tiny appended "drumstick." (Drawn from photomicrographs in Barr, M. L., 1960. "Sexual dimorphism in interphase nuclei," *American Journal of Human Genetics,* **12:**118–27.)

like that of the autosomes, is in an attenuated form throughout the nucleus and hence not visible. The other X chromosome remains in compact form, so that it stains deeply and is identifiable as a Barr body.

Figure 15.5, B, shows a drawing of a white blood cell from a female. The irregular stained portion is the nucleus, with its appendage, called a "drumstick," which is found in the white blood cells of women but not in those of men. This forms another trait by which cells of females differ from those of males.

The Lyon Hypothesis   In this connection we may appropriately mention an idea that is gaining wide acceptance. It is called the **Lyon hypothesis**, after Dr. Mary Lyon, a British geneticist who specializes in the genetics of mice. This hypothesis is that in any given cell of a female the genes in the attenuated X chromosome are active, producing their appropriate phenotypic effects, whereas the genes in the compact chromosome composing the Barr body are inactive. This hypothesis helps to explain the common observation that X-linked genes have no more effect on a homozygous female than they do on a hemizygous male, although the female has two X chromosomes and the male only one. Various other phenomena in which some cells of a heterozygous female differ from other cells in the expression of X-linked traits fit the hypothesis (Lyon, 1962). For example, a female mouse may be heterozygous for certain X-linked color genes and have a mottled appearance, apparently because one gene is active in cells composing certain areas of the skin, whereas its allele is active in cells of other areas. Apparently the "decision" as to which X chromosome shall be inactive in a given cell (and all cells derived from it) is made early in embryonic development. A more extensive discussion of the Lyon hypothesis is found in McKusick (1964).

If the conclusion that the Barr body represents one of the X chromosomes is correct, then in any individual there should be a correlation between the number of X chromosomes and the number of Barr bodies. We should expect to find that the number of Barr bodies is one less than the number of X chromosomes. We have seen that this relation holds for normal males and females. What about individuals who have an abnormal number of X chromosomes?

Usually XO individuals (Turner's syndrome) have no Barr bodies in their cells. Although they are sterile females, they resemble males in this respect. Occasional individuals suffering from this syndrome do have one Barr body, however, as well as the normal number of chromosomes (46). In such cases one of the two X chromosomes present is considered to be an abnormal one, an isochromosome (see pp. 251–252, and Figs. 16.4, p. 252, and 16.5).

Persons with Klinefelter's syndrome, with an XXY constitution, usually have *one* Barr body. In this respect, and frequently in breast development as well, they resemble females.

Someone may ask at this point: If the Lyon hypothesis is correct, why are XO and XXY individuals abnormal? If in a normal female one of the two X chromosomes is inactive, why does the one X chromosome in an XO individual not suffice to produce a normal female? Moreover if one X chromosome of an XXY individual is inactive, why does not the one active X chromosome, combined with the effect of the Y chromosome, result in a normal male? Doubtless we shall know much more about these matters in the future. Lyon (1962) has pointed out that Barr bodies are not visible in the cells of early rat embryos. Perhaps, then, *both* X chromosomes may be active in early embryonic development before one of them becomes condensed to form a Barr body. Such early activity of two X chromosomes may be necessary for normal female development, or in the presence of a Y chromosome (as in XXY individuals) two X chromosomes may cause abnormal development. It is probable, too, that the X chromosome forming a Barr body is not *completely* inactive. Other explanations are possible, but we await further research.

The general rule we have mentioned, correlating the number of X chromosomes and the number of Barr bodies, holds for individuals with larger numbers of X chromosomes, at least insofar as maximum number of Barr bodies is concerned. Thus, many cells of an XXX individual contain two Barr bodies; many cells of an XXXX or XXXXY individual contain three. In other cells of an XXXX individual only one or two Barr bodies have been seen (Carr *et al.*, 1961). Why are not three Barr bodies seen in all the cells of such an individual? Probably there are reasons not yet known to us, but doubtless the reasons not all cells of a normal female show a Barr body apply here also (p. 239).

Sex Chromosome Mosaics

All of the cells of an individual are the lineal descendants, through repeated cell divisions, of the fertilized ovum from which the individual arose. Hence, if the fertilized ovum contained two X chromosomes, we should expect all of the cells of the individual to contain two X chromosomes (although one might be in the form of a Barr body between mitoses). If the fertilized ovum contained an X chromosome and a Y chromosome, we should expect all cells of the individual to be similarly constituted. As far as we know at present, this expectation is usually realized, but with increasing frequency we are learning about exceptions. These are cases in which some parts or tissues of an individual have a certain number of sex chromosomes, whereas other parts or tissues have a different number. Such an individual is called a **sex chromosome mosaic**.

How could such a mosaic come into being? To take a simple case, suppose that an ovum contains two X chromosomes. When it divides, the chromatids of one X chromosome fail to separate (they undergo nondisjunction), with the result that one daughter cell contains three X

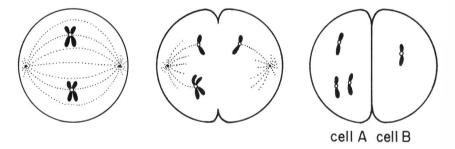

cell A cell B

FIG. 15.6 Origin of an X-chromosome mosaic by nondisjunction in the first mitotic division of a fertilized ovum containing two X chromosomes. Autosomes have been omitted from the diagram.

chromosomes, whereas the other contains only one (Fig. 15.6). Then all of the cells comprising parts of the body derived from Cell A (Fig. 15.6) by subsequent mitoses would have the XXX constitution, and all of the cells comprising parts of the body derived from Cell B would have the XO constitution. Such a mosaic would be designated XXX/XO.

An XXX/XO individual has been discovered and studied (Jacobs *et al.*, 1960). She was of low normal intelligence with many of the symptoms of Turner's syndrome (of feminine phenotype but lacking vagina, uterus, and breast development; no menstruation). Study of buccal smears revealed that 37 percent of the mucosal cells had two Barr bodies. Chromosome counts were made on four samples of living tissue: (1) bone marrow from the sternum; (2) white blood cells; (3) skin from the left shoulder; (4) skin from the right leg. Most of the cells had either 45 or 47 chromosomes. Disregarding a few cells with different chromosome numbers, the chromosome counts on the four samples were as follows:

Tissue	Chromosome Number	
	45	47
1. Sternal marrow	67	0
2. Blood	71	11
3. Skin, left shoulder	18	28
4. Skin, right leg	15	20
Total	171	59

Thus we see that, on the whole, nearly three times as many cells had 45 chromosomes as had 47 but that the different samples varied greatly in this respect. For example, no sternal marrow cells had 47 chromosomes, whereas in the skin samples the number of cells containing 47 outnumbered those containing 45.

Cells containing 45 chromosomes were found to lack one of the medium-sized chromosomes (see next chapter). This was considered to be an X chromosome and so the constitution of these cells was regarded as XO (44 autosomes plus one X chromosome). Cells containing 47 chromosomes had an additional medium-sized chromosome and were considered to be of XXX constitution (44 autosomes plus three X chromosomes).

Thus the individual was an XXX/XO mosaic of the type we have been discussing. The authors suggest that her mosaicism may have originated by nondisjunction in the first division of the fertilized ovum, as in Figure 15.6. It is, of course, entirely possible that nondisjunction could occur in a mitosis in some later stage of embryonic development. However, nondisjunction at a later stage would affect fewer of the cells of the body, perhaps only the cells of a single organ or part of an organ, as compared to the widespread effect in the present example. Evidently in her case the proportion and distribution of XO cells were sufficient to produce the symptoms of Turner's syndrome as in an XO individual who is not a mosaic.

Much more complicated mosaics have been described and new ones are continually being discovered. XX/XXY, XO/XX/XXX, and XO/XYY are only three examples now known. Although they are interesting in themselves, they illustrate no new principles as compared to the case we have discussed, and therefore we shall not consider them further.

Most of the cases studied so far have come to attention because of some abnormality, physical or mental. It would be most valuable to know to what extent *normal* people exhibit mosaicism. Is our assumption really justified that most cells of normal people contain the same number of sex chromosomes that the fertilized ovum did? Recent researches demonstrate that cells within the body may differ in the number of chromosomes. Thus a large proportion of liver cells are tetraploid, containing twice as many chromosomes as other cells have: 92 instead of 46. We need a knowledge of normal variation in chromosome numbers to use as a basis for judging the significance of variations in numbers in abnormal individuals. Medical science necessarily devotes more attention to abnormal individuals than to normal ones. Hence, important as it is, information about normal individuals is acquired more slowly.

PROBLEMS

1. How many Barr bodies would we expect to find in the cells of people with the following sex-chromosome constitutions: XXXY, XXYY; XX/XXY mosaic; XO/XX/XXX mosaic; XO/XYY mosaic.

2. If an XXY individual *were* to produce sperm cells, what kinds would he produce with regard to sex-chromosome content? If he married a normal woman, and no nondisjunction were involved in the production of her ova, what types of offspring would be expected?

3. If in Fig. 15.2 nondisjunction of the X chromosomes had occurred in *both* the first and second meiotic divisions, what type of ovum would have been produced? What would have resulted from its fertilization by a Y-bearing sperm cell? What would be the total number of chromosomes (autosomes plus sex chromosomes) in this fertilized ovum? How could an unfertilized ovum containing three X chromosomes be produced by the female represented in the diagram?

4. If in Fig. 15.4, A, nondisjunction of the X and Y chromosomes had occurred in *both* first and second meiotic divisions, what types of sperm cells would have been produced? If these sperm cells fertilized normal ova, what types of offspring would have arisen?

5. If in Fig. 15.4, A, nondisjunction of the X chromosomes had occurred as shown but nondisjunction of the Y chromosomes had occurred in *both* divisions, what types of sperm cells would have been produced, and what would have resulted from their fertilization of normal ova?

6. Males having an XYY constitution are known. How could such an individual be produced by parents having the normal constitution of sex chromosomes, through the occurrence of a single nondisjunction?

REFERENCES

Barr, M. L., 1959. "Sex chromatin and phenotype in man," *Science,* **130**: 679–85.

Carr, D. H., M. L. Barr, and E. R. Plunkett, 1961. "An XXXX sex chromosome complex in two mentally defective females," *Canadian Medical Association Journal,* **84**:131–37.

Hauschka, T. S., J. E. Hasson, M. N. Goldstein, G. F. Koepf, and A. A. Sandberg, 1962. "An XYY man with progeny indicating familial tendency to nondisjunction," *American Journal of Human Genetics,* **14**:22–30.

Jacobs, P. A., D. G. Harnden, W. M. Court Brown, J. Goldstein, H. G. Close, T. N. MacGregor, N. Maclean, and J. A. Strong, 1960. "Abnormalities involving the X chromosome in women," *Lancet,* **1**:1213–16.

Lyon, M. F., 1962. "Sex chromatin and gene action in the mammalian X-chromosome," *American Journal of Human Genetics,* **14**:135–48.

McKusick, V. A., 1964. *On the X Chromosome of Man.* Washington, D. C.: American Institute of Biological Sciences.

Polani, P. E., M. H. Lessof, and P. M. F. Bishop, 1956. "Colour-blindness in 'Ovarian Agenesis' (gonadal dysplasia)," *Lancet,* **2**:118–20.

Stewart, J. S. S., and A. R. Sanderson, 1960. "Fertility and oligophrenia in an apparent triplo-X female," *Lancet,* 1960, **2**:21–23.

16.

CHROMOSOMAL ABERRATIONS
OF THE AUTOSOMES

In the broad sense, the word "mutation" may be used to include any changes in the chromosomes and their constituent genes. In Chapter 3 we discussed mutations that involve changes in the structure of the DNA molecule. These are frequently called **gene mutations**, or **point mutations**, to distinguish them from mutations that involve visible changes in the chromosomes, called **chromosomal mutations** or, better, **chromosomal aberrations**. At the present time, we cannot see the changes involved in gene mutations; they are too small to be seen even with the electron microscope. However, if more powerful electron microscopes are developed—as seems to be in the offing, these minute changes in molecular structure may become visible. Perhaps the best way to distinguish between gene mutations and chromosomal aberrations is to say that gene mutations consist of changes of structure *within* molecules of DNA, whereas chromosomal aberrations consist of changes of structure involving aggregates of great numbers of such molecules. The distinction may prove to be more or less artificial, yet it is useful.

Chromosomal aberrations are of two types: (1) changes in the number of chromosomes and (2) changes in the structure of individual chromosomes.

Changes in number may be of two orders: (1) changes in terms of complete haploid sets and (2) changes in numbers involving less than a haploid set. A haploid set is the complement of chromosomes found in a germ cell following meiosis. A human spermatogonium, for example, contains 46 chromosomes comprised of 23 pairs; 46 is the diploid number. A human sperm cell contains 23 unpaired chromosomes, one from each of the 23

246

pairs. This is a haploid set.

Change in number by less than a haploid set is called **aneuploidy**, or sometimes **polysomy**. In theory the change may be either the loss or the gain of a chromosome. Because normal functioning is dependent on a full and balanced complement of chromosomes, loss of a chromosome is likely to be lethal. An individual having one chromosome less than normal is called a **monosomic**. In the preceding chapter we described one example: individuals who have one X chromosome but lack either a second X chromosome or a Y chromosome. Such XO individuals are monosomics. That they are viable, although abnormal, is probably attributable to the fact that a single X chromosome is "self-sufficient" (e.g., in men), and the Y chromosome is relatively inert (except in the matter of normal testicular development in men). However, it seems that loss of any one of the autosomes cannot be tolerated.

Addition of a single chromosome to the normal diploid set is called **trisomy**. The initial n is frequently used to designate the number of chromosomes in a haploid set. Thus normal individuals with two of each kind of chromosome are $2n$. Trisomic individuals are $2n + 1$. In plants, especially, tetrasomic individuals ($2n + 2$) and even aneuploids of higher order are known, but we shall not be concerned with them.

The XXX woman we described in the preceding chapter was a trisomic (44 autosomes plus three X chromosomes). Presently we shall describe a case of trisomy involving an autosome: mongolism or the trisomic-21 condition. Here we may note that the mechanism by which aneuploidy occurs is usually nondisjunction. In Chapter 15 we diagramed nondisjunction of the X chromosomes. Autosomes undergo nondisjunction at times in the same manner. In this way germ cells having an extra chromosome arise, and trisomic individuals are produced when such a germ cell unites with one having the normal haploid number.

Increase in the number of chromosomes by complete haploid sets is called **polyploidy**. In the preceding chapter we mentioned that many human liver cells are **tetraploid**, $4n$, meaning that they have four complete haploid sets of chromosomes in place of the usual two sets. Such a tetraploid liver cell would arise when a cell prepares for mitosis by duplicating its chromosomes but then fails to divide: the 46 chromosomes originally present have duplicated themselves, making a total of 92, all of which remain in the one cell instead of being distributed to two daughter cells. Recall that in man $n = 23$; hence $4n = 92$.

In plants, especially, entire individuals may be polyploid. They arise from germ cells that are *diploid* ($2n$) instead of the normal haploid (n) in constitution. In Figure 16.1 we illustrate how such a diploid ovum may be produced by what we may call roughly "complete nondisjunction"—complete failure of chromosomes in the primary oöcyte to separate. Failure of the primary oöcyte to form a first polar body would produce the same

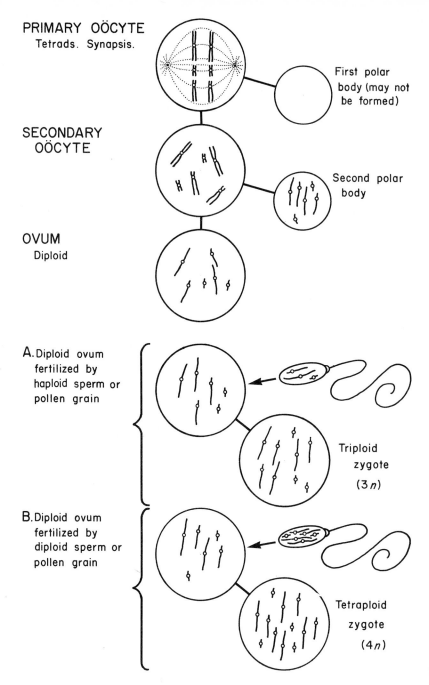

PRIMARY OÖCYTE
Tetrads. Synapsis.

First polar body (may not be formed)

SECONDARY OÖCYTE

Second polar body

OVUM
Diploid

A. Diploid ovum fertilized by haploid sperm or pollen grain

Triploid zygote (3*n*)

B. Diploid ovum fertilized by diploid sperm or pollen grain

Tetraploid zygote (4*n*)

FIG. 16.1 Polyploidy arising by production of diploid ova in a plant having three pairs of chromosomes. In meiosis the first polar body does not form, or if it forms does not contain chromosomes. A. Triploid zygote produced when a diploid ovum is fertilized by a haploid pollen grain. B. Tetraploid zygote formed when a diploid ovum is fertilized by a diploid pollen grain.

result. Similarly, if meiotic division fails to occur, diploid pollen grains may be produced as well. Although polyploidy is important in plants, it is rare in animals, apparently because it upsets the mechanism of sex determination. We noted in the preceding chapter that an increase in the number of X chromosomes is usually detrimental. Polyploidy is almost unknown in man save as it occurs in the cells of some tissues of the body, e.g., liver, bronchial epithelium, and amnion.

A very abnormal individual has been discovered, however, who had 69 chromosomes in most of his cells: three of each kind of autosome, two X chromosomes, and a Y chromosome (Böök and Santesson, 1960). Such cells are triploid, $3n$. Because some cells were diploid ($2n$), having 46 chromosomes, the individual was evidently a mosaic (pp. 242–243).

Turning to chromosomal aberrations that consist of structural changes in individual chromosomes, we note that these may be classified into four categories: (1) deletions, (2) duplications, (3) inversions, and (4) translocations. To these should perhaps be added a fifth: formation of isochromosomes.

From experiments, geneticists have amassed much knowledge concerning structural changes in single chromosomes of plants and animals, especially of the fruit fly, *Drosophila*, with its "giant" banded salivary gland chromosomes (p. 30). Although the small, densely staining human chromosomes do not give much visible evidence of structural changes of this type, a beginning has nevertheless been made: at certain stages, banding can be seen in human chromosomes. Moreover, we must remember that human cytogenetics is still an infant.

(1) **Deletions** or deficiencies. A chromosome may fragment and then recombine, but with a portion missing (Fig. 16.2, II). The chromosome is thereby shortened, but in the absence of distinctive banding such as that which characterizes the salivary gland chromosomes of *Drosophila* we have difficulty in telling exactly what portion is missing. In Figure 16.2 we have used letters to represent genes but, of course, we cannot see the genes in actual chromosomes. We could probably arrange suitable breeding experiments in various organisms to determine which genes are missing, but man does not lend himself to such experimentation. If the missing piece contains important genes, (a) a gamete containing the deleted chromosome may not be viable, or (b) a zygote containing the deleted chromosome paired with a normal one from the other parent may not be viable, or (c) a zygote containing the deleted chromosome may not be viable *if* it happens to receive a deleted chromosome from the other parent, also. In this latter case the zygote would be homozygous for the deletion (in terms of Fig. 16.2, it would be completely lacking in genes *H*, *I*, and *J*, and so, if these genes were important at all, the zygote would be likely to die). On the other hand, a heterozygote for the deletion (e.g., a zygote having *H*, *I*, and *J* in one chromosome but not in its partner)

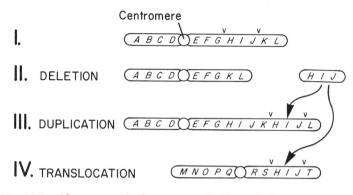

FIG. 16.2 Chromosomal aberrations. I. Normal chromosome, with letters representing gene loci. II. Deletion of the "HIJ" section. III. Duplication or repeat. The "HIJ" section becomes attached to a homologous chromosome. IV. Translocation. The "HIJ" section becomes attached to a non-homologous chromosome, as evidenced by the different letters it contains.

might survive if the genes "in single dose" could perform their functions.

(2) **Duplication** or repeat. When a deletion occurs, what happens to the deleted portion? Usually it is lost, but it may become attached to the homologous chromosome, causing a section of the chromosome to be repeated (Fig. 16.2, III), where there are two "*HIJ*" sections). The duplicated piece may or may not be placed next to the section that it duplicates. The visible result is a lengthening, usually slight, of the chromosome. Repeats in the banded salivary gland chromosomes of *Drosophila* can easily be identified, but because of the density of human chromosomes we shall probably be slow in demonstrating such duplication in them. This does not mean that duplication does not occur in man, but only that we have difficulty observing it.

(3) **Translocation**. When part or all of one chromosome becomes attached to a chromosome not homologous to it (not a member of the same pair), translocation is said to have occurred (Fig. 16.2, IV). At times non-homologous chromosomes may *exchange* portions, even whole arms. This is called reciprocal translocation. In our discussion of mongolism we shall describe a case of translocation in man.

(4) **Inversions**. Sometimes a chromosome will divide into fragments, and then the fragments will recombine, but one or more of them will be in a reversed relationship to the others. If the inversion is confined to one arm of the chromosome, it is called **paracentric** (Fig. 16.3, II). If the inverted portion includes the centromere, it is called **pericentric** (Fig. 16.3, III). As shown in the figure, pericentric inversions are more likely to

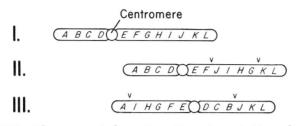

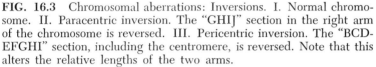

FIG. 16.3 Chromosomal aberrations: Inversions. I. Normal chromosome. II. Paracentric inversion. The "GHIJ" section in the right arm of the chromosome is reversed. III. Pericentric inversion. The "BCD-EFGHI" section, including the centromere, is reversed. Note that this alters the relative lengths of the two arms.

change the shape of chromosomes than are paracentric ones, and hence have a greater chance of being seen in preparations of densely stained chromosomes, such as those with which most studies of human chromosomes are made.

We might expect that the last two chromosomal events, translocations and inversions, would have little genetic effect because no genes are missing or duplicated. This might be true if each gene performed its function all by itself, like a lone artisan in his home workshop, but in point of fact, the function of a gene is frequently influenced by its position in relation to other genes: **position effect**. As we saw in Chapter 3, genes function by synthesizing proteins, which serve as enzymes. This synthesis is a chain reaction more like an assembly line in a manufacturing plant. If one man in an assembly line inserts a bolt, and another man screws a nut onto it, this second man usually must be near the first one, not down at the other end of the line, especially if the bolt must be fastened before the next process in assembly can occur. It appears that similar assembly lines of genes function in much this way. Thus, changing the position of the genes may change their phenotypic effect.

(5) **Formation of isochromosomes.** As we have noted, a typical chromosome consists of two "arms" separated by a centromere. The arms are not alike in genetic content, a fact we have indicated in our diagrams by using the letters of the alphabet in normal sequence (Fig. 16.4, I). An **isochromosome** is a chromosome in which the centromere is in the middle and the two arms *are* alike in genic content (although typically they are mirror images in arrangement). Figure 16.4, II, illustrates such chromosomes and the manner in which they may arise from normal chromosomes. When a daughter cell receives one of these isochromosomes, the genetic effect is that of deletion and duplication combined. For example, one cell will have genes *ABCDE* in a double dose and completely lack

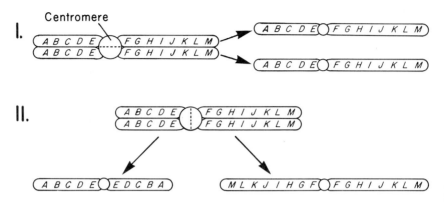

FIG. 16.4 Formation of isochromosomes compared to formation of normal chromosomes. I. Formation of normal daughter chromosomes from a metaphase chromosome consisting of two chromatids and one centromere. The centromere is shown dividing in a plane parallel to the long axis of the chromatids (dotted line). II. Formation of isochromosomes. The centromere divides abnormally, as indicated by the dotted line transverse to the long axis of the chromatids.

genes *FGHIJKLM*, whereas another cell will have genes *FGHIJKLM* in duplicate but will lack genes *ABCDE*. Both the lack of some genes and the presence of others in a double dose may have important consequences.

Knowledge of human isochromosomes and their significance is in its infancy. We may mention one suspected case involving the X chromosome. As we noted in the preceding chapter, persons with Turner's syndrome (XO) usually do not have a Barr body in the nucleus (pp. 240–241). They are sometimes said to be *chromatin negative*. Occasionally, however, a person with Turner's syndrome does have one Barr body in the nucleus; she is *chromatin positive*. In some cases (Polani, 1962), one normal X chromosome was found to be present, as well as a large additional chromosome with a median centromere, resembling autosome No. 3 (Fig. 16.6). It was suspected that this was an isochromosome consisting of the long arms from two X chromosomes. Radioactive tracers gave evidence that the two arms of the presumed isochromosome were indeed identical to each other. If this interpretation is correct, the corresponding two short arms were both missing. Thus, the only short arm present was that possessed by the single normal chromosome, as in the usual XO condition (Fig. 16.5). This would suggest that the genes for normal ovarian development (and for other bodily traits that Turner's syndrome patients exhibit) are located in the short arm of the X chromosome and must be present in duplicate if normal development is to occur, as in normal XX females.

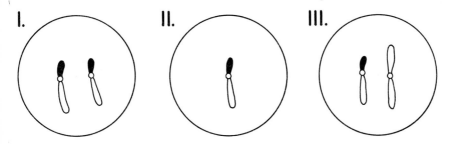

FIG. 16.5 Possible explanation of cases of Turner's syndrome having two X chromosomes, one an isochromosome. I. Normal female. Two X chromosomes, with a total of two short arms (black). II. Turner's syndrome with the usual XO constitution. One X chromosome, with one short arm. III. Turner's syndrome with one normal X chromosome and one X chromosome an isochromosome consisting of two long arms. Total: One short arm, as in the XO condition.

The Normal Human Karyotype

Recent technical improvements have made possible great advances in the study of human chromosomes. It is now possible to remove a bit of tissue by biopsy, grow the tissue in tissue culture, cause many of the cells to undergo mitosis up to the metaphase stage, and then stop there, and treat the cells in such a way that the chromosomes on the metaphase plate are well spread out and relatively easy to count and study. The drug colchicine inhibits spindle formation in cells, causing them to remain in the metaphase stage instead of progressing on through anaphase and telophase. Treatment with a hypotonic (watery) solution swells the cells and causes dispersion of the chromosomes. Chromosomes are flattened and spread out by allowing the tissue to dry, or by applying pressure to the cover slip after the tissue is mounted on a microscope slide.

When a cell with the chromosomes nicely dispersed (not overlapping) is found, an enlarged photograph is made. Then the picture of each chromosome is cut out, and the pictures are arranged in homologous pairs and in sequence from the largest pairs to the smallest ones. Such a diagrammatic arrangement of the chromosomes is called a **karyotype**. Figure 16.6 is a drawing of the karyotype of a normal male, and was made from a photographic montage of the kind described.

We note immediately that each chromosome is represented by a *double* structure. This is because each chromosome had duplicated itself and was at the metaphase stage of mitosis (Fig. 3.2, p. 28). If mitosis had continued, the centromere (represented by the round white dot) would have divided, releasing the two chromatids from each other. Then one chro-

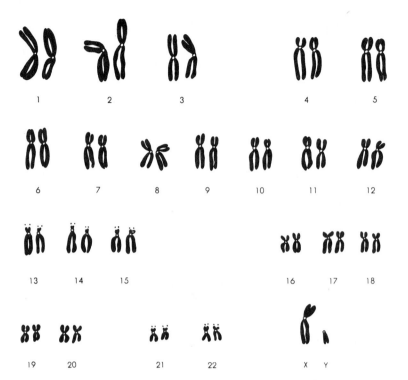

FIG. 16.6 Karyotype of the metaphase chromosomes from a somatic cell of a male. (From Victor A. McKusick, *HUMAN GENETICS.* © 1964. By permission of Prentice-Hall, Inc., Englewood Cliffs, N. J.)

matid (now a "daughter chromosome") would pass to one pole of the spindle, the other chromatid to the other pole.

The chromosomes are designated by number, beginning with the largest pair (Fig. 16.6). This means of designation was agreed on by workers in the field at a meeting in Denver in 1960. In the Denver system, the chromosomes are also divided into seven groups. This grouping is convenient, for it is frequently very difficult to distinguish among chromosomes within one group.

Group 1–3 (also called A) consists of the three largest pairs. The centromere of each chromosome is median or nearly median in position. This is called *metacentric* (Fig. 16.6 and Fig. 16.8).

Group 4–5 (or B) consists of two slightly smaller pairs in which the centromere is nearer one end than the other (*submetacentric*).

Group 6–12 (or C) is composed of the relatively numerous medium-sized chromosomes. Some are metacentric, some submetacentric. The X chromosome belongs in this group; it is not placed with the others in Figure 16.6 but is placed with them in Figure 16.8 and in Figure 15.3.

Group 13–15 (or D) is comprised of three pairs, which are nearly as large as those in Group 6–12 but have the centromere placed so near one end that the short arm is very short indeed (called *acrocentric*). All of them have satellites, tiny masses of chromatin attached to the short arm (represented by dots in Fig. 16.6).

Group 16–18 (or E) consists of three somewhat smaller pairs, which are metacentric or submetacentric, and lack satellites.

Group 19–20 (or F) is composed of the two smallest metacentric pairs.

Group 21–22 and Y (or G) includes the two smallest acrocentric autosomes, and the Y chromosome, which is also acrocentric. Chromosomes 21 and 22 have satellites (Fig. 16.6). The Y chromosome is typically larger than the others, but the size varies. Interestingly, this size difference is hereditary, passed on from father to son.

We note that members of one group can be distinguished very clearly from members of other groups—by size, placement of the centromere, presence or absence of satellites, and sometimes by other peculiarities. In many cases, however, chromosomes within one group cannot be distinguished with certainty from other members of the same group. Thus many of the medium-sized chromosomes of Group 6–12 look very much alike, and the X chromosome looks much like other members of the group. We might wonder, in fact, how a cytologist finding, for example, 17 of these medium-sized chromosomes in a cell can determine which chromosome pair is trisomic. Are there, perhaps, three No. 6 chromosomes, or three No. 9's, or three X chromosomes? In this case, investigation of the number of Barr bodies (p. 239) in the nuclei of interphase cells can be of assistance. If two Barr bodies are found, it is probable that trisomy involves the X chromosomes. If only one Barr body is present, an autosome is probably present in triplicate. Identification will become more certain as research in this most active field continues.

Mongolism or Trisomy 21

One of the commonest forms of mental defect is that called **mongolism.** About one birth in 600 is that of a mongoloid. The name is unfortunate because it suggests some connection with the Mongolian race. Occasional mongoloids have skin pigmentation or an eye fold (epicanthus) faintly suggestive of Oriental features, but the resemblance is purely coincidental. To avoid unfortunate implications, the name **Down's syndrome** is sometimes used, as is **Trisomy 21**, for reasons that will soon be evident. (In our discussion we shall use the term "mongoloid" without capitalization to make plain that no reference to the Mongolian race is intended.)

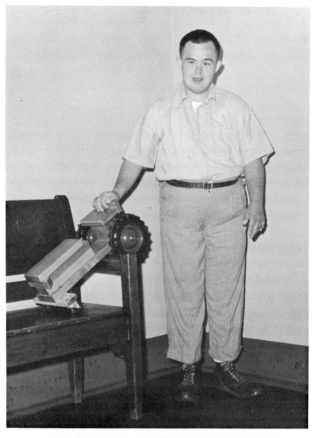

FIG. 16.7 Mongoloid boy (Down's syndrome)—age 25 years, Stanford-Binet IQ 26. The round, rather flat face and its expression are typical, as are the short stature and the stubby fingers. (Photo by Jim Reid. Courtesy of Dr. Raymond M. Mulcahy, Superintendent, Brandon Training School.)

Children with Down's syndrome (Fig. 16.7) vary in their degree of mental deficiency, but in most cases it is severe. Typical mongoloids also have a syndrome of physical traits, including short stature, stubby fingers, a large, fissured tongue, and a round head.

There have been many theories as to the cause of mongolism, but in 1959 it was discovered that mongoloids usually have 47 chromosomes instead of the normal 46 (Lejeune, Gautier, and Turpin, 1959). The additional chromosome was found to be one of the tiny satellited chromosomes of Group 21–22. By convention it is usually designated as 21. Thus, mongoloids are "trisomic 21" (Fig. 16.8).

How does mongolism arise? In almost all cases, the parents are normal.

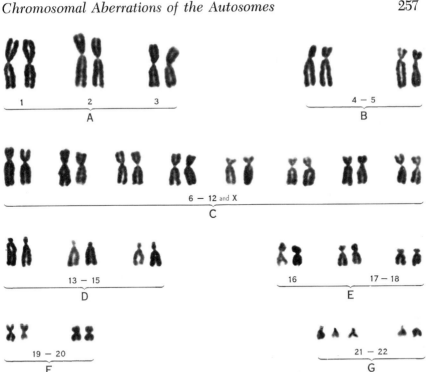

FIG. 16.8 Karyotype of a female mongoloid (Down's syndrome; Trisomy 21). Note the three No. 21 chromosomes, as well as the two X chromosomes. (Courtesy of Dr. Victor A. McKusick.)

Nondisjunction in production of the ovum or sperm is doubtless involved in most instances. Figure 16.9 shows nondisjunction in the first meiotic division of oögenesis, leading to production of an ovum containing two No. 21 chromosomes. Ova containing two No. 21 chromosomes may also be produced by nondisjunction in the second meiotic division, rather than the first. The trisomic condition follows when such an ovum is fertilized by a normal sperm containing one No. 21 chromosome (as shown below the horizontal line in the figure). Nondisjunction in spermatogenesis may lead to production of sperm containing two No. 21 chromosomes. When such a sperm fertilizes a normal ovum containing one No. 21 chromosome, a trisomic-21 condition also results.

In this connection, we may note that although mongoloids may be born to mothers of any age, there is a marked tendency for them to be born to older mothers, the remainder of whose children have, usually, been normal. This tendency has been recognized for a long time, and its causes have been much debated. It is interesting to note that in the fruit fly, *Drosophila*, the tendency to nondisjunction in oögenesis increases with the age of the parents.

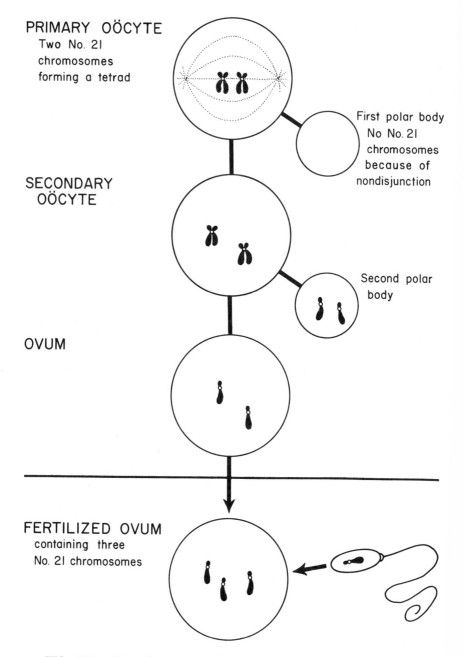

PRIMARY OÖCYTE
Two No. 21
chromosomes
forming a tetrad

First polar body
No No. 21
chromosomes
because of
nondisjunction

**SECONDARY
OÖCYTE**

Second polar
body

OVUM

FERTILIZED OVUM
containing three
No. 21 chromosomes

FIG. 16.9 Mongolism. Above the line: Origin of trisomy 21 through nondisjunction in production of an ovum. Below the line: Fertilization of an ovum containing two No. 21 chromosomes by a normal sperm containing one No. 21 chromosome.

In mammals, all of the oöcytes a female will ever have are present at birth or shortly thereafter. Evidence from mice indicates that as the oöcytes in the ovary grow older, they may exhibit an increased tendency to undergo nondisjunction. Perhaps this is also true of human oöcytes.

Occasional mongoloids are found to have 46 rather than 47 chromosomes. In such cases, one of the chromosomes is usually found to be exceptionally long. The conclusion seems warranted that the exceptional chromosome has the substance of a No. 21 chromosome fused to another chromosome, an example of translocation (p. 250). Usually the translocation involves a chromosome of Group 13–15 and is designated "15/21." At times, two of the tiny Group 21–22 chromosomes seem to be united, forming a so-called 21/22 or 21/21 chromosome.

A mongoloid with a 15/21 chromosome also has the two regular No. 21 chromosomes. Hence, although the observed number of chromosomes is not increased over the normal 46, the *substance* of three No. 21 chromosomes is present, as it is in mongoloids who have three separate No. 21 chromosomes.

Study of the parents of a mongoloid with such a translocation chromosome usually reveals that one parent has 45 chromosomes. One of them is the 15/21 chromosome, in addition to which there is one No. 21 chromosome and one No. 15 chromosome. The parent is normal, but he or she may produce a germ cell containing both the translocation chromosome and a No. 21 chromosome. Such a germ cell, uniting with a normal one from the other parent, would produce a mongoloid child (Fig. 16.10). A parent of this kind could also produce offspring of normal phenotype who could in their turn produce mongoloid offspring. This affords a basis for the *inheritance* of mongolism.

In the more common cases in which three separate No. 21 chromosomes are present, a hereditary predisposition to nondisjunction might form a basis for apparent inheritance of mongolism.

Most mongoloids do not themselves become parents. When they do, what would we expect concerning their offspring? If the primary spermatocytes, or oöcytes, of a mongoloid contain three No. 21 chromosomes, disjunction would always produce germ cells containing one No. 21 chromosome and germ cells containing two No. 21's. Half of the germ cells should be of one type, half of the other. Hence, with fertilization involving normal cells, half of the offspring should have two No. 21's, half should have three. Data are few, but such as they are they indicate that when the mother is mongoloid (no male mongoloids have been known to father children), half of the offspring are in fact mongoloid, and half are normal, as predicted.

We note that knowledge concerning the chromosomal basis of mongolism is relatively recent. There are many questions we should like answered. Do the symptoms of mongolism ever arise in the *absence* of

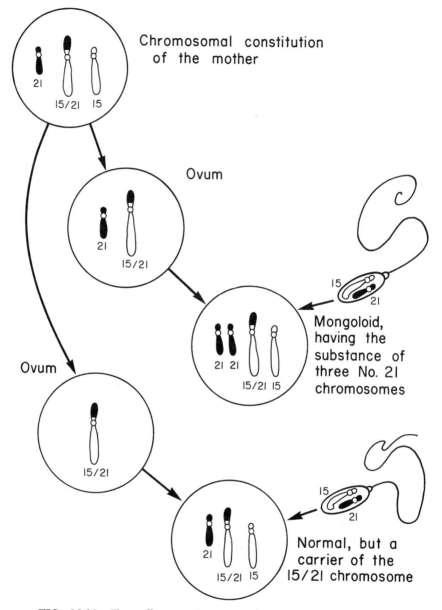

Chromosomal constitution
of the mother

Ovum

Ovum

Mongoloid,
having the
substance of
three No. 21
chromosomes

Normal, but a
carrier of the
15/21 chromosome

FIG. 16.10   Two offspring of a woman having a 15/21 translocation chromosome. In addition to the two types of ovum shown, such a woman can produce other types; those having one No. 21 and one No. 15 will give rise to normal offspring who will not be carriers of the 15/21 chromosome. In all cases, normal sperm are shown fertilizing the ova, although at times the 15/21 chromosome may be carried by sperm.

a triplicate condition of the substance of the No. 21 chromosome? Do people ever have three No. 21 chromosomes without developing the symptoms of mongolism? Here again (see p. 244) we note the lack of a basic knowledge of chromosomal variation possible in *normal* individuals. Why is it that having two of these tiny chromosomes is normal, whereas having three of them leads to such severe abnormality? Future research on the biochemical and metabolic differences between mongoloids and normal individuals may be expected to suggest what goes wrong in embryonic development when three instead of two of these chromosomes are present. We may suspect that abnormality of the enzyme systems in the embryo, based on abnormal genetic constitution, forms the basis for the defect, but just what the abnormalities are remains to be seen.

A much more complete discussion of the chromosomal basis of mongolism, including a variety of modifications in chromosomal constitution encountered in individual case histories, is found in Hamerton (1962). For our present purpose, mongolism has afforded an example of two chromosomal aberrations in man: trisomy and translocation. In some cases, formation of an isochromosome may also be involved (pp. 251–252). In this instance the isochromosome would consist of the long arms of two No. 21 chromosomes. If a normal No. 21 chromosome were also present, the total effect would be that of triplication of the No. 21 chromosome.

We are just at the dawn of knowledge concerning the pathological consequences of chromosomal aberration. For instance, the incidence of childhood leukemia is about twenty times as great in mongoloids as it is in normal children. In some leukemic mongoloids the number of small chromosomes is increased above the number usually found in mongoloids, resulting in total chromosome counts above 47. Within the next few years we shall doubtless know much more than we do now about the chromosomal basis of leukemia in children.

A chromosomal basis is at least suspected for a variety of other pathological conditions (see summary in Fraccaro, 1962). Knowledge is advancing rapidly. In most cases, trisomy is implicated, as in mongolism. The trisomy usually involves the smaller chromosomes, although larger chromosomes (e.g., Group 6–12) may be involved in some cases. We might anticipate that, because of their greater genic content, change in the number of large chromosomes would have more severe consequences than would change in the number of the small chromosomes, and that this change would amount at times to a lethal effect.

Because of the difficulty of observing structural change in the densely staining metaphase chromosomes, knowledge of the pathological effects of structural aberrations of chromosomes (pp. 249–252) lags behind knowledge of the effects of changes in number. Yet a beginning has been made, and we may be sure that in the future we shall learn much more about the effects of human deletions, duplications, translocations, and inversions. An exciting future is ahead for the infant science of human cytogenetics.

PROBLEMS

1. What would be the result if the tetraploid zygote shown in Fig. 16.1, B, gave rise to an embryo in which some of the primary oöcytes failed to form first polar bodies? How many haploid sets would the resulting ova contain? What would result if the ova were fertilized by haploid pollen grains? By diploid pollen grains?

2. Suppose that in human oögenesis nondisjunction of both the X chromosomes and the No. 21 chromosomes occurred in the first meiotic division, the first polar body receiving neither type. If the resulting ovum were fertilized by a Y-bearing sperm, what would be the genotypic and phenotypic nature of the offspring produced?

3. How might nondisjunction in the production of the ovum result in offspring having both Turner's syndrome and mongolism?

4. In Fig. 16.10 we have shown two types of ovum that a woman of normal phenotype but having a 15/21 translocation chromosome might produce. What other types of ovum might she produce? Which of these would give rise to offspring that would be normal both in genotype and phenotype?

5. A mongoloid woman may have 46 chromosomes, one of them being an isochromosome consisting of the long arms of two No. 21 chromosomes. If such a woman reproduces, and her husband is normal, what proportion of her children will be expected to be mongoloids?

REFERENCES

Böök, J. A., and B. Santesson, 1960. "Malformation syndrome in man associated with triploidy (69 chromosomes)," *Lancet*, 1960, 1:858–59.

Fraccaro, M., 1962. "Autosomal chromosome abnormalities." In J. L. Hamerton (ed.). *Chromosomes in Medicine*. London: National Spastics Society. Pp. 184–203.

Hamerton, J. L., 1962. "Cytogenetics of mongolism." In J. L. Hamerton (ed.). *Chromosomes in Medicine*. London: National Spastics Society. Pp. 140–83.

Lejeune, J., M. Gautier, and R. Turpin, 1959. "Étude des chromosomes somatiques de neuf enfants mongoliens," *Comptes Rendus de l'Académie des Sciences, Paris*, 248:1721–22.

Polani, P. E., 1962. "Sex chromosome anomalies in man." In J. L. Hamerton (ed.). *Chromosomes in Medicine*. London: National Spastics Society. Pp. 73–139.

17.

MUTATIONS:
RATES AND EFFECTS

In Chapter 4 we stated that "when a gene undergoes chemical change so that an altered phenotypic effect is produced, we say that a mutation has occurred." Mutations of this type are called **gene mutations** or **point mutations**. The latter name represents the idea that the mutation arises as a change at a certain point in the chromosome, the point at which a gene is located. However, if a gene is composed of a portion of a DNA molecule comprising many nucleotide pairs (see Chap. 4), is a gene really a "point" in any literal sense of the term? Perhaps, as has been suggested, the term "point mutation" should be reserved for changes involving a single nucleotide pair in a DNA molecule. Here we may be accused of splitting hairs, and therefore, we shall follow common usage in employing the terms gene mutation and point mutation to denote changes in single genes (even while we recognize that modern research makes it increasingly difficult to define the limits of a gene).

Used broadly, the term "mutation" encompasses any change in the chromosomes of cells, at least any change that involves the DNA. Because the chromosomes, with their DNA, control heredity, mutations are hereditary by definition. Mutations may occur in body (**somatic**) cells or in germ cells. **Somatic mutations** are not passed on from one generation to the next, but are passed on from the somatic cell in which they occur to other somatic cells arising from that one by mitosis. Thus, in the embryo of a plant, a cell may undergo a mutation so that chlorophyll is not produced. If, in subsequent development, that cell gives rise to branches with leaves, those branches and leaves will be white. According to one widely recognized theory, somatic mutations may be involved in the production of

263

cancer; a cancer may start from a cell that has undergone mutation in the genetic mechanism that controls cell division. The result would be that the cell would "lose control," and divide and subdivide in the unregulated fashion characteristic of malignant tumors.

Our main concern is genetics, and therefore our attention will be focused principally on **germinal mutations.** This term may be used to include all changes in the chromosomes of germ cells, including the gene or point mutations mentioned previously.

In Chapter 4, we noted that gene mutations may occur in one of two ways. The nucleotide pairs in a DNA molecule may become *rearranged*, with a resultant effect on the phenotype, or one nucleotide pair may be *exchanged* for another, so that a triplet sequence ATC, for example, becomes changed to AAC. As an example, we cited the case of sickle-cell hemoglobin, **Hb S**, which differs from normal hemoglobin, **Hb A**, by substitution of glutamic acid for the normally present valine at one point in the chain of amino acids composing the molecule. We suggested that change in one nucleotide in a triplet of three nucleotides of the DNA molecule might account for the change from normal to abnormal hemoglobin. We have still to explain the cause of such nucleotide exchange— as in all of science, one explanation demands another.

The process of gene mutation is frequently pictured as a *copying error*. Before the invention of printing, manuscripts were copied by hand, sometimes repeatedly. Occasionally the scribes made mistakes, so that the copy was not exactly like the original. In somewhat similar fashion, copies of the DNA molecule are made every time a chromosome duplicates itself in preparation for mitosis or meiosis (Fig 4.2, p. 42). Usually the copying is precise, so that the replica is exactly like the original, but occasionally errors creep in. These errors are the mutations; if they are large errors, the effect is probably lethal, but if the errors are not great enough to cause death they may nevertheless produce a phenotype that is altered in some way.

So our questioning is pushed back one step further; we now ask: What causes errors in replicating the DNA molecule? In general, we may say that the factors concerned must lie in the microenvironment surrounding the chromosomes within the cell. One cause of mutations is believed to be **thermal agitation**, which we may picture as heat-induced movement of molecules (both inside and outside the chromosomes).

We also know of a variety of chemicals that can cause genes to mutate (mustard gas was perhaps the first to be recognized). For the most part, these chemicals are not normal constituents of cells. We can readily, understand that it is much easier to add an unusual chemical and note its effect than it is to determine the mutagenic (mutation-causing) action of normal cell constituents. However, some of the observed mutation rate may be caused by chemicals that cells normally encounter.

Starting with the classic results of Dr. H. J. Muller (1927), who won a Nobel Prize for this research, we have much evidence that mutations are also produced by radiations. These radiations include ionizing radiations such as X-rays, neutrons, and cosmic rays, and nonionizing radiation such as ultraviolet light. Apparently, radiations may act in two general ways. They may strike a chromosome and its included DNA directly, producing a break in the chromosome or a change in the molecule, or they may alter the microenvironment (mentioned above), producing changes in chemical compounds within the cell. These changes then affect the DNA of the chromosomes, producing mutations.

Mutation Rate

How frequently does mutation occur? There have been many investigations of natural mutation rates in experimental plants and animals, and all indicate that mutation is a rare event. Summarizing data from the mouse and the fruit fly, *Drosophila*, the United Nations Scientific Committee on the Effects of Atomic Radiation stated that the rates found "mostly range between 10^{-5} and 10^{-6} per locus per tested gamete"* (UN, 1958). Hence only one gamete in 100,000 to 1,000,000 gametes will contain a mutation in any one gene in which we may be interested. This is a very low rate, yet it may be even higher than the rates for many genes. The great difficulty of measuring the rate of something that occurs only once in a million times is evident. Huge numbers of individual entities, gametes in this case, must be available if the investigator is to have a fair chance of observing even a few of the rare occurrences. Accordingly, the mutations picked for study in mice and flies may well be ones that oblige by occurring with greater frequency than do most mutations. In bacteria, where obtaining vast numbers of individuals is no problem, mutation rates as low as 10^{-9} per gene per cell have been measured (on the average, only one bacterial cell in a *billion* shows mutation of the gene being investigated).

Turning to man, we note that, despite the difficulties, geneticists attempt to estimate the rate of mutation of human genes. Most easily detected are mutations of recessive genes to form fully penetrant, dominant ones. In such cases, the mutated gene produces a phenotypic effect in every individual who inherits the gene. For example, if in a kindred lacking Huntington's chorea (pp. 73–75) an individual appears who has that abnormality, we may conclude that a new mutation has occurred in a germ cell of a parent and has been inherited by the individual offspring.

*For those unacquainted with this method of designating small fractions, we state that 10^{-5} is 0.00001, and 10^{-6} is 0.000001.

Thus, in theory, one could compute the mutation rate at which the gene for Huntington's chorea is produced by calculating the proportion of people who have the disease (are Hh) but who were born to parents neither of whom had it (they were hh). To obtain the mutation rate per gene (the rate at which h mutates to form H), this proportion of people would be divided by two, for either the h gene from the mother or the one from the father might have mutated to produce the H gene. For example, if among 1,000,000 people 40 were found to have Huntington's chorea although their parents did not have it, the mutation rate indicated would be:

$$\frac{40}{1,000,000} \times \frac{1}{2} = 0.00002 \text{ (or 2 mutations per 100,000 genes)}$$

[Check: 1,000,000 people possess 2,000,000 genes at the locus concerned. $2,000,000 \times 0.00002 = 40$]

The method sounds simple, but it is beset with difficulties. Errors of diagnosis, difficulty in determining true parentage, the fact that different genes may mutate to produce the same abnormality, the fact that non-hereditary traits (phenocopies) may appear and be indistinguishable from gene-determined traits—these are a few of the sources of uncertainty (Crow, 1956; UN, 1962).

Even greater difficulty is experienced in measuring the rate at which dominant genes mutate to form their recessive alleles. If the genes are in the autosomes, the mutant phenotype is shown only by homozygotes; in these one of the two recessive genes may be a newly formed one but the other may have been inherited from distant ancestors. Thus rates of mutation cannot be determined by direct observation and counting. Methods of estimating such rates are based on principles of population genetics, utilizing certain assumptions, and they yield results of uncertain significance (Crow, 1956). If, on the other hand, the genes are in the X chromosomes, the probem is somewhat simpler, for *males* will show the phenotype produced by an X-linked gene even if the gene is recessive.

Perhaps it is surprising that any consensus can be reached in the face of varied methods of investigation and of the attendant difficulties, yet similarity of results "makes it reasonable to assume that the average mutation rate in man is about 1/100,000 per locus per generation" (UN, 1962). Doubtless there is much variation from this estimated average. Perhaps the genes we observe to mutate, and hence are able to study, come to our attention because they have a particularly high rate of mutation.

In summary, we may at least conclude that genes are very stable entities, rarely undergoing change.

What is the total frequency of spontaneous mutations? What proportion of gametes will contain a new mutation of some one of the genes present? We could answer this question (a) if we knew the rate at which individual genes mutate, and (b) if we could assume that all genes mutate at the same rate, and (c) if we knew how many genes there are in the chromosomes of a gamete. Unfortunately, each "if" represents a big uncertainty.

How many genes are there in a gamete? The best estimates we have are for *Drosophila*; it is thought that a gamete of this fly contains between 5000 and 10,000 genes (a zygote or other diploid cell containing about double that number, of course). Perhaps man has about four times as many, a gamete containing between 20,000 and 42,000 of them (Spuhler, 1948). Let us take the figure of 30,000; if all of these genes mutated at the rate of 1/100,000, 30 percent of the gametes would be expected to contain a new mutation ($30,000 \times 0.00001 = 0.30$). Actual estimates are as high as this, or higher. Despite the unavoidable uncertainties, we may conclude that because of the large number of genes, even low mutation rates per gene result in mutations of one gene or another being common. Probably they occur in all of us, and a considerable proportion of the gametes produced by each of us contains at least one new mutation (plus mutant genes inherited from ancestors).

Significance of Mutations

Are mutations "good" or "bad"? An organism, be it fly or man, is like a highly complex machine in that for perfect functioning all parts must work together smoothly. Both fly and man are highly adapted for a particular mode of existence. Each represents the product of age-long processes of evolution always tending to produce more and more perfect adaptation to the needs of existence. Although each may not be perfect in its own sphere, each is well up toward what is sometimes called its "adaptive peak." Each is a highly successful organism in its own way.

If we take a smoothly running machine and hit it with a hammer, we *may* improve the running of the machine, but the chances are against doing so. We are far more likely to injure the machine so that it runs poorly, or does not run at all.

Mutation is something like that—it is an accident to a chromosome or to a gene in a chromosome. Because the machine is already running well, such an accident is more likely to do harm than it is to be of benefit (although we must never forget the possibility that it may be of benefit). Thus, we should expect that most mutations to modern, well-adapted organisms would be deleterious. That is what we do, in fact, observe.

However, we cannot leave the matter there. We have spoken of modern, well-adapted organisms. Well adapted to what? Obviously, to their environments. Adaptation only has meaning with reference to an environmental setting. Hence it is that in large measure whether a mutation is beneficial or harmful depends on the environment of the organism in question. Doubtless there are some mutations so harmful that they cannot be of benefit in any conceivable environment. In man, *pseudohypertrophic muscular dystrophy*, which is dependent on an X-linked gene and always kills boys in their teens, would seem to be an example. Yet great numbers of mutations are harmful in one environment and beneficial in another.

For example, a mutation that changed the physiology of an organism so that it required a food, vitamin, or chemical compound not available in its environment would certainly be detrimental. Indeed, if the requirement could not be met, the mutation would be lethal. Such a mutation occurs once in a billion times or so in the much-studied colon bacillus, *Escherichia coli*. Presumably from time immemorial, on rare occasions a mutation has occurred which results in its possessor's being unable to live without the antibiotic streptomycin. A cell with this mutation would promptly die unless streptomycin were present. Hence this is a lethal mutation in an environment lacking the antibiotic, but in a test tube culture containing streptomycin the previously lethal mutation suddenly becomes most valuable (Demerec, 1950). Cells not possessing the mutation die by the million, but the cell with the mutation thrives and gives rise to a new streptomycin-dependent population. The mutation, lethal under usual conditions encountered by the bacillus, becomes highly beneficial in the new environment containing streptomycin.

In much the same way, mutations in house flies conferring resistance to the insecticide DDT would be of no value in an environment devoid of DDT, and they might even be harmful. However, as soon as man started using DDT, a great premium was placed on these very mutations. Flies died by the millions, but the fortunate possessors of these mutations survived and became the ancestors of the DDT-resistant strains that plague us today.

We might multiply the examples, but these two will suffice to emphasize the point that the harmfulness or beneficialness of many, if not most, mutations depends on the environment. We cannot answer the question: Is the mutation to streptomycin-dependence in *E. coli* a harmful mutation? until we know whether or not the environment contains streptomycin.

We have labored this point at some length to counteract the impression many people have that there is something essentially harmful about mutations, that they are always bad. As we have seen, mutations are genetic changes, and change in and of itself is neither intrinsically good nor intrinsically bad. We may have change for the better or change for the worse. To a great extent, environment determines which it shall be.

As a matter of fact, most biologists today regard mutations as the raw materials utilized in the evolution of organisms. Progressive evolution by this means would hardly be possible if mutations were always changes for the worse. This is a very large subject, which we can do no more than touch on here, but in general, we may point out that plants and animals have not always been as well-adapted to as many means of livelihood ("environmental niches") as are the species we observe about us today. For example, at one time there were no vertebrates (back-boned animals) living on land; all vertebrates were fishes of one kind or another. The terrestrial environment was vacant. The geologic record shows that certain fishes gave rise to descendants that could adapt to life on land. Genetic change, probably of a mutational nature, must have been involved. This is only one of countless examples. Whenever the environment changes, or a new environment becomes available to a group of organisms if they have the capability of entering it, a premium is placed on hereditary traits different from those that were formerly most valuable.

Here it might be well to note that mutations do not occur because they are needed. They are genetic accidents, as we have stressed, and they occur at random in the sense that they occur at a fairly constant rate with no regard to possible utility. Furthermore, they occur perhaps not in all but in several directions in haphazard fashion. From our knowledge of the mutation process in general, we should expect, for example, that occasionally mutations may arise in *E. coli*, making their possessors *more* susceptible to streptomycin than are normal cells. If streptomycin is present, such cells are quickly weeded out, of course, and leave no progeny. Progressive evolutionary change occurs when a mutation useful in a given environment *chances* to occur. (For a discussion of this and other factors important in evolution, see Moody, 1962).

Natural Selection

The occurrence of mutation by itself does not suffice to produce evolutionary change. What happens to mutations when they do occur? In the preceding discussion we have spoken of the death of large numbers of organisms not possessing a given mutation in a given set of circumstances, of a "premium" being placed on possession of a mutation, of the occurrence of "weeding out." In each case, we have reference to what, following Darwin (1859), is called **natural selection**. In the endeavor to live and reproduce in a given environment, individuals or groups of individuals possessing certain traits succeed better than do individuals possessing other traits, and they leave larger numbers of offspring. The essential idea of natural selection, then, is **differential fertility**: one group of organisms producing more offspring than does another group.

Our example of streptomycin-dependence in *E. coli* demonstrated natural selection in an extreme form. In a broth containing streptomycin all the cells except the ones having the mutation die, and, of course, leave no progeny, whereas the streptomycin-dependent cells do leave progeny. However, in many cases, the differential is not as great as it is in such an all-or-none situation (and perhaps it would not be with *E. coli* if sufficiently dilute solutions of streptomycin were employed, so that some cells not possessing the mutation in question could nevertheless survive).

We may surmise that in the case of the development of DDT-resistant flies the application of DDT was not usually sufficient to kill *all* flies not possessing genetically determined resistance to the insecticide; rather, what probably happened in most cases was that of, perhaps, a thousand offspring more were the progeny of resistant flies than were the progeny of nonresistant ones. If this differential fertility continued for a few generations, the resistant flies in a given region would almost or entirely replace the nonresistant ones.

These two examples, *E. coli* and flies, have stressed differential *survival,* followed by reproduction of the surviving group. Natural selection does not always involve differential survival. This is particularly true of the operation of natural selection on man, our point of greatest interest at present. *Differential fertility, and hence natural selection, is operative whenever possessors of one genotype leave fewer offspring than do possessors of another genotype.* As we noted earlier (p. 195), men who have hemophilia, in past generations, at least, have usually not married and produced children. As a result of their failure to do so, the gene for hemophilia tends to die out, to undergo what Muller and others have called "**genetic death**" (meaning death of a *gene,* not of a person necessarily). The fact that the gene does not eventually disappear from the gene pool is due in greatest measure to the occurrence of new mutations from the normal gene to the hemophilic gene, thereby replenishing the store.

Mongolism (pp. 255–261) and many other human abnormalities result in their possessors either producing no children or producing fewer children, on the average, than do normal people. These are all examples of natural selection at work. Thus we see how incorrect it is to think, as some people have, that natural selection is confined to plants and lower animals. Natural selection operates in human populations and will continue to do so until the day when all people of all types produce exactly the same number of children who live to reproductive age in their turn. And that will be a long time, if ever.

Varying Effects and Relationships of Mutations

A subject of interest and concern at the present time is the probable effect on future generations of increasing the number of mutations. What is likely to be the genetic effect if we are exposed to more X-rays and radioactive substances than past generations have been? To what extent is increased radiation cause for alarm? Before we can form an intelligent opinion on such questions we must inquire into the interrelationships of changed and unchanged genes and into the nature of the human gene pool.

We have spoken of gene mutations as being either dominant or recessive. It would be well at this point to remind ourselves of the meaning of these terms. A dominant gene is one that produces a phenotypic effect in a heterozygote, whereas a recessive gene is one that produces no phenotypic effect in a heterozygote (Chap. 2). Thus, if *A* is dominant and its allele *a* is recessive, *AA* and *Aa* individuals are indistinguishable in phenotype, the gene *a* having no effect in the *Aa* individual. Unfortunately, not all genetic situations are as clear-cut as this. At times, in a heterozygote, gene *A* may have the principal effect, but gene *a* may have some effect; in this case *Aa* individuals differ from *AA* individuals in some manner. This forces us to use qualifying terms, designating degrees of dominance. We may say that *A* is incompletely dominant or that *a* is partially dominant (i.e., not wholly recessive). Indeed, as knowledge increases, we learn of more and more instances in which heterozygotes differ in some respect from homozygotes for the dominant gene. Conceivably, in fact, the terms "dominant" and "recessive" may eventually disappear from genetical parlance. At present, however, it is convenient to use them, remembering that there are, in fact, all shades or degrees of dominance.

In discussing the effects of mutations it will be convenient to recognize two categories: (a) a normally occurring recessive gene mutates to form a dominant allele; (b) a normally occurring dominant gene mutates to form a recessive allele.

Mutation from Recessive to Dominant   Suppose that people normally have the genotype *aa*; what will be the effect when in some germ cell *a* mutates to form *A* (and this germ cell unites with an *a*-containing one from the other sex to form an *Aa* zygote)?

In the first place, gene *A* may be so abnormal that the resulting individual is not viable. The zygote or the embryo or infant that develops from it may be destroyed. Such a gene is said to be **lethal**, or to be **sub-**

lethal if the individual is born but dies in infancy or childhood. Death may occur at any stage; the effect is the same, that of removing the gene before it can be passed on to a following generation. This is an example of the "genetic death" we referred to earlier. We might note that while the genetic effect of early spontaneous abortion, still-birth, death in infancy, or death in childhood is the same, the emotional impact upon the parents may be very different in the four cases.

In the second place, gene A may not be lethal, but it may result in lowered vitality or perhaps in sterility. If Aa individuals are not as healthy as aa individuals, they may produce fewer children, on the average. If so, the gene A would be possessed by few, if any, of the next generation. This would afford an example of natural selection. Needless to say, if Aa individuals are sterile, the A gene will not be passed on (A will suffer immediate "genetic death").

On the other hand, gene A may be neither lethal nor detrimental; it may be actually beneficial. Here we recall our earlier discussion and note that "beneficial" implies an environmental setting. The effect of the gene is beneficial in a certain environment. (The gene for sickle-cell hemoglobin is beneficial in regions of Africa where malaria is common; it is not beneficial in countries, such as much of the United States, where malaria is almost unknown.) If the benefits conferred by the gene lead to increased success in survival and reproduction, then the gene will increase in frequency as generations pass. If AA and Aa individuals both enjoy the benefits, as compared to aa individuals, gene A may eventually entirely replace gene a in the gene pool through the action of natural selection. (If, on the other hand, the benefits are not of a sort that increases fertility, the relative frequency of gene A will not be increased in this manner. As we noted earlier, natural selection operates through differential fertility.)

An interesting case arises when gene A is beneficial to heterozygotes (Aa) but detrimental to homozygotes (AA). The classic example is the gene for sickle-cell hemoglobin: heterozygotes have increased resistance to malaria; homozygotes suffer a severe, and often fatal, anemia (pp. 50–52). Here we have two opposing forces. When AA individuals die at an early age or fail to reproduce, A genes are lost from the gene pool. When Aa individuals survive some unfavorable aspect of the environment better than do "normal" aa individuals, leaving proportionately more offspring than do the latter, the gene A tends to increase in relative frequency in the gene pool. The result of these two opposing forces is establishment of an *equilibrium* between the frequencies of genes A and a. Although detrimental to homozygotes, gene A does not disappear entirely, because it is beneficial to heterozygotes.

The preceding paragraph illustrates the difficulty of separating genes into the categories "dominant" and "recessive." If the AA genotype is detrimental and the Aa genotype is beneficial, we .cannot say that gene

A produces the same effect in homozygotes and heterozygotes. For example, in what sense is the gene for sickle-cell hemoglobin, Hb^s, dominant? The red blood cells of both $Hb^s Hb^s$ and $Hb^s Hb^A$ individuals *sickle* (assume bizarre shapes when deprived of oxygen). Even here, there is a difference in degree, a double dose of the Hb^s gene causing somewhat more drastic deforming of the cell than does a single dose. Overlooking this, we can say that gene Hb^s is dominant because it causes red blood cells of both homozygotes and heterozygotes to sickle. However, in its other effects such dominance is not demonstrated. As we noted earlier (p. 51), genes Hb^s and Hb^A may be classed as codominant, for each gene produces its own type of hemoglobin whenever it is present.

In its effects on viability in the face of malaria, genes Hb^s and Hb^A evidently interact in some way to produce a result that neither $Hb^s Hb^s$ nor $Hb^A Hb^A$ homozygotes attain. Such an interaction of genes to produce a superior phenotype in a heterozygote is called **heterosis** or **hybrid vigor** or sometimes **overdominance**. With reference to their heterotic effect, neither gene is properly termed dominant to the other. Both combine to produce the phenotypic effect. This suggests that a gene may be dominant in some of its phenotypic effects but not in others.

Mutation from Dominant to Recessive   Suppose that most members of a population are homozygous for a dominant gene (let us call it B), but that from time to time the gene mutates to form a recessive allele (b). What will happen to this recessive allele?

If the gene is completely recessive, it will produce its phenotypic effects only in homozygotes (bb). Let us suppose that this is the case. Obviously bb individuals may be at either an advantage or a disadvantage as compared to BB and Bb individuals. If they enjoy an advantage, reflected in the production of proportionately greater numbers of offspring, the relative frequency of gene b will increase as generations pass. This increase will be slow, especially at first when the gene is rare, for when a recessive gene is rare it is found mostly in heterozygotes (who, we are assuming, do not enjoy its advantages). When a gene is rare, homozygotes are usually produced only when heterozygotes chance to marry each other (and then only one fourth of the offspring, on the average, are homozygous-recessive).

If, on the other hand, bb individuals suffer a disadvantage compared to both BB and Bb individuals, the gene will slowly decline in relative frequency. Again, the slowness of the decline is occasioned by the fact that natural selection will act only on homozygotes. They may die, or they may merely suffer some defect that reduces the relative number of offspring produced. As we shall see later in our discussion of selection (Chap. 22), as long as selection operates only on homozygotes, the change in frequency of the gene will be small. This is because heterozygotes far outnumber homozygotes for rare recessive genes, and the rarer the gene becomes the more the heterozygotes outnumber the homozygotes.

As mentioned earlier, complete recessivity, in which Bb individuals are exactly like BB individuals, is probably much rarer than the converse. Evidence points to the fact that in most cases heterozygotes differ from homozygotes in some way. In this event, of course, gene b is not strictly recessive at all, because it does combine with B to affect the phenotype of the Bb heterozygote. The effect of gene b in heterozygotes may be either detrimental or beneficial.

If the effect is detrimental, this fact may mean that the heterozygote has poorer health or is less fertile than are the normal BB homozygotes. This fact, combined with the disadvantage suffered by bb homozygotes, would be likely to result in rapid elimination of the gene from the gene pool, much more rapid elimination than would result from selection involving bb individuals alone (see above). As a matter of fact, are genes that are detrimental to homozygotes also usually detrimental to heterozygotes? We lack evidence on this question as far as man is concerned, but evidence from the much-analyzed fruit fly, *Drosophila*, indicates that in this insect genes that are lethal to homozygotes (e.g., bb individuals die) on the average lower the chances of survival of heterozygotes by 5 percent or more, and genes that are merely detrimental to homozygotes are also commonly detrimental, in a lesser degree, to heterozygotes. However, this is not always the case. Sometimes genes that are highly detrimental to homozygotes are actually beneficial to heterozygotes. This leads us back to heterosis again. In this case our hypothetical gene b confers an advantage on the heterozygote, and natural selection will tend to establish an equilibrium in the gene pool, so that neither B nor b will disappear from it (see above). The point of equilibrium will be determined by the advantage enjoyed by the heterozygotes (Bb) relative to the disadvantage suffered by the homozygotes (bb).

We now turn our attention to the vital question of genetic changes likely to be induced by radiations, man-made and otherwise (Chap. 18).

PROBLEMS

1. Suppose that a man is homozygous *AA*. If he produces five billion (5000 million) sperm cells, how many of them will contain the mutant allele, *a*, if the estimated mutation rate quoted from the UN report (p. 266) applies to this locus?

2. If the man mentioned in question No. 1 has 30,000 gene loci and they all mutate at the rate mentioned, how many of his five billion sperm cells will be expected to contain a new mutation of some one of the genes?

3. In a population of 2,000,000 people, 48 were found to show a certain dominant trait but to be the offspring of parents who did not show it. Estimate the mutation rate producing the dominant gene concerned.

REFERENCES

Crow, J. F., 1956. "The estimation of spontaneous and radiation-induced mutation rates in man," *Eugenics Quarterly*, 3:201–8.

Darwin, C., 1859. *The Origin of Species by Means of Natural Selection*. (Available in many reprint editions, e.g.—Collier Books series, The Crowell-Collier Publishing Company, New York; Mentor Books series, New American Library, New York; Modern Library series, Random House, New York.)

Demerec, M., 1950. "Reaction of populations of unicellular organisms to extreme changes in environment," *American Naturalist*, 84:5–16.

Moody, P. A., 1962. *Introduction to Evolution*, 2nd ed. New York: Harper & Brothers.

Muller, H. J., 1927. "Artificial transmutation of the gene," *Science*, **66**:84–87. (Reprinted in J. A. Peters (ed.), 1959. *Classic Papers in Genetics*. Englewood Cliffs, N. J.: Prentice-Hall, Inc. Pp. 149–55.)

Spuhler, J. N., 1948. "On the number of genes in man," *Science*, **108**:279–80.

UN, 1958. *Report of the United Nations Scientific Committee on the Effects of Atomic Radiation*. General Assembly Official Records: 13th Session, Supplement 17 (A/3838). New York: United Nations.

UN, 1962. *Report of the United Nations Scientific Committee on the Effects of Atomic Radiation*. General Assembly Official Records: 17th Session, Supplement 16 (A/5216). New York: United Nations.

18.

THE HUMAN GENE POOL
AND THE EFFECTS
OF RADIATION

The Gene Pool

We return to the question of the probable effect on future generations of increasing the number of mutations—through radiation or otherwise. Our discussion so far will have made evident the meaninglessness of the question: Are mutations good or bad? Each mutation must be judged on its own merits in the light of (a) the environment facing the possessor of the mutant gene, and (b) the interaction of the mutant gene with its allele and with other genes possessed by the individual. Even so, on the whole, is the increase of mutations likely to be detrimental to future generations?

Students of the subject are divided on this question, and with our present knowledge, a final answer is not possible. Our point of view will vary depending on what we consider the normal nature of the human gene pool to be. There are two main points of view and all shades of opinion between the two.

The two points of view have been termed: (a) the classical hypothesis and (b) the balance hypothesis (Dobzhansky, 1955).

The Classical Hypothesis   According to the classical hypothesis, mankind has a high degree of homozygosity for genes that produce normal phenotypes. This homozygosity for the "good" genes has been favored by natural selection operating throughout all of human evolution. Hence, at the present time, any change is likely to be a change for the worse. We readily understand that proponents of this point of view are concerned by the "load of mutations" we already have and by any tendency to increase the load.

Muller (1950) calculated that in *Drosophila* one gamete in every twenty "contains a new spontaneously arisen lethal or detectable detrimental gene that arose within the span of the very last (parental) generation." He concluded that the rate was probably higher in man, with his greater number of genes and higher body temperature. Furthermore, Muller concluded that a large proportion of human mutations gives evidence of some degree of dominance—usually to the detriment of heterozygotes. Calculations based on certain assumptions led him to the conclusion that "each individual, on the average, carries 8 slightly dominant, detrimental mutant genes in heterozygous condition." From this point of view, any agent such as radiation that increases the number of such detrimental mutations would be cause for concern.

The Balance Hypothesis   According to the balance hypothesis, on the other hand, mankind is characterized by a high degree of heterozygosity. Proponents of this view conclude that "the adaptive norm is an array of genotypes heterozygous for more or less numerous gene alleles, gene complexes, and chromosomal structures. Homozygotes for these genes and gene complexes occur in normal outbred populations only in a minority of individuals, and make these individuals more or less inferior to the norm in fitness" (Dobzhansky, 1955).

Stated baldly, we can contrast the two points of view as follows: According to the classical hypothesis, it is normal to be homozygous, abnormal to be heterozygous; according to the balance hypothesis, it is normal to be heterozygous, abnormal to be homozygous. Which point of view is correct? Probably both points of view are, for it may be normal to be homozygous for some genes, whereas it may be normal to be heterozygous for certain other genes.

Within the last few years, a large body of experimental evidence has been accumulated, which indicates that wild populations of lower animals do, in fact, possess a high degree of heterozygosity (for survey and bibliography, see Spiess, 1962). In these cases, heterozygosity for many genes and gene complexes underlies the production of the normal phenotype. This is simply another way of saying that heterozygotes exhibit some degree of heterosis (pp. 273–274). The value of a given gene to a population frequently seems to be determined by its effect on heterozygotes possessing it, rather than by its effect when homozygous. As Dobzhansky (1955) expressed it: "A genetic good mixer becomes superior to a genetic rugged individualist."

Furthermore, experimental evidence indicates that in some cases, at least, populations that are highly heterozygous are superior in various ways to populations that have been rendered relatively homozygous (see, for example, Beardmore *et al.*, 1960). Populations that are highly heterozygous frequently seem to enjoy enhanced viability and adaptability to changing conditions—to have the ability for self-regulation in the face of changing environment, an ability referred to as **genetic homeostasis** (Lerner, 1954).

Now if heterozygosity is normal, what will be the effect of increasing that heterozygosity by the production of additional new mutations? Proponents of the balance hypothesis, unlike those of the classical hypothesis, might expect that increasing heterozygosity by production of new mutations would be beneficial rather than detrimental. Indeed, elaborate experiments by Wallace (1958) have indicated that, under some circumstances, the viability of populations of fruit flies can be increased by causing new mutations to be produced by radiation.

So the matter stands. The two points of view are not mutually exclusive. Clearly, many mutations are harmful to their possessors, even to possessors who have them "in single dose" (are heterozygous). On the other hand, we find mutations that are beneficial to possessors who have them in single dose (even though having them in double dose may be harmful). Further research will be needed before we can be sure which situation is the more common. However, recognition of the fact that mutations *can* be beneficial will perhaps reduce somewhat our concern for the genetic future of mankind in this atomic age.

In this connection, it is interesting to note that one's judgment as to whether or not a gene is "good" depends on many factors aside from genetic considerations. We cited Wallace's extensive experiments demonstrating that heterosis (overdominance) is common in *Drosophila*. However, a heterotic gene is not necessarily a "good" gene in the *social* sense. Dr. Wallace (1961) has pointed out that we have a *moral* obligation to prevent even one death in our descendants if we can do so by reducing our exposure to radiation. Hypothesizing a lethal gene that increased the general health of heterozygotes by 1 percent, he commented: "It would still be legitimate to ask whether this is a 'desirable' or 'undesirable' gene, whether it is 'right' for two hundred persons to enjoy an advantage of 1% (an advantage which would certainly not be recognized as such by the individuals involved) at the expense of one person who forfeits his life—perhaps in an agonizing manner." Dr. G. R. Fraser (1962) commented along this same line: "It is even doubtful if the very considerable increase of resistance to malaria postulated for heterozygotes for the sickling gene is sufficient to balance the misery and early death of homozygotes with the full disease picture. It is easy to see, however, that such a mechanism might under more unfavorable circumstances make all the difference between survival and extinction of the species." Fraser concluded that the genetic load of mutations is the price a species pays for having "the building stuff of evolution."

The Genetic Load

We have spoken of the "load" of mutations. This figure of speech is a way of expressing the fact that all of us have certain genes that reduce health and fertility in some manner and to some degree. Sometimes the effects of these genes are serious; sometimes the disabilities are so slight that we are not conscious of them. Some of these detrimental mutations are new, in the sense that they occurred in the ovum or sperm from which the individual in question originated. Some of the mutations are old, in the sense that they have been inherited from more or less distant ancestors.

Insofar as these mutant genes affect fertility they have a tendency to disappear from the gene pool. For example, if a new dominant mutation in a gamete is lethal, it will be eliminated from the gene pool immediately because an individual developing from that gamete cannot live. Similarly, if a new dominant mutation in a gamete causes sterility, the gene will be eliminated from the gene pool immediately because the resulting individual will produce no offspring. These are extreme cases. Suppose, by contrast, that a gamete develops a new lethal mutation that is fully recessive, by which we imply that heterozygotes are entirely normal. Then the mutation will not be eliminated from the gene pool immediately but will be passed along from heterozygote to heterozygote, as generations pass, until sooner or later two heterozygotes chance to marry each other. When this happens, some of the potential offspring will inherit the gene in double dose and will be killed by it. Thus the quantity of this gene in the gene pool will be depleted.

On an earlier page we quoted Muller (1950) as stating that many recessive lethal genes are detrimental to heterozygotes as well as to homozygotes, i.e., they exhibit some degree of dominance. We can readily see that when this is true, elimination of the gene from the gene pool occurs more rapidly than it does when the gene is completely recessive. Not only are genes lost when homozygotes die, as just noted, but, also, genes are lost when heterozygotes produce fewer offspring, on the average, than do homozygotes for the normal allele.

Again, we recall that many mutations are not lethal at all; they merely reduce the fitness of individuals, including the average number of off-spring they produce. If possessors of genotypes *aa* and *Aa* produce fewer offspring, on the average, than do possessors of genotype *AA*, gene *a* will tend to disappear from the gene pool as generations pass. If possessors of gene *a* produce nearly as many offspring, on the average, as do individuals lacking that gene, the gene will persist in the gene pool for many generations. On the other hand, if possessors of gene *a* suffer a considerable reduction in offspring produced, the gene will be expected to disappear from the gene pool more rapidly. The point is that, be it slowly or rapidly, detrimental genes do have a tendency to disappear from the gene pool, to undergo genetic death. This is the action of natural selection mentioned earlier.

If detrimental genes are constantly being removed from the gene pool, what replenishes the supply of them? Obviously it is the process of mutation we have been discussing. As genes are being eliminated, new ones are being added by mutation. Hence a population may be thought of as existing in a state of dynamic equilibrium: natural selection is constantly removing gene *a* from the gene pool; the mutation process is constantly adding new genes of this type whenever gene *A* mutates to form its allele, gene *a*. If the two opposing forces balance each other, an equilibrium is maintained. The frequency of gene *a* in the gene pool maintains a constant level. A bird feeder will provide an analogy. We can maintain a constant level of seed in our feeder if we add seed at the top at the same rate that the birds are eating seed at the bottom. The birds are analogous to the forces of natural selection; the adding of seed is analogous to the production of new mutations. The quantity of seed in the feeder is analogous to the genetic load.

How can the quantity of seed in the feeder be increased? Obviously this may occur in two ways. (1) We may add seed faster than it is being eaten by the birds. This is analogous to increasing the rate at which mutations occur, by increasing the amount of radiation, for example. (2) We may decrease the number of birds eating the seed. This is analogous to reducing the forces of natural selection. We have emphasized that natural selection operates whenever possessors of one genotype leave fewer offspring, on the average, than do possessors of an alternative genotype. If this differential is reduced, the forces of natural selection are reduced. Until recently, for example, sufferers from phenylketonuria died young or suffered such great disability that they did not produce children. Thus the gene pool of the new generation had a reduced frequency of the gene in question. This was natural selection in action. However, modern medical developments are likely to result in phenylketonurics being able to lead normal lives and pass on their genes to children. Thus the forces of natural selection will be reduced, with the result that the gene will increase in frequency in the gene pool, just as the amount of seed in the bird feeder increases when the birds no longer eat as much as they did formerly. Parenthetically, we should note, however, that natural selection will not be entirely elminated from this situation unless and until the time arrives when phenylketonurics produce as many children, on the average, as do persons who are not homozygous for this gene.

We might cite many other examples of instances in which modern medical techniques are reducing the disabilities suffered by possessors of genotypes that formerly were more or less severe handicaps. As human beings we must rejoice over these medical successes. Yet geneticists are sometimes worried that the gene pool of future generations will come to possess ever higher frequencies of these detrimental genes, until the time arrives when a great amount of people's time and energy "would be devoted chiefly to the effort to live carefully, to spare and to prop up their own feeblenesses, to sooth their inner disharmonies and, in general, to doctor themselves as effectively as possible. For everyone would be an invalid, with his own special familial twists." (This picturesque quotation is from "Our load of mutations" by Muller, 1950, a paper in which the interested reader will find an extended discussion of the problem, and a suggested solution.)

So far, we have spoken of the process of mutation as the force that tends to keep the gene pool supplied with a given gene. As noted previously (pp. 273–274), however, when heterozygote superiority (heterosis) occurs, that in itself will tend to keep a gene detrimental to homozygotes from disappearing from the gene pool. If, for example, *aa* individuals are sterile, but *Aa* individuals produce, on the average, more offspring than do *AA* individuals, gene *a* will be passed on to descendants. Thus in some cases, at least, heterosis abets the process of mutation (**mutation pressure**) in maintaining a constant frequency of a gene in a gene pool. Such a situation, in which alternative alleles remain at more or less constant relative frequencies, is an example of genetic polymorphism (see Chap. 24). An example is the maintenance of the sickle-cell hemoglobin gene (Hb^s) at a frequency of as high as 20 percent in the gene pools of some African populations living in malarial regions, even though homozygotes seldom if ever pass on the gene to offspring.

We turn now to consideration of the effects of radiation on our genetic load. Clearly, by increasing the mutation rate we can increase the load, just as we can increase the amount of seed in our bird feeder if we increase the rate at which we pour in the seed (assuming in this case that the birds continue to eat at a constant rate).

Radiation and the Mutation Rate

On an earlier page (p. 264) we noted that a variety of physical and chemical factors may cause genes to mutate. One of the physical factors is radiation. We single it out for attention because it is the one that is most likely to increase in our modern world, and we wonder what the effects of this increase will be.

In the first place we should note that we are all subjected to some radiation throughout our lives. This background radiation arises from cosmic rays, radiation from radioactive minerals in rocks and soil, and radioactive isotopes in air, water, and food consumed.

How much background radiation does the average person receive? Only the most approximate of estimates can be given because environmental conditions vary greatly. For example, people who live in brick houses receive slightly more radiation than do people who live in wooden ones. In general the amount is very small indeed. Estimates usually are of the order of 3 or 4 roentgen units spread over a 30-year period. This is about the amount of radiation one receives when two or three X-ray pictures are taken. Thus the international group of scientists that constitute the United Nations Scientific Committee on the Effects of Atomic Radiation estimated that, on the average, the dose received by the gonads amounts to 126 mrem* per year (UN, 1962). (0.126 × 30 = 3.78 rem in a 30-year period.) The committee estimated that those 126 mrem are comprised as follows: 50 mrem from cosmic rays, 50 from terrestrial radiation, 26 from radioactive isotopes entering the body in air, water, and food—elements of the radium and thorium series, potassium-40, and carbon-14, for the most part (UN, 1962, Table I, p. 21).

From results of experiments with plants and animals we may infer that this low level of natural radiation may be responsible for some of our "spontaneous" mutations. As far as we know, there is no amount of radiation so small that it may not cause mutation. Yet experiments suggest that only a small proportion of the observed mutation rate (p. 266) would be caused by radiations totalling such a small amount. In this connection it would be of great interest to know whether or not the mutation rates are increased in people who live in regions where they are exposed to more radiation than most people receive. People who live at high altitudes receive greater cosmic radiation than do people at low altitudes—3 to 6 times the amount mentioned in the preceding estimate. People who live on certain types of soil receive more radiation than do people living on other soils. For example, in Travancore State in India some 100,000 people live on a soil of monazite sand (containing radioactive thorium). It is estimated that they may receive from 50 to 150 units of radiation (roentgens or the equivalent) in a 30-year period (Gopal-Ayengar, 1957). Do

---

*A word is in order about the units in which radiations are expressed, for different studies employ different terms. The most frequently employed unit is the roentgen (r), based on amount of ionization produced. The rad is a unit based on the amount of energy absorbed by the material being radiated. The rem is the biological equivalent of the rad, taking into account the difference in biological effectiveness of different sources of radiation—X-rays, gamma rays, etc. Mrem (millirem) is one-thousand of a rem. The use of different units may seem confusing but need not concern us greatly since r, rad, and rem are of similar magnitude.

they have a higher mutation rate than do people who receive only the 3 or 4 units in a 30-year period? Here is a fertile field for investigation. At present, we can note with interest that apparently normal populations can live under widely varying intensities of background radiation. This may lead us to anticipate that people who receive the 3 or 4 units in a 30-year period could have this amount increased without alarming consequences.

How much is the radiation we receive from natural sources likely to be increased by radiations resulting from human activities? These latter radiations fall into two main categories: (1) Medical radiations (such as diagnostic and therapeutic X-rays) and radiation exposure received by persons whose occupations place them in contact with radiation-producing equipment (e.g., X-ray technicians and radiologists). (2) Fall-out from the testing of nuclear weapons. The United Nations committee quoted p. 282 (UN, 1962) estimated that during the period of 1954-1961, world population on the average experienced a genetic risk from medical and occupational exposures that was about one third of that from natural sources. They concluded that "the comparative genetic risk from fall-out is about one-tenth of that from natural sources."

Hence a person born in 1931 may have received by 1961, 3 or 4 r of natural radiation plus about 0.4 r from weapons testing. Although any increase is undesirable, such a small increase is hardly justification for grave concern, particularly when we recall the wide limits of natural radiation within which normal populations live. Thus, to a considerable extent, alarm over the effects of testing nuclear weapons has been unjustified. We should remember, however, that the estimates are world-wide averages and do not apply to populations living near testing sites; radiation received by survivors of atomic warfare would be another matter entirely.

The probable genetic effect of fall-out from the testing of atomic weapons is overshadowed by the possibility of genetic damage from the medical and industrial use of X-rays and radioactive materials. We noted above the world-wide estimate that such sources may increase the genetic risk from natural radiations by about one third. In a country such as the United States, in which radiation diagnosis and therapy is widely used, the risk may well be greater, equalling if not exceeding the dosage received from natural sources (Glass, 1957). Although this dosage is of a different order of magnitude from that expected from fall-out, it is still relatively small. Nonetheless, it remains true that *any* amount of radiation, no matter how small, *may* cause a mutation. Hence, because many mutations, at least, are detrimental, it is important to reduce radiation exposure of the gonads to a minimum. Modern radiologists are well aware of this, and improved methods are steadily reducing the amount of radiation received by the gonads when X-rays are employed for diagnosis. Obviously, protection of the gonads of children, before and after birth, and of young people before the end of their reproductive life is especially important.

Acute Radiation Versus Chronic Radiation   Natural radiation is of low intensity and is received very slowly. Radiations from X-rays and other sources employed in medicine are ordinarily of relatively high intensity and are given in a short period of time. This may be called *acute radiation* in contrast to the *chronic radiation* mentioned first. Are the two types of radiation equivalent in mutation-inducing potency? When the rate is slow, is there anything at all comparable to healing and repair?

A great body of information has been accumulated to show that when sperm cells (of fruit fly or mouse) are radiated, the number of mutations depends on the total dosage of radiation and is independent of the rate at which that radiation is given. For example, if sperm cells receive 100 roentgen units of X-rays in 10 minutes, a certain average number of mutations will be induced. If they receive 100 units of radiation slowly, spread over 10 days, perhaps, the same average number will be induced. This has been found true over a range of dosages from 5 r to 6000 r. There-fore, it is generally agreed that with mature sperm cells the induction of mutations varies with dosage and is independent of rate. In theory, at least, even the smallest amount of radiation will produce its proportionate effect, whether the amount is given slowly or rapidly.

This independence of rate does not seem to be true of spermatogonia and oöcytes, however, stages of meiosis in which much of mammalian germ plasm remains during the greater parts of the lives of individuals. In extensive experiments on mice, Dr. W. L. Russell and his collaborators have demonstrated that a certain dosage of radiation produces *fewer* mutations if it is given slowly than it does if it is given rapidly (Russell *et al.*, 1958; Russell, 1963, a, b). It would seem that, unlike sperm cells, these metabolically active spermatogonia and oöcytes have some capabil-ity that we may think of as repair. Granted that there is no amount of radiation so small that it may not produce a mutation, to what extent does this ability to repair protect the germ plasm against low-rate or chronic radiation? We recall that man has reached his present stage of evolution in a world in which he is constantly subjected to natural radiation of very low intensity. It would be strange if the body had not developed some capability of coping with this factor in the environment. To what extent will this protective ability function to keep the germ plasm buffered against mutations in a world in which man himself is increasing the amount of radiation? We shall await with great interest further investiga-tions on the relationship between dose rate and mutation frequency. In the meantime we may take some comfort in the thought that perhaps chronic, low-level radiation from natural sources and from fall-out (barring atomic warfare) may not constitute as severe a threat to the genetic well-being of future generations as we had feared it would. At the same time, we stress again the potential genetic danger from medical radiation because it is usually of the acute type.

Antimutagenic Agents Can anything be done to protect cells against the mutagenic effects of radiations? It was thought formerly that radiation caused a mutation by making a direct hit on the gene in question, located in its chromosome. This is the "target theory" of mutagenesis. As noted previously (p. 265), more recent investigations have indicated, on the other hand, that the radiation may cause a chemical change in some of the constituent compounds of the cell (changing some molecules of water to hydrogen peroxide, for example) and that these changed constituents then react with the gene to produce the mutation. We have evidence that there may be a time interval between the change in the cell constituent and the change in the gene. In theory, and hopefully in practice, during that time interval some agent might operate to neutralize the changed cell constituent or in some way protect the gene from it. A substance that can do this is called an *antimutagenic agent*. We shall know much more about such agents in the future.

Tentative Conclusions

What, then, can we conclude? Obviously, in the face of so many uncertainties and differing opinions, dogmatic statements would be out of place.

At the present time, it seems that indiscriminate increase in human mutations, through radiation or otherwise, should be avoided. Although some mutations may increase viability or well-being, it is unlikely that most of them do so. At this point we need much additional investigation. What proportion of new mutations can be expected to exert the effects of heterosis and thus prove of value to their possessors? Answering this question will entail much investigation of the actual genetic structures of human populations, as well as of the interactions between phenotype and environment. We recall that heterosis usually, if not always, involves an environmental setting in which the genotype concerned is heterotic (as when Hb^A Hb^S individuals are favored when the environment contains malaria). How common is this type of situation? We have seen evidence for theorizing that human populations are highly heterozygous in many gene loci, and that in this heterozygosity may reside some of the homeostatic properties of the population, making possible the success of the population and its adaptability to changing conditions. Even so, to what extent would these homeostatic properties be increased still further by increasing the number of mutations and hence the amount of heterozygosity? If there is an increase, would the value of it be commensurate with the price paid in terms of ill-adapted and abnormal homozygotes (pp. 278–279)? We may suspect that we cannot have our genetic cake and eat it, too, but we must have many more facts before we can make valid value judgments.

We have been asking a few of the many important questions for which future investigations must supply the answers. The questions crowding in on us are legion. A fine summary of them is presented in the report of the Committee on the Genetic Effects of Atomic Radiation of the National Academy of Sciences—National Research Council (see National Academy of Sciences, 1960).

PROBLEMS

1. If a 100 r dose of X-rays administered to sperm cells produces 3 mutations per thousand cells when given within a span of 10 minutes, how many mutations will be produced when a 100 r dose is spread evenly over a 10-day period? How would your answer differ if the question specified spermatogonia or oöcytes instead of sperm?

2. To what extent is it true that the genetic risk arising from 3 r of X-rays received by the gonads in medical practice is greater than that from 3 r of cosmic rays?

3. Gene a is lethal in the homozygous state. Nevertheless, the gene pools of some populations contain fairly high percentages of this gene. Judging by analogy with known cases, what is likely to be the explanation for this fact?

REFERENCES

Beardmore, J. A., T. Dobzhansky, and O. A. Pavlovsky, 1960. "An attempt to compare the fitness of polymorphic and monomorphic experimental populations of *Drosophila pseudoobscura*," *Heredity*, 14:19–33.

Dobzhansky, T., 1955. "A review of some fundamental concepts and problems of population genetics," *Cold Spring Harbor Symposia on Quantitative Biology*, 20:1–15.

Fraser, G. R., 1962. "Our genetical 'load.' A review of some aspects of genetical variation," *Annals of Human Genetics*, 25:387–415.

Glass, B., 1957. "The genetic hazards of nuclear radiations," *Science*, 126:241-46.

Gopal-Ayengar, A. R., 1957. "Possible areas with sufficiently different background-radiation levels to permit detection of differences in mutation rates of 'marker' genes." In *Effect of Radiation on Human Heredity.* Geneva: World Health Organization. Pp. 115–24.

Lerner, I. M., 1954. *Genetic Homeostasis.* New York: John Wiley & Sons, Inc.

Muller, H. J., 1950. "Our load of mutations," *American Journal of Human Genetics,* **2**:111–76.

National Academy of Sciences, 1960. *The Biological Effects of Atomic Radiation.* Summary Reports, 1960. Washington, D. C.: National Academy of Sciences–National Research Council.

Russell, W. L., 1963a. "The effect of radiation dose rate and fractionation on mutation in mice." In F. H. Sobels (ed.). *Repair from Genetic Radiation Damage.* New York: The Macmillan Company. Pp. 205–17.

Russell, W. L., 1963b. "Genetic hazards of radiation," *Proceedings of the American Philosophical Society,* **107**:11–17.

Russell, W. L., L. B. Russell, and E. M. Kelly, 1958. "Radiation dose rate and mutation frequency," *Science,* **128**:1546–50.

Spiess, E. B., 1962. "Introduction." In E. B. Spiess (ed.). *Papers on Animal Population Genetics.* Boston: Little, Brown & Company. Pp. xi-lxxi.

UN, 1962. *Report of the United Nations Scientific Committee on the Effects of Atomic Radiation.* General Assembly Official Records: 17th Session, Supplement 16 (A/5216). New York: United Nations.

Wallace, B., 1958. "The average effect of radiation-induced mutations on viability in *Drosophila melanogaster," Evolution,* **12**:532–56.

Wallace, B., 1961. "Heterotic mutations." In L. I. Gardner. *Molecular Genetics and Human Disease.* Springfield, Ill.: Charles C Thomas. Pp. 212–30.

19.

MULTIPLE BIRTHS

Twins may be thought of as the darlings of human geneticists. Their special position in the affections of investigators in this field arises from the fact that there are two kinds of twins, and that in one of these kinds we find the only human example of individuals with exactly the same genotype. Hence we can study them with regard to a certain trait and attempt to answer the question: How much depends on heredity, how much on environment? Note that we do not ask: Is the trait caused by heredity or by environment? The more we learn about such things, the more we realize that most traits are the result of the interaction of heredity *and* environment.

Dizygotic and Monozygotic Twins

The two kinds of twins just referred to are usually called "fraternal" and "identical." Identical, however, is too strong an adjective. No two individuals, not even the most similar of twins, are alike in every detail (i.e., identical). Geneticists, therefore, prefer to use a term that refers to the differing origin of the two types of twins—the fact that in one type the members of the pair arise from separate ova, whereas in the other type the two members arise from a single ovum. So instead of speaking of fraternal twins, we call them **dizygotic twins** (two-egg twins) and use the initials **DZ** in referring to them. Similarly, identical twins (Fig. 19.1) are called **monozygotic** or **MZ** (one-egg twins).

In the production of DZ twins, two ova are ovulated simultaneously by the mother, and each is fertilized by a different sperm cell. Each resultant

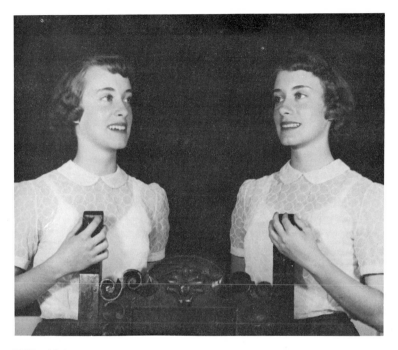

FIG. 19.1 Monozygotic twins Carolyn and Carol. (Photo by H. B. Eldred.)

embryo becomes separately implanted in the wall of the uterus and undergoes its own independent development. In general, DZ twins are no more alike than are other brothers and sisters in the same family, each of whom, of course, also arose from a separate ovum and a separate sperm. The DZ twins merely happen to be simultaneous instead of consecutive. Nevertheless, in the next chapter we shall mention some embryonic processes that may cause members of a pair of DZ twins to be more alike than we should expect them to be (pp. 305–307).

Monozygotic twins, on the other hand, arise from a single fertilized ovum, and hence the genes they inherit are the same. Embryologists, like geneticists, are handicapped by their inability to experiment with human beings, and therefore we know little about the actual embryology of MZ twinning in man. Judging from observations on lower mammals, however, we may conclude that the single ovum, by a series of mitoses, produces an embryonic mass of cells. Ordinarily this mass would develop into a single embryo, but occasionally, as a result of influences as yet unknown, the mass may become subdivided into two masses, each of which will develop into an embryo. In the armadillo, which as we noted (p. 232) regularly produces monozygotic quadruplets, the embryonic mass divides into four masses by a sort of budding process (Patterson, 1913). Human monozygotic quadruplets also occur at times and doubtless originate in a comparable manner.

We should note that the *time* of separation of the embryonic masses may vary. It might occur as early as the two-celled stage (following the first mitosis of the fertilized ovum). Probably such early separation is not common in mammals; at least we know that it is not the program followed by armadillo embryos. Evidence suggesting that such early separation may occur in man, at least rarely, is afforded by a pair of twins consisting of a normal male and an individual with Turner's syndrome (Turpin *et al.*, 1961). Blood groups and reciprocal skin grafting indicated the strong probability that this was an MZ pair. The chromosomal constitution was XY and XO, respectively. Suppose that an XY zygote underwent mitosis and in the process one daughter cell failed to receive a Y chromosome (through "anaphase lag," perhaps). If the two daughter cells then separated and each produced an embryo, one would be XY, the other XO, as in this case.

We do not know how late in embryonic development separation is still possible, but incomplete separation as in conjoined or so-called Siamese twins probably represents a belated attempt of an embryonic mass to form two embryos. In this connection, we may note the interesting but still mysterious fact that although separate MZ twins are usually very similar to each other, Siamese twins are frequently very dissimilar to each other. Moreover, they show a greater tendency to "mirror imaging" (e.g., tendency of the right side of one twin to resemble the left side of his partner more than his right side resembles his own left side). It would seem that the embryonic mass had begun to form one embryo, with right and left sides, before something caused it to partially divide into two. The alternative suggestion has been made that conjoined twins might be produced by the partial fusion of two originally separate embryonic masses. In this case, the twins would be dizygotic, which would explain why they are usually dissimilar. Although it is not impossible, such an embryonic fusion seems highly improbable (but see Aird, 1959).

We might mention the *possibility* that there is a third kind of twin formation: a large polar body might be fertilized and develop into an embryo. This happens in some invertebrates. In man, if an ovum and its second polar body (Fig. 3.8, p. 36) were both fertilized (by different sperm, of course), then the resulting twins would have the same genes from their mother but would differ in the genes received from their father. At present this remains only a possibility; no certain instance of its occurrence has been demonstrated, although some have been suspected.

Frequency of Multiple Births

A study of births occurring in the United States during a 22-year period indicated that among the white population one delivery in 92.4 gave rise to twins (in a total of 50,000,000). For the colored population the rate was 1 in 73.8. The ratio of triplets to single births was 1:9828 among whites, 1:5631 among colored people (Guttmacher, 1953). The rate of multiple births is highest among Negroes and lowest among Orientals; Caucasians occupy an intermediate position.

Here we might appropriately mention a generalization usually called **Hellin's law**, although various people have had a hand in its formulation. According to this idea, if $1/n$ represents the fraction of births giving rise to twins, $1/n^2$ would represent the fraction of births giving rise to triplets, $1/n^3$ the fraction giving rise to quadruplets, and so on. That this may be a useful rule of thumb is indicated by data on 120,061,398 pregnancies occurring in a total of 21 countries over a 10-year period. The ratio of twin births to single births was 1:85.2. The ratio of triplet births to single births was 1:7628.7 or $1:(87.3)^2$. The ratio of quadruplet births to single births was 1:670,734 or $1:(87.5)^3$ (Greulich, 1930). Clearly the "law" is a mere approximation at best; not all data fit it as well as do these given as an example.

Hellin's law does not differentiate between the likelihood of the occurrence of the two types of twins. What proportion is dizygotic, what proportion monozygotic?

Proportion of Monozygotic and Dizygotic Twinning Weinberg (of Hardy-Weinberg fame) formulated a means of estimating the answer to this question. We consider first the frequencies of DZ twinning. For our purposes the approximation that the sex ratio at birth is 1:1 is sufficiently accurate. In other words, the chance for a male birth is ½, the chance for a female birth is ½. What are the chances that a pair of DZ twins will consist of two boys? The chance that the first-born twin will be a boy is ½, the chance that the second-born twin will be a boy is ½. Hence the chance for a boy-boy pair is ½ × ½ = ¼. In the same manner, the chance that both members of a DZ pair of twins will be girls is ½ × ½ = ¼. The total chance that the DZ pair will be of like sex (either boy-boy *or* girl-girl) is ¼ + ¼ = ½. Therefore, the other half of DZ pairs must consist of unlike-sexed pairs (boy-girl pairs).*

* This can be calculated directly. (a) Chance that first-born is a boy = ½; chance that second-born is a girl = ½; total chance for this combination = ½ × ½ = ¼. (b) Chance that first-born is a girl = ½; chance that second-born is a boy = ½; total chance for this combination = ½ × ½ = ¼. Total chance that one twin will be a boy, the other a girl = ¼ + ¼ = ½.

According to calculation, then, one half of the DZ twins consists of pairs differing in sex. Such pairs can, of course, be easily recognized. Suppose that we have 1000 pairs of twins of all kinds and that among them 310 are boy-girl pairs. How many of the 1000 pairs are monozygotic? According to our calculation the 310 boy-girl pairs represent *half* of the *dizygotic* pairs. Thus the total number of DZ pairs must be twice 310, or 620. Then the number of *monozygotic* pairs must be 1000 − 620 = 380, or 38 percent, which is approximately the figure usually obtained from actual data.

FIG. 19.2 The Fischer quintuplets, the only living quintuplets in the United States. Born September 14, 1963. It is thought that three of the sisters form a set of monozygotic triplets, the other sister and the brother having developed from separate ova. (Photograph by Wayne Miller, © 1965 The Curtis Publishing Company.)

Although twins are not uncommon, triplets are rare, and quadruplets and quintuplets are so unusual as to be always newsworthy (Fig. 19.2). These multiple births of higher order may arise in a great variety of ways. They may all arise from one ovum, as the Dionne quintuplets are believed to have done; or each may arise from a separate ovum; or there may be combination of the two types of origin. For example, Corner (1955) reported on four recently recorded sets of quadruplets whose placentas and embryonic membranes had been studied carefully (see pp. 297–299). In one case, four ova were evidently involved. In a second case, three ova had participated, one giving rise to an MZ pair (in other words, the quadruplets consisted of one DZ pair and one MZ pair). In the third case, there were three girls, all of whom had developed within one amnion (an indication of monozygosity, p. 298) and one boy, who had a separate placenta and amnion; evidently only two ova were involved here. In the fourth case, all four quadruplets evidently arose from one ovum and were monozygotic. In other instances other combinations of monozygosity and the production of two or more ova are found.

Inheritance of Twinning

From our discussion so far, we can readily understand that monozygotic twinning and dizygotic twinning are two separate, and presumably unrelated, phenomena. Hence we should not be surprised to find that they differ in many ways. For example, they differ in what is called **repeat frequency.** A woman who has had one pair of DZ twins is more likely to have a second pair (compared to the chance of having a DZ pair among women in general). This is not true of a woman who has had one pair of MZ twins; with regard to a second pair her chances are the same as they would have been if she had not had the first pair. Evidently some women have a tendency to DZ twinning. Evidence indicates that this tendency is probably hereditary. At any rate, a difference in repeat frequency is a respect in which DZ twinning and MZ twinning are not alike.

Another respect in which they differ concerns the relationship between incidence and the age of the mother. The tendency to produce DZ twins increases up to about age 39, and then decreases sharply (Fig. 19.3). On the other hand, the frequency of MZ twinning varies little with the age of the mother. Dizygotic twins may originate in either of two ways: (a) two separate follicles in the ovaries may rupture simultaneously, each releasing its ovum, or (b) one follicle may contain two or possibly more ova, which are released when the follicle ruptures. (A follicle is a tiny "bubble" containing liquid in which the ovum floats. This "bubble" gradually works its way to the surface of the ovary and ruptures, releasing its

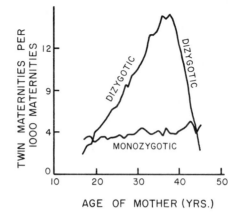

FIG. 19.3   Rates of monozygotic and dizygotic twinning related to the age of the mother. (Redrawn from Bulmer, M. G., 1959. "The effect of parental age, parity and duration of marriage on the twinning rate," *Annals of Human Genetics*, **23**:454–58.)

ovum or ova.) It would seem that older mothers have a tendency either to produce more follicles that mature simultaneously or to produce more follicles containing more than one ovum (polyovular) than have younger mothers. We need more information than we have at present on which of these two modes of origin of DZ twins is commoner. Furthermore, do *both* modes vary with the age of the mother? Are *both* subject to hereditary tendencies?

Although DZ twinning and MZ twinning seem to be unrelated processes, the occurrence of both in the same woman sometimes makes us wonder (e.g., the quadruplets just discussed). Perhaps only coincidence is involved —two relatively rare events happening to occur simultaneously. Certainly we should need positive evidence before we concluded that something other than coincidence was involved. After all, we know of other rare conditions that happen to occur together in an occasional individual. Be that as it may, some women give evidence of having a remarkable tendency to multiple births (frequently of both types). Davenport (1919) learned of a woman who was married three times and had multiple births by all three husbands. Her pregnancies totaled as follows: seven pairs of twins, five sets of triplets, three sets of quadruplets. (Two sets of the quadruplets and two of the triplets resulted in miscarriages.) She reported that both her mother and her mother's mother had had only twins, triplets, and quadruplets. In all candor we should report that Dr. Davenport commented that she had "certain mental limitations," and that he was unable to obtain independent information concerning her mother and her mother's mother.

Many pedigrees have been assembled showing the occurrence of several or many pairs of twins within a few generations. Here a word of caution is in order. As we have seen, twinning is not really a rare event. Consequently, even if there were no hereditary tendency involved, we should expect that by chance some pedigrees would include several sets of twins. We must be careful not to select pedigrees for their "curiosity value," i.e., because they happen to include an unusual number of sets of twins. On the other hand, if no hereditary tendency were involved, the chance of occurrence of four successive generations like those shown in Figure 19.4 would be relatively slight. This pedigree is of particular

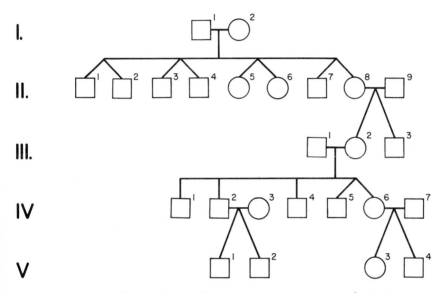

FIG. 19.4 Pedigree showing four successive generations of twinning: a total of eight pairs of twins. (Based on data in Taylor, C. E., 1931. "Four generations of heterosexual twins with prepartum amenorrhoea in two generations," *British Medical Journal*, 2:384).

interest in that four of the eight sets of twins are of unlike sex, thereby demonstrating that a tendency to DZ twinning is involved. Note that I-1 had *only* twins in her family.

The best evidence of a hereditary tendency to twinning is derived from studies of the incidence of twinning among the relatives of parents who have twins. In general, the results of various studies indicate that among the brothers, sisters, aunts, uncles, cousins, etc., of a mother of DZ twins there is an increased incidence of twinning, as compared to the incidence in the population as a whole. Somewhat mysteriously, this is also true of the relatives of a father of DZ twins. However, it is *not* true of the relatives of parents who have MZ twins. Accordingly, we conclude that the tendency to DZ twinning is inherited but that the tendency to MZ twinning is not.

We mentioned racial differences in the amount of twinning that occurs. Here, too, these differences are limited almost entirely to the amount of DZ twinning, not MZ twinning (Nance, 1959).

PROBLEMS

1. An investigation of the population of a certain city disclosed 500 pairs of twins, classifiable as follows: 166 boy-boy pairs, 170 girl-girl pairs, 164 boy-girl pairs. About how many of the pairs were probably monozygotic?

2. Judging from Fig. 19.3, how much more likely are 30-year-old women to have DZ twins than they are to have MZ twins? 40-year-old women?

REFERENCES

Aird, I., 1959. "Conjoined twins—further observations," *British Medical Journal,* 1959, 1:1313–15.

Corner, G. W., 1955. "The observed embryology of human single-ovum twins and other multiple births," *American Journal of Obstetrics and Gynecology,* 70:933–51.

Davenport, C. B., 1919. "A strain producing multiple births," *Journal of Heredity,* 10:382–84.

Greulich, W. W., 1930. "The incidence of human multiple births," *American Naturalist,* 64:142–53.

Guttmacher, A. F., 1953. "The incidence of multiple births in man and some of the other unipara," *Obstetrics and Gynecology,* 2:22–35.

Nance, W. E., 1959. "Twins: an introduction of gemellology," *Medicine,* 38: 403–14.

Patterson, J. T., 1913. "Polyembryonic development in *Tatusia novemcincta,*" *Journal of Morphology,* 24:559–662.

Turpin, R., J. Lejeune, J. La Fourcade, P. L. Chigot, and C. Salmon, 1961. "Présomption de monozygotisme en dépit d'un dimorphisme sexuel: sujet masculin XY et sujet neutre Haplo X." *Comptes Rendus de l'Académie des Sciences, Paris,* 252:2945–46.

20.

THE TWIN METHOD
IN HUMAN GENETICS

Determination of Zygosity

Before twins can be used in studies of the role of heredity, accurate determination must be made as to whether each pair is monozygotic or dizygotic. In a sense, everything hinges on accuracy in this matter.

Twin pairs consisting of one boy and one girl are automatically identified as being dizygotic. In most studies this is the least interesting group because hereditary differences may be obscured by differences between the sexes. For example, if one were studying the hereditary component in stature, there would be little profit in comparing the difference in height between members of a pair of MZ boy twins with the difference in height between members of a DZ boy-girl pair, simply because in this latter case one twin is a boy, the other a girl.

For this reason, we are most interested in like-sexed pairs of twins. The problem then becomes: Among like-sexed pairs how can we determine which ones are monozygotic, which ones dizygotic?

The Embryonic Membranes

Human embryos are enclosed within two membranes, an inner **amnion** and an outer **chorion**. Figure 20.1 shows a pair of twin embryos about five weeks of age. Note that in this case each embryo is enclosed within its own amnion, but that the two amnions are enclosed within one chorion.

Note, too, that the umbilical cords connected to the embryos run in different directions; this suggests that the placentas (p. 150) are separate. Sometimes the placentas may be so close together that they join to form one.

The situation shown in Figure 20.1 is typical of *monozygotic* twins. Usually MZ twins have separate amnions but a common chorion. Oc-

umbilical cords

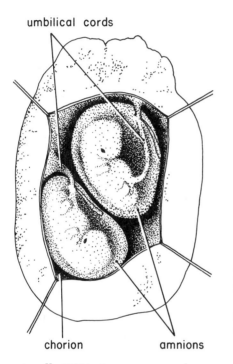

chorion   amnions

FIG. 20.1 Twin embryos of about five weeks of age. Each has its own amnion, but both are enclosed within one chorion. (Redrawn from Fig. 2, J. C. Potter, *Anatomical Record,* 34:255.)

casionally MZ twins may even share a common amnion. This difference is presumably related to a difference in the time at which separation of the embryonic mass into two parts occurred (pp. 289–290). If separation occurred late, only after the chorion and amnion were both formed, then both twins would lie within one amnion. As far as determination of zygosity is concerned, this rule seems warranted: *If the twins are enclosed within one chorion* (and in some cases amnion), *they are monozygotic.* There is speculation about the possibility of two originally separate chorions merging into one, but if this ever occurs, it is so rare that it introduces little error into the general rule.

Dizygotic twins, on the other hand, have separate amnions and chorions. Figure 20.2 shows separate placentas, as well, but sometimes the placentas may lie close together and merge to form one. Placentas are of little aid in determining zygosity. Moreover, we cannot conclude that because twins have separate chorions they are dizygotic. About 33 percent of MZ twin

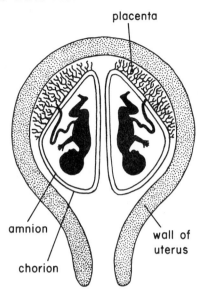

placenta

amnion

chorion

wall of
uterus

FIG. 20.2 Dizygotic twin fetuses in separate chorions. (Redrawn from *Fundamentals of Human Reproduction* by E. L. Potter. Copyright © 1948, McGraw-Hill Book Co., Inc. Used by permission of McGraw-Hill Book Company.)

pairs have separate chorions. In these cases separation of the embryonic mass into two parts presumably occurred very early, perhaps as early as the two-celled stage (Nance, 1959).

Thus, in some cases, accurate investigation of the embryonic membranes at the time of birth will aid in determining zygosity, and in some cases it will not. If it can be determined definitely that there is only one chorion, then the twins are almost certainly monozygotic. However, if there are two chorions, the evidence is of little value. Furthermore, in many cases accurate study of the membranes was not made at the time of birth. As a result of all these factors, the zygosity of only a minority of an investigator's pairs of twins is determinable from data on the embryonic membranes.

The Similarity Method

For the most part, decisions concerning zygosity are based on an extension of the method employed by people generally in deciding whether a given pair of twins is identical or not. We ordinarily base our judgment on how much the twins look alike. Geneticists employ the same principle except that they utilize many traits other than similarity in physical appearance. Blood groups are particularly useful because their genetic basis is simple and well established.

The recent investigation by Osborne and De George (1959) may be taken as a typical example of methods of diagnosing zygosity. In their investigation, the blood of the twins was tested for the following antigens: A_1, A_2, B, O; M, N, S; C, D, E, c of the Rh series; Kell, Duffy, and P. The mode of inheritance of most of these was discussed in Chapter 9. However, we did not mention Kell, Duffy, and P. Like the others, each of these is an antigen whose presence or absence from a red blood cell is demonstrable by using suitable antiserums. The presence or absence of each is dependent on a single pair of genes.

If the members of a pair of twins did not agree with regard to all fourteen of these antigens, the pair was considered dizygotic. If the members of a pair of twins *did* agree with respect to all fourteen antigens, did this fact prove that the twins were monozygotic? Unfortunately not. Osborne and De George found that five pairs of unlike-sexed twins agreed with respect to all these antigens. These five pairs were surely dizygotic, yet they had the same fourteen antigens. How could this be? Evidently it reflected the genetic situation in the family. We can readily understand, for example, that if both parents belonged to blood group O, all the children would too, whether or not they were dizygotic twins. If one parent were homozygous for blood group B and the other parent belonged either to B or O, all the children would belong to group B. The same principle applies to the other antigens. In general we can say then that although disagreement proves dizygosity, agreement does not prove monozygosity. The greater the number of traits employed, the greater will be the probability that dizygotic twins will differ in at least one of them.

What, then, did Osborne and De George do at this point? They added to the blood tests other traits having a fairly well established mode of inheritance. The traits they found most useful were the following: hair color, eye color, eye detail pattern, ability or inability to roll the tongue lengthwise, ability or inability to taste PTC (phenylthiocarbamide), earlobe form, chin form, and presence or absence of hair on the middle phalanx of the fingers. Utilization of these traits increased the chance of detecting dizygosity. It is still possible, of course, that some dizygotic twins would agree on all these traits as well as on all blood tests, but the chance is relatively small. The error introduced would have the effect of causing investigators to include in their monozygotic group an occasional pair of DZ twins who were very similar to each other. This would in fact constitute a very small source of error.

The criteria employed by Osborne and De George have been cited as typical. Other investigators, employing the same principle, include a somewhat different list of traits, although emphasis is always placed on antigens. Sometimes investigators make a point of determining how frequently other members of the family, and friends, mistake the twins for each other.

In summary, we note that the similarity method of zygosity diagnosis cannot *prove* monozygosity, but it can make the conclusion that a given pair is monozygotic highly probable, and for practical purposes that is sufficient. As usual where probability is involved, mathematical expression of the probability is possible and useful. Interested readers will find a concise treatment of the mathematics in Steinberg (1962).

Utilization of the Twin Method

Alternative Traits   When members of a pair of twins agree with regard to a certain trait, we usually say that they are *concordant*; when they disagree, we say that they are *discordant*. Using these terms, we may make the following general proposition: *If a genetic component is concerned in producing a certain trait, concordance in MZ pairs should exceed that in DZ pairs.* The greater the genetic component the greater the difference between MZ and DZ pairs is likely to be. This proposition follows from the fact that MZ twins are genetically identical (except for the rare occurrence of somatic mutation in one of them), whereas DZ twins are no more alike genetically than are other brothers and sisters in the same family. We should not forget, however, that they are *as* alike as are other brothers and sisters in the same family. The similarity may be considerable.

To a degree, the alternative traits we are now considering are an extension of the alternative traits we employed when we first used the similarity method to separate our twins into MZ and DZ categories. Possessing antigen A_1 is the alternative of lacking that antigen, for example. However, the alternative traits employed in our diagnosis had a well-established and usually a simple genetic basis; the alternative traits we are now investigating are much less clear-cut in genetic basis. Indeed, we are usually asking the question: Does the trait involve any genetic component at all?

As examples we shall take measles and schizophrenia (the commonest type of mental disorder or insanity). Each is an alternative trait in the sense that one either does or does not have measles, and one either has the symptoms of schizophrenia or one does not have them.

Table 20.1 presents the cumulative results of many investigations concerning the concordance of twins for the two conditions. In the case of measles we note that concordance is high in *both* MZ and DZ pairs. This indicates that if one twin develops measles the other one usually does, too, whether the twins are monozygotic or dizygotic. Thus we would conclude that the genetic identicalness of the MZ pairs has little or no effect on the likelihood of having measles. The only clue that a slight genetic component may be involved in resistance to measles lies in

TABLE 20.1. Twin studies: Concordance and discordance for measles and schizophrenia, in percentage.

	MZ Twins Percent		DZ Twins Percent	
	concordant	discordant	concordant	discordant
Measles	95	5	87	13
Schizophrenia†	80	20	13	87

(Data cited from Stern, 1960.)

†Average of results of investigations in five countries: England, Germany, Japan, Sweden, United States.

the fact that concordance is slightly lower in DZ twins than it is in MZ twins. If the difference between 95 percent and 87 percent is statistically significant, we may suspect that a difference in genetic constitution may influence resistance to the disease. This would not seem to be improbable, of course, but we would still conclude that the principal factor is environmental: a matter of whether or not the measles virus enters one's environment.

Turning to schizophrenia, we find a very different picture. The cumulative results of many studies indicate that if one MZ twin becomes schizophrenic, the other one does, too, in 80 percent of the cases. If one DZ twin becomes schizophrenic, the other one develops the symptoms in only 13 percent of the cases. Evidently here the genetic identicalness of the MZ twins has a large effect. It is noteworthy that in many cases the members of an MZ pair were not living together (i.e., were not sharing the same environment) when the symptoms developed. There are many striking cases of MZ twins who were completely out of contact with each other but who nevertheless developed schizoid symptoms almost simultaneously. On the other hand, many of the DZ pairs were living in the same environment when one developed the symptoms but the other did not.

The evidence indicates, then, that there is an important hereditary component in the tendency to develop schizophrenia. There is also an important environmental component. A person may have a tendency to schizophrenia, but if his life is sufficiently placid, he may never become schizoid. Emotional stresses and strains, especially in adolescence and the young adult years, trigger the development of the symptoms. Yet some people subjected to such stresses develop schizophrenia, whereas others do not. What is the difference? Evidence from the study of twins indicates an important genetic component in this difference.

The difference in percentage of concordance does not in itself tell us anything about the nature of the genetic component. Other investigations have shown that the genes involved are probably recessive rather than dominant. Two of our criteria of recessiveness apply especially: children develop schizophrenia even though neither parent has done so; there is an increased incidence of consanguinity among the parents of schizophrenics (see pp. 116–120).

It is not likely, however, that the difference between schizophrenics and non-schizophrenics depends on a single pair of genes. This has been suggested (e.g., Huxley *et al.*, 1964), but it seems unlikely until and unless a simple biochemical basis for the disorder can be found. We recall the relatively simple biochemical basis of phenylketonuria (p. 423). In this case, profound mental effects result from failure of a single gene-controlled enzyme. However, at the present time, the biochemical basis of schizophrenia appears to be more complicated and hence likely to have a more complex biochemical foundation (progress in exploring the biochemical mysteries of schizophrenia is summarized by Kety, 1959).

The twin method, which we have discussed with regard to measles and schizophrenia, has been applied to the determination of genetic components in many other human traits, normal and pathological. The principles are the same in each case, so we need not list further examples. For those interested in further details and examples, an extensive discussion is available in Stern (1960), Chapters 26 and 27.

Pitfalls to be Avoided   Just in case some reader may think that the twin method has created utopia for human genetics, we may well pause at this point to mention some of the limitations of the method.

In the first place, an old enemy rears its head: the problem of ascertainment (pp. 67–69). In the case of schizophrenia, for example, how do we learn of a pair of twins to be included in our investigation? Obviously we learn of them because at least one of the pair has developed schizophrenia. Now, are the chances *equal* that we shall have brought to our attention (a) a pair in which both twins develop the trait and (b) a pair in which only one twin develops the trait? In fact, we might argue that we are twice as likely to learn of the concordant pair because there are two schizoid individuals involved, either one of whom might be brought to our attention and so inform us of the existence of this twin pair. As we might expect, the difference in likelihood of ascertainment in the two cases has been given mathematical expression; a correction factor for it can be incorporated in calculations. We mention the existence of the problem here, and note the fact that geneticists are aware of it.

A correlated pitfall lies in basing surveys on *published* cases. As I write, I have before me reference to a paper recounting how both members of a pair of MZ twins developed schizophrenia at age 21 although they had had no contact with each other for five years (Gardner and

Stephens, 1949). This is truly an interesting case and one well worth publishing, but is it likely that if only one twin had become schizophrenic, the authors would have thought it worth their while to write a paper about the case—or that the editors of our overcrowded scientific journals would have thought the paper worth publishing? Perhaps, but the chance is rather small. Thus, if we were to rely only on surveys of published accounts we would acquire very biased data—biased in favor of concordance. Workers in the field are well aware of this, of course, and attempt insofar as possible to obtain first-hand data with as complete ascertainment as possible of both concordant and discordant pairs. It is heartening to note that the data on schizophrenia (Table 20.1) include so many discordant DZ pairs. This suggests that if there *had* been large numbers of discordant MZ pairs they would have been ascertained, too.

In a complex psychological trait like schizophrenia, there are many variables, and often we cannot adequately assess their significance. Parental attitudes toward identical twins frequently differ from attitudes toward twins who are not "look-alikes." The parents may wish either to accentuate the similarity (by dressing the twins alike) or to de-emphasize the similarity so that each member of the pair may become an independent, self-sufficient individual. In each case, what is the psychological effect on the twins? Does this effect have any influence on the subsequent development of the symptoms of schizophrenia? Frequently there is greater uniformity in the environment shared by two MZ twins than there is in the environment shared by DZ pairs (even though the latter are living together in the same home). This is particularly true if the DZ twins are of different sexes. Does this difference have any effect on concordance and discordance in developing schizoid symptoms? The question has been investigated, and results available at present seem to indicate that such differences exist but that they can, at most, account for only a little of the difference in concordance between MZ and DZ pairs (Kety, 1959).

Frequently there seem to be stronger psychological and emotional bonds between MZ twins than there are between DZ twins. Does this mean that more psychological stress is produced when MZ twins grow up and separate? Kety (1959) stated: "One cannot assume that environmental similarities and mutual interactions in identical twins, who are always of the same sex and whose striking physical congruence is often accentuated by parental attitudes, play an insignificant role in the high concordance rate of schizophrenia in this group." As checks on the significance of these factors, Kety suggested (a) investigations on MZ twins separated at birth and reared in different homes, and (b) "careful study of schizophrenia in adopted children, with comparison of the incidence in blood relatives and in foster relatives."

A beginning has been made on investigation of schizophrenia in MZ twins reared apart. Shields (1962) reported three cases from the literature and added a fourth from his own investigation. All four pairs were concordant. Although the numbers are small, the cases certainly suggest that sharing the same environment is not essential to concordance in MZ twins. Yet even here the twins were not separated at birth. They shared the same environment during the first months of life as well as, of course, the same intra-uterine environment before birth. This is mentioned not to imply that factors in prenatal and neonatal environment play a large role in predisposition to schizophrenia, but rather to emphasize possible pitfalls and to indicate something of the complexity of "the nature-nurture problem."

The literature on the genetics of schizophrenia is extensive. More detailed consideration of the topic is not possible here, but interested readers are referred to Kallmann (1946, 1953, and 1962) for accounts of original investigations and for references to the literature.

So far we have presented some of the more prominent pitfalls to be avoided by investigators using the twin method. Others might be cited (see, for example, Price, 1950), but at present we shall mention only one more variable encountered in studies of twins. The variables we have discussed might cause MZ twins to be similar, but *not* because they have the same genes; rather, we have suggested situations in which environmental factors might cause MZ twins to be similar *regardless* of genes. Such factors in operation might mimic the effect of having the same genes and thus lead an investigator to false conclusions concerning the genetic basis of a trait. They might do so unless he is aware of them, and can design his investigation to compensate for them.

The variable we mention now has the effect of causing dizygotic twins to be more similar than their genes would cause them to be. This has the effect of increasing the amount of concordance between members of DZ pairs, and hence of decreasing the difference in concordance between MZ and DZ pairs. As a result, heredity might seem to be less important than it actually is.

Many years ago, it was discovered that when twins are produced in cattle, the embryonic membranes frequently are connected in such a way that the blood vessels join, so that blood from one fetus can flow into the other. If one fetus is male, the other female, the sex hormones of the male enter the female body with harmful effect, usually causing her to be sterile (a *freemartin*) (Lillie, 1916). More recently, it was discovered that not only hormones but also cells or small masses of cells can be transplanted from one twin to the other through the connected circulatory systems. DZ twin calves usually have exactly the same red blood cell antigens even though they differ in the genes concerned. Suppose, for example, that one twin has a gene for a certain antigen, whereas the other twin lacks this gene; yet both twins have the antigen. This is interpreted to indicate that during early development blood-forming cells (hematopoietic tissues) have actually been transplanted from the twin having the gene to the twin lacking the gene. This twin develops some blood cells possessing the antigen, but other blood cells, produced by his own hematopoetic tissues, lack it (Owen, 1945). Because they have some cells of one kind and some of the other, such calves are said to be **red blood cell** (erythrocyte) **mosaics** or **chimeras**. Male twins (or female twins not having a male as the co-twin) are fertile, and when they are bred they do not pass on to their offspring the genes for the production of the antigen contained in cells received from the co-twin by the transplantation process (Stone *et al.*, 1960).

Examples of red-blood-cell mosaicism have also been found in human twins, although they are rare. Usually the circulatory systems of human twins are not connected, but, as mentioned above, in some cases both MZ twins and DZ twins may share a common placenta (Fig. 20.3). In some instances, an actual joining (*anastomosis*) of embryonic blood vessels has been demonstrated (Price, 1950; Nance, 1959). This should make possible the exchange of hormones, and even cells, between the twins; the existence of mosaicism indicates that this does, in fact, occur. In one case (Booth *et al.*, 1957) of unlike-sexed twins, 86 percent of the brother's cells were of group A_1 and 14 percent of group O. He was a secretor (pp. 140–142), secreting antigens A and H in his saliva (p. 140). His sister possessed 99 percent of group O cells and 1 percent of group A_1 cells. She was a secretor but had only antigen H in her saliva. Evidently, then, she was genetically of group O, whereas her brother was genetically of group A_1.

Further evidence of mosaicism in this case was afforded by the white blood cells. Some of these cells in the brother showed "drumsticks" on their nuclei, a characteristic of the leucocytes of *females* (Fig. 15.5, p. 240). This suggests that he had received ancestral white blood cells from his co-twin.

This case throws an interesting sidelight on another test that has been suggested for distinguishing between MZ and DZ twins. As is generally known, transplantation of tissue from one MZ twin to the co-twin is usually successful, whereas transplantation of tissue between other brothers and sisters, even DZ twins, usually is not. In the DZ case we are discussing, however, skin grafts were transferred from one to the other and survived successfully. Evidently the embryonic interchange of blood-forming tissues had included creation of an antigenic similarity of the kind necessary for successful transplantation. Thus we may conclude that successful tissue transplantation is not a certain means of determining whether twins are monozygotic or dizygotic.

In another case of mosaicism between unlike-sexed twins, both twins had a mixture of O and A red blood cells (Nicholas *et al.*, 1957). The sister secreted antigen H, but not A, in her saliva, thus demonstrating that she was genetically of group O (although 51 percent of her red blood cells

placenta

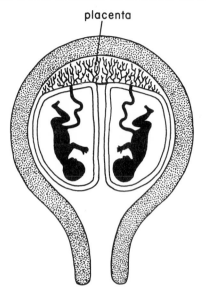

FIG. 20.3 Dizygotic twin fetuses with separate amnions and chorions but with a single placenta. (Redrawn from *Fundamentals of Human Reproduction* by E. L. Potter. Copyright © 1948, McGraw-Hill Book Co., Inc. Used by permission of McGraw-Hill Book Company.)

contained antigen A). She married a man of group O and produced three children. As was to be expected, all three belonged to group O.

The O cells in both the woman and her twin brother were of blood type MNs (pp. 158–159), whereas the A cells in both were of type Ns. This adds further evidence of mosaicism. Mosaicism was also shown in the white blood cells; in both twins only a small proportion of these cells showed "drumsticks." Without mosaicism a larger proportion of the female's leucocytes would have been expected to display this feature, whereas none of the male's leucocytes would have been expected to do so.

We also note that the female twin demonstrated her fertility by producing children. In no human case described so far has there been evidence of the freemartinism found in cattle (p. 305).

Thus, we see that mechanisms exist by which one twin can influence the other. In the case of dizygotic twins, this may lead to greater similarity (concordance) than the genes would have produced alone. In the blood groups, for example, the concordance may mimic that produced by homozygosity (both twins have all the antigens produced by the genes of either one, although careful tests reveal that each individual red blood cell does not have all the antigens, as it would have in homozygosity).

Our knowledge of these matters is comparatively recent. We do not know the extent to which it is possible for one twin to influence the other. We have spoken of one DZ twin influencing the other; this may also occur with MZ twins. Perhaps differences between MZ twins may arise in this way, through such mechanisms as changes in oxygen and hormonal concentrations at critical periods in development (Nance, 1959). Here is another area in which we are just at the threshold; we shall await future findings with great interest.

While we are speaking of twins influencing one another, we should mention that the mere physical fact of two fetuses developing together in one uterus is a form of influence—through crowding, possible competition for nourishment, and the like. It is a noteworthy fact that the death rate, both before and immediately after birth, is greater for twins than it is for children born singly. This may be due in part to the fact that twins may sometimes influence each other adversely.

PROBLEMS

1. A husband and wife have the following genotypes relative to ABO blood groups, M-N blood types, Rh, the secretor trait (pp. 140–142), and the tasting of PTC (the gene for tasting, T, is dominant to the gene for non-tasting, t).

$$I^A I^O L^N L^N R r Se Se T t \quad \times \quad I^B I^O L^M L^M R r se se T t$$

They have a pair of male twins both of whom belong to group O, type MN, are Rh positive, are secretors and nontasters. Does this agreement form strong evidence that the twins are monozygotic? In answering, compute the chances that if one member of a *dizygotic* pair of twins born to these parents is a male having the traits listed, the other member of the dizygotic pair will be a male having them also.

2. With regard to trait A, concordance of MZ twins is 90 percent, and concordance of DZ twins is 80 percent. With regard to trait B, concordance of MZ twins is 90 percent, and concordance of DZ twins is 30 percent. With regard to which trait would genetic factors seem to be the more important?

3. A husband belongs to blood group O, his wife to group B. They have a pair of unlike-sexed twins. Most of the red blood cells of the girl react with anti-B antibodies, but a small percentage of the cells fail to do so. Most of the red blood cells of the boy do not react with anti-B although some of them do. What is the probable cause of this situation?

   If the girl eventually marries a man of group O, and the boy marries a woman of group O, what types of offspring may each expect to have?

REFERENCES

Booth, P. B., G. Plaut, J. D. James, E. W. Ikin, P. Moores, R. Sanger, and R. R. Race, 1957. "Blood chimerism in a pair of twins," *British Medical Journal,* 1957, 1:1456–58.

Gardner, E. J., and F. E. Stephens, 1949. "Schizophrenia in monozygotic twins," *Journal of Heredity,* **40**:165–67.

Huxley, J., E. Mayr, H. Osmond, and A. Hoffer, 1964. "Schizophrenia as a genetic morphism," *Nature*, 204:220–21.

Kallmann, F. J., 1946. "The genetic theory of schizophrenia. An analysis of 691 twin index families," *American Journal of Psychiatry*, 103:309–22.

Kallmann, F. J., 1953. *Heredity in Health and Mental Disorder*. New York: W. W. Norton & Company, Inc.

Kallmann, F. J. (ed), 1962. *Expanding Goals of Genetics in Psychiatry*. New York: Grune & Stratton, Inc.

Kety, S. S., 1959. "Biochemical theories of schizophrenia," *Science*, 129:1528–32; 1590–96.

Lillie, F. R., 1916. "The theory of the free-martin," *Science*, 43:611–13.

Nance, W. E., 1959. "Twins: an introduction to gemellology." *Medicine*, 38:403–14.

Nicholas, J. W., W. J. Jenkins, and W. L. Marsh, 1957. "Human blood chimeras. A study of surviving twins," *British Medical Journal*, 1957, 1:1458–60.

Osborne, R. H., and F. V. De George, 1959. *Genetic Basis of Morphological Variation*. Cambridge, Mass.: Harvard University Press.

Owen, R. D., 1945. "Immunogenetic consequences of vascular anastomoses between bovine twins," *Science*, 102:400–401.

Price, B., 1950. "Primary biases in twin studies," *American Journal of Human Genetics*, 2:293–352.

Shields, J., 1962. *Monozygotic Twins*. London: Oxford University Press.

Steinberg, A. G., 1962. "Population genetics: special cases." In W. J. Burdette (ed.). *Methodology in Human Genetics*. San Francisco: Holden-Day, Inc. Pp. 76–91.

Stern, C., 1960. *Principles of Human Genetics*, 2nd ed. San Francisco: W. H. Freeman & Company.

Stone, W. H., D. T. Berman, W. J. Tyler, and M. R. Irwin, 1960. "Blood types of the progeny of a pair of cattle twins showing erythrocyte mosaicism," *Journal of Heredity*, 51:136–40.

21.

THE TWIN METHOD:
QUANTITATIVE TRAITS

In the preceding chapter we discussed the twin method of determining genetic components in alternative traits. We then considered pitfalls to be avoided in twin studies, including some variables introduced by aspects of the twinning process itself. Now we turn our attention to traits involving differences in the amount of something, as in height, weight, and intelligence. Insofar as such traits are genetically determined, the genetic basis is that of multiple genes, polygenes (Chap. 11). What can we learn by applying the twin method to study of such traits?

As in our discussion of alternative traits, we may begin by stating a general proposition: *If genetic components are involved in the production of quantitative traits, the average difference between members of pairs of MZ twins should be less than the difference between members of pairs of DZ twins* (or, more concisely, the intrapair variance in MZ twins should be less than it is in DZ twins).

In Chapter 20 we mentioned the investigation of Osborne and De George (1959), using it as an example of the similarity method of determining zygosity. The investigation, conducted by Dr. Richard H. Osborne and Dr. Frances V. De George at the Columbia-Presbyterian Medical Center in New York, under the auspices of the Institute of the Study of Human Variation, of Columbia University, dealt with traits of the kind we are now discussing, and so we may well draw our examples from it.

This investigation differed from most of its predecessors in that it included adult twins only (twins over 18 years of age). The twins were not selected because they possessed any particular traits. The group consisted of voluntary participants of whom the investigators had learned in a variety of ways. The zygosity of the participants was determined as described previously (pp. 299–300).

The results of the study were expressed in terms of "mean intrapair variance," a statistic indicating the average amount of difference between co-twins. This variance was calculated by the formula: $\Sigma\ x^2/2n$. In this formula, the capital sigma indicates summation; "n is the number of twin pairs, and x the difference between the two members of a twin pair for a given measurement."

Stature

Results of the study of stature are summarized in Table 21.1, without including the statistical tabulations which demonstrated that differences are significant. We note immediately that the intrapair difference is much greater for DZ pairs than it is for MZ (almost 5 times as great for male twins, and 14 times as great for female twins). From this we may conclude that there is a strong genetic component in stature. We may find surprising the fact that males differ from females in the difference between MZ pairs and DZ pairs. The small number of DZ male pairs may have contributed to this, but the authors concluded that it was due largely to the somewhat amusing circumstance that women were more cooperative than men about having their measurements taken. Thus, when the same individual was given the same measurement at different times the results of the two measurings were more nearly the same if the subject was a woman than it was if the subject was a man. "A similar difference between the sexes is noted in all measurements requiring the subjects' physical cooperation in application of the measurement technique."

Table 21.1 includes only like-sexed pairs. As we should expect, the variance in unlike-sexed pairs (114.789) was much greater than the variance in either DZ or MZ like-sexed pairs.

TABLE 21.1. Mean intrapair variances in stature between like-sexed pairs of twins.

	Number of twin pairs	Variance
Male MZ pairs	25	1.604
Male DZ pairs	10	7.581
Female MZ pairs	34	1.387
Female DZ pairs	27	18.329

Reprinted by permission of the publishers from R. H. Osborne and F. V. De George, *Genetic Basis of Morphological Variation*. Cambridge, Mass.: Harvard University Press, Copyright, 1959, by The Commonwealth Fund.

These results by Osborne and De George corroborate earlier twin studies indicating that one's genes are important in determining one's stature (cf., Newman, Freeman, and Holzinger, 1937).

Weight

Table 21.2 presents the intrapair variances for weight. We note that they are much greater than are those for stature. This indicates in general that a twin differs more from his co-twin in weight than he does in stature. We also see that male MZ twins are closely similar to male DZ twins in variance. Even in the case of the female twins the difference in variance between MZ and DZ pairs is not statistically significant. Accordingly, the authors drew the conclusion "that after the end of the growth period, weight, in essentially healthy people, is predominantly under environmental influence." (Roughly, this is a way of saying that it depends in large part on how much you eat and how much physical work you do.)

TABLE 21.2.   Mean intrapair variances in weight between like-sexed pairs of twins.

	Number of twin pairs	Variance
Male MZ pairs	25	62.400
Male DZ pairs	10	65.450
Female MZ pairs	34	38.515
Female DZ pairs	27	66.722

Reprinted by permission of the publishers from R. H. Osborne and F. V. De George, *Genetic Basis of Morphological Variation.* Cambridge, Mass.: Harvard University Press, Copyright, 1959, by The Commonwealth Fund.

Earlier studies with twins had indicated a genetic component in weight. However many of the twins in these studies were children. In the investigation by Newman, Freeman, and Holzinger (1937), for example, mean intrapair weight difference was 10.0 pounds for like-sexed DZ twins, 4.1 pounds for MZ twins, but the average age of the subjects was 13 years. Accordingly, Osborne and De George concluded that "in the twin studies of growing children the hereditary influence measured by intrapair weight differences is principally associated with growth rate." As we all know, children have periods when they grow rapidly, other periods when they grow slowly. If, as may well be, such rates are under genetic control, we might expect MZ twins to resemble each other more in pattern of growth than do DZ twins. If so, measurements taken at any given time would show less intrapair difference between MZ twins than between DZ twins, on the average.

Interested readers will find in the book by Osborne and De George (1959) similar data concerning inheritance of other body measurements (e.g., arm length, trunk length, and chest circumference). The results on stature and weight have sufficiently illustrated the principles of the twin method applied to such traits. Now we turn our attention to another subject, possible hereditary components in intelligence within the range of normality.

Intelligence

Do "normal people" differ genetically with respect to intelligence? We cannot enter into an extensive discussion of this large and much-debated question, which has been argued from every conceivable point of view. One extreme view is that everyone comes into the world with the *same* intellectual endowment and that differences in intellectual attainment depend solely on differences in environment (including differences in training and education). Probably few people would subscribe to so bold a statement as this; after all, we do seem to sense that there was some difference between Einstein's mind and ours that was not entirely dependent on a difference in upbringing and education. Yet many people conclude that the effects of environmental differences are more important than genetic differences in determining intelligence. In no other field has the "nature-nurture question" been so hotly debated. What evidence is obtainable by application of the twin method?

We must note at the outset one real handicap in attempting to answer this question. Aside from the fact that intelligence is difficult to define, there is no exact and objective means of measuring the native intellectual endowment with which a person is born. There are accurate scales for studying weight but nothing comparable for measuring intelligence. Tremendous ingenuity has entered into the devising of intelligence tests, and serious attempts have been made to devise "culture-free" tests. Even the best of them, however, are only partially successful in separating what is innate from what is acquired in intelligence. Most tests employ language; this immediately introduces the effects of different environments and education. Nonverbal tests attempt to avoid the difficulty but one can go only so far in measuring intelligence without the use of words. What kind of test can measure with reasonable objectivity and completeness the native intelligence of both a college graduate and a person with no schooling? Or that of a child and that of an adult? Surprisingly, some tests are partially successful in meeting such demands, and the best of them are the best means we have available. In the discussion that follows, intelligence is of necessity defined as "that which intelligence tests measure." Hopefully there is good correlation between what intelligence tests measure and what we think of as native intellectual endowment: "the brains we are born with."

The underlying theory in applying the twin method to the study of intelligence is the same as that applied to the study of stature and weight. If there is a hereditary component in intelligence, intrapair variance in MZ twins should be less than it is in DZ twins. Many studies have indicated that this is in fact the case. A review of the extensive literature would be out of place here, but we offer as a typical example the results obtained by Newman, Freeman, and Holzinger (1937) on the same twins referred to in our discussion of weight. These investigators gave the Stanford-Binet test to 50 MZ pairs and 52 like-sexed DZ pairs. The average intrapair difference for the MZ pairs was 5.9 IQ points; for the DZ pairs it was 9.9 points. Woodworth (1941) applied a correction to compensate for the fact that "retest of the same person within a week usually shows some shift of score up or down, averaging about 5 points of IQ." This correction reduced the MZ difference to 3.1 points, the DZ difference to 8.5 points. Thus, the DZ pairs differed about 2.7 times as much as did the MZ pairs (Woodworth, 1941). If we may assume that the environment of DZ pairs raised together is not significantly more different than the environment of MZ pairs raised together, then the increased intrapair variance of DZ twins may be ascribed to the fact that the co-twins differ genetically.

It is convenient to express the intrapair differences in terms of a statistic known as the *correlation coefficient*. Without describing the method of calculating this coefficient we may state that if co-twins always agreed exactly in IQ score, the coefficient would be 1.0, whereas if there were no relation at all between what one scored and what the other one did, the coefficient would be O.

Applying the correction mentioned above to the data of Newman, Freeman, and Holzinger, Woodworth (1941) found that the correlation coefficient for MZ pairs was 0.93, whereas that for DZ pairs was 0.66. If there is a genetic component in intelligence, we should expect the correlation of DZ pairs to be fairly high because the co-twins share the same parents. (Only unrelated pairs of persons in differing environments would be expected to show correlation coefficients approaching O; see Figure 21.1.)

Through the years, many studies have yielded similar results. Blewett (1954) summarized these results with the statement that "the level of correlation between intelligence test scores of identical twins is generally above 0.90, whereas correlations for fraternal pairs tend to be lower, ranging upwards from 0.50."

Although the evidence seems conclusive that there is a genetic, as well as an environmental, component in determining one's performance on intelligence tests, we have little basis for drawing conclusions as to the mode of inheritance. It is safe to conclude that many genes must be involved in such a complex trait. Actually, intelligence is not a single trait at all; it is comprised of many component parts. "It is, for instance, rather common to find someone who is highly gifted verbally but who is poor in numerical ability or in the ability to understand mechanical principles and vice versa" (Vandenberg, 1962). Recent investigations have attempted to break down intelligence into these component parts and to identify the ones that seem to be most strongly gene-controlled. Thus Blewett (1954) employed Thurstone's Primary Mental Abilities Test (PMA) in testing 52 pairs of like-sexed twins aged 12 to 15 years; half were boy-boy pairs, half were girl-girl; half were monozygotic, half dizygotic. He found the usual difference in correlation coefficients in the PMA test as a *whole,* but observed that this difference was not maintained within the various parts of the test. Hence he concluded that there is a larger hereditary component in verbal comprehension and word fluency than there is in such abilities as numbers and spatial factors. Vandenberg (1962), also employing the PMA test, obtained results indicative of a hereditary component in verbal completion, addition of numbers, and word fluency. This was part of a large study under the direction of Dr. Lee R. Dice at the University of Michigan's Institute of Human Biology. A great variety of tests was given to 82 pairs of like-sexed twins of high school age (45 MZ and 37 DZ). Aside from the PMA tests, there were various cognitive and achievement tests, tests of motor skills, tests of perceptual skills, sensory tests and measures of musical ability and interests, and tests concerning personality. As might be expected, evidence of a genetic component was obtained in some instances but not in others.

Investigators in the Psychometric Laboratory of the University of North Carolina studied 142 pairs of twins, with an average age of 14 years (Thurstone *et al.,* 1953). They employed 34 tests, which yielded 53 test scores. They found that large intrapair differences were more frequent in DZ pairs than they were in MZ pairs. They found that tests in which there were significant differences between DZ and MZ twins involved visual, verbal, and motor functions.

Thus "intelligence" is being dissected into its components. Although tests for these components frequently lack the precision we might desire, better tests will be constructed, and utilization of them in the study of twins will contribute greatly to our understanding of the role of heredity in intelligence.

Most of the investigations we have described utilized children and young people in school, largely because it is relatively easy to ascertain twins through school administrators and teachers, and to secure cooperation in the testing program. Schoolchildren are used to being tested, whereas many adults find it an annoyance and an interference with the day's work. Nevertheless, there is interest in older twins. It has been suggested that differences between young DZ twins may disappear with the passage of years. According to this view, genetic elements may be important in determining intellectual development during childhood but cease to be important in later life. Dr. Lissy F. Jarvik (1962) of the New York State Psychiatric Institute gave a battery of tests to 134 like-sexed pairs of twins 60 years of age and older. Two years later most of them were given the same tests a second time. A smaller number survived to take the tests six years later, and 17 individuals were available to take the tests a fourth time, after a two-and-a-half-year lapse. The initial testing showed that "the scores of one-egg twin partners were more similar than those of two-egg twins even after the age of 60, indicating the persistence during adult life of gene-specific differences in mental functioning." Subsequent tests demonstrated no significant change in intrapair correlations.

Heredity Constant, Environment Varied

In designing an experiment, scientists seek to introduce only one variable factor at a time, keeping all other factors constant. To determine the roles of heredity and environment, we should wish to set up two parallel experiments, (1) one in which the heredity is constant but the environment is varied; and (2) another in which the environment is constant but the heredity is varied. Of course, we cannot set up such experiments with human beings at all, but an approximation of the first type of experiment is afforded when monozygotic twins are separated early in life and raised in separate environments. In such cases, the heredity is constant, whereas the environment is varied because the twins are living in separate homes, with different cultural and educational atmospheres. At this point, however, the comparison to an experiment breaks down, for the "experimenter" has no control over the degree of difference in the two environments. The two homes may be very similar or very different. The separated twins may receive about the same amount of schooling or they may receive very different educations. As is usual in human genetics, we must take our "experiments" as we find them.

Dr. H. J. Muller reported on such a pair of separated twins in 1925. The investigation conducted at the University of Chicago by Newman, Freeman, and Holzinger (1937), to which we referred earlier, included 19 pairs of separated twins; a twentieth pair was added in 1940 by Gardner and Newman. Occasional cases have increased the list since that time, and an extensive investigation has been carried on by Dr. James Shields

Lecturer in the Institute of Psychiatry in London, whose book on the subject (1962) contains a summary of previous investigations.

The 20 cases in the University of Chicago study received the attention of a cooperating team: Dr. H. H. Newman, a zoologist, Dr. F. N. Freeman and Dr. I. C. Gardner, psychologists, and Dr. K. J. Holzinger, a statistician. In 11 of these 20 pairs, separation had occurred not later than 1 year of age; 8 pairs were separated between their first and second birthdays; one pair was 3 years of age, and another 6 years when separation occurred. Despite the fact that they were being reared apart, and in many cases without knowledge of the co-twin's existence, the twins continued to be remarkably alike in many psychological traits.

The average difference in IQ was 7.5 points, which we may compare with the 5.9 points of difference shown by the 50 pairs of MZ twins reared together (p. 314). If the corrections recommended by Woodworth (1941) are applied, these figures become 6 points and 3 points, respectively. Evidently being reared apart did make a little difference in average attainment on intelligence tests, but not enough difference to mask the underlying similarity determined by the identical inheritance.

Of more interest than the average difference is the distribution of differences (first part of Table 21.3). We note that 8 of the 20 pairs differed by 4 points or less (4 pairs by only 1 point). At the other extreme, only 4 pairs differed by 15 points or more (the greatest difference was 24 points). A study of sibling pairs (not twins) reared apart showed 17 percent of the pairs differing by *more* than 24 points; the average difference was 15.5 points.

Attainment on intelligence tests is known to be affected by education. Newman and his colleagues therefore established criteria for estimating the similarity of educational opportunities enjoyed by the twins. As we might expect, the investigators found a high correlation between IQ and the education received, the coefficient being 0.791. In general, the greater the difference in educational opportunity experienced by the separated twins the greater the difference in IQ. Thus, in the pair showing the 24 points of difference, one twin had a college degree and was a teacher, whereas her sister's education consisted of only three years of grade school. (The data correlating educational opportunity with IQ are nicely summarized for the original 19 pairs in Table 15 of Osborn, 1951. The twentieth pair was studied when the twins were in the same college; their IQ difference was 3 points [Gardner and Newman, 1940].)

The conclusion reached was that monozygotic twins have an inherited tendency to similarity of response in testing. Small environmental differences cause little or no deviation in this inherited similarity, but larger differences may produce detectable effects. Dr. Newman concluded that in only 4 of the 20 pairs "were there any very striking differences, exceeding those of some identical twins reared together. The remaining sixteen

TABLE 21.3.   Distribution of intrapair differences in intelligence test scores made by twins reared together and twins reared apart.

| | No. of pairs | Intrapair differences | | | |
		0–4 points	5–9 points	10–14 points	15 or more points
Newman *et al.*, 1937, and Gardner & Newman, 1940					
MZ, apart	20	8 pairs, 40%	5 pairs, 25%	3 pairs, 15%	4 pairs, 20%
Shields, 1962°					
MZ, apart	37	32%	30%	14%	24%
MZ, together	34	44%	21%	23%	12%
DZ	7	14%	14%	14%	57%

°From Table 8, p. 60, of Shields, J., 1962. *Monozygotic Twins.* London: Oxford University Press.

cases show no greater mean differences than did the fifty pairs of identical twins reared together. It might be concluded then that in these sixteen cases, although we know of many differences in their environments, these differences were not sufficiently large to reach the threshold of effectiveness" (Gardner and Newman, 1940).

These statistics only dimly reveal a wealth of interesting information concerning the 20 pairs of twins. This information is presented in the form of case histories in the references cited and also in Newman (1940). As samples we will summarize two cases briefly.

Gladys and Helen were the given names of the twins who differed by 24 IQ points. They were separated at 18 months of age and did not meet again until they were 28 years old. Helen was adopted twice, the second time by a childless farmer and his wife who were determined to give her every advantage. She graduated from a good college and taught school for 12 years. Gladys was adopted by a Canadian railroad conductor. Her schooling was interrupted in the third grade when the family moved to an isolated part of the Canadian Rockies so that her foster father could recuperate from tuberculosis. Although the family later returned to Ontario, Gladys did not resume her schooling. She worked in a knitting mill and then as a salesgirl in various stores. Finally, she got a job in a printing establishment and worked up to a position as assistant to the proprietor. Both Helen and Gladys married; Helen had one child, Gladys two.

Dr. Newman's comment concerning Helen was that "she had acquired considerable social polish, showed much facility in social intercourse and possessed a good deal of feminine charm." Concerning Gladys he wrote: "She had always been a hard worker and had not acquired any of the social ease and polish possessed by her sister. She was a business woman without airs or coquetry" (Newman, 1940).

Because the subject under discussion is intelligence, we have said nothing of the personality tests also given the 20 pairs of separated twins. As we might expect, Gladys and Helen scored very differently on these tests, the differences no doubt arising from the great differences in their lives. In the matter of intelligence, Helen had an IQ score of 116 on the Stanford-Binet test, whereas Gladys scored 92. Thus Helen was "high normal," and Gladys was "low normal." Thirteen years' difference in the amount of schooling showed its effect in ability to cope with an intelligence test although innate ability was probably the same for both.

We choose the second pair of twins because of the curious similarities of their lives. Such similarities are often encountered by students of twins—too often, it would seem, to be matters of mere coincidence.

Edwin and Fred were separated at about one year of age and were reared as only children in their respective homes. When they were small they attended the same school, noticed how much they looked alike, but did not suspect that they were brothers. Later their families moved to different cities, and the twins did not meet again until they were 25 years old. Dr. Newman stated: "The oddest feature about these twins is that, although neither one knew of the other's existence, they lived strangely parallel lives. They were both reared as only children of childless foster parents, both under the impression that they were own children. They had about the same amount of education, were both interested in electricity and both became expert repair men in different branches of the same large telephone company. They were married the same year to young women of about the same age and type. Each had a baby son and each owned a fox terrier dog named Trixie. Believe it or not!"

The twins differed slightly in the amount of schooling, Edwin having had one year of high school, Fred three years. On the Stanford-Binet test Edwin scored 91 and Fred 90. In other tests, including those of personality, the twins showed themselves to be strikingly similar. Dr. Newman commented: "From this case one might be led to infer that the identical heredity and closely similar environments had interacted to produce almost identical results" (Newman, 1940).

We have already mentioned the investigation by Shields (1962) in Great Britain. The subjects consisted of 88 pairs of MZ twins, 44 of them brought up in different homes, 44 brought up together. A smaller number of DZ pairs was also studied. Most of these twins were ascertained when they responded to an appeal made in connection with a television program. Most of the separated pairs had been parted within the first six months of life. They were reared in different homes for at least five years during childhood. Their ages ranged from 8 years to 59 years, but most of them were in their 30's or 40's. Hence, on the average, they were older than the twins studied by Newman and his colleagues (25.7 years).

The pairs varied greatly in degree of separation and in degree of similarity of the environments in which the co-twins were raised. "Some lived in different towns and knew nothing of their being one of twins until they were grown up. Others went to school together, being brought up by relatives in the same town. Varying degrees of contact in adult life were found."

Dr. Shields' investigation involved many tests: stature, weight, intelligence, personality, and others. Two intelligence tests were employed, a nonverbal test called Dominoes and the Synonyms section of the Mill Hill Vocabulary Scale. Combining the results of the two tests, we find that the average intrapair difference for the separated twins was 9.46 points; for the twins reared together, it was 7.38 points. For a small group of DZ twins it was 13.43. The correlation coefficients were, respectively, 0.77 and 0.76 (0.51 for the DZ pairs).

In the lower portion of Table 21.3 we present the distribution of intrapair differences. Note that there is little difference between the MZ twins reared together and those reared apart, although the proportion of twins showing very little difference (0-4 points) is slightly greater for the twins reared together than it is for those reared apart. The proportion of twins showing 15 or more points of difference is greater for the twins reared apart than it is for the twins reared together (but note how much greater is the proportion of DZ twins in this category).

The main impression is the striking similarity of MZ twins whether reared together or reared apart. Separate rearing of the twins in this study seemed to make less difference than it did in most of the cases studied by Newman and his co-workers. Dr. Shields concluded: "This may be because Newman's sample included more pairs than ours that differed widely in schooling and cultural background." Detailed case histories of the twins are given by Shields (1962).

Twin studies afford strong evidence of an important genetic component in intelligence. There is also an important environmental component in the extent to which innate ability is brought to fruition. The situation is somewhat analogous to photographic film. We place the film in the camera and snap the shutter. The film then contains what is called a "latent image," which may be likened to one's hereditary endowment. The picture is not visible until the film has been treated with the proper chemicals (environment). If the picture is imperfect, the fault may lie either in the latent image (heredity) or in the developer (environment). Both must be perfect if the picture is to be perfect.

Earlier, we mentioned two types of experiments we should like to perform: (1) heredity constant, environment varied; (2) environment constant, heredity varied. To a degree, this second kind of experiment is performed when DZ twins live together in the same home. However, because they are the children of the same parents, DZ twins exhibit much less genetic diversity than do unrelated children. Hence, they afford investigators only a small range of variation for study. More revealing are investigations of unrelated children reared together (in foster homes or in institutions). To what extent will common environment cause children with dissimilar heredities to resemble one another more than they would if each child had been reared by his own parents? In degree of intelligence, will foster children bear closer resemblance to their biological parents or to their foster parents? These are only two of the questions we can ask that have bearing on the roles of heredity and environment. Obtaining unequivocal answers is difficult for many reasons; the problems involved are ably analyzed in Woodworth (1941). For example, many foster children are illegitimate, and therefore one can seldom secure the cooperation of the biological father for any testing program. Again, adoption agencies frequently try to match the foster home to the social and economic rank of the home from which the child came. Thus the contrast an investigator would like to see is minimized, the foster parents and biological parents being all about on a level. Despite these and other difficulties, progress has been made and evidence obtained that intellectual development is conditioned by both heredity and environment.

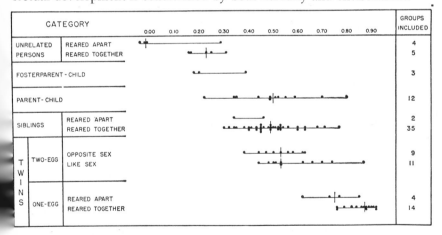

FIG. 21.1 Correlation coefficients for intelligence test scores from 52 studies. Over two thirds of the coefficients were derived from IQ's, the remainder from special tests (e.g., Primary Mental Abilities). Midparent-child correlation was used when available, otherwise mother-child correlation. Correlation coefficients obtained in each study are indicated by dark circles; medians are shown by vertical lines intersecting the horizontal lines, which represent the ranges. (From Erlenmeyer-Kimling, L., and L. F. Jarvik, 1964. "Genetics and intelligence: a review," *Science*, **142**:1477–79. Copyright 1964 by the American Association for the Advancement of Science.)

We conclude our discussion of the hereditary contribution to intelligence by presenting an illuminating chart prepared by Dr. L. Erlenmeyer-Kimling and Dr. Lissy F. Jarvik of the New York State Psychiatric Institute (Fig. 21.1). The chart summarizes data from 52 studies, carried on in eight countries on four continents over a period of 50 years. Each dark circle on the chart represents a correlation coefficient obtained from these studies. Over two-thirds of the coefficients relate to IQ scores, the remainder to special tests, such as the Primary Mental Abilities Test mentioned earlier. Despite the diversity and heterogeneity of the tests included, the general trend is obvious: the greater the degree of relationship the more similar the individuals are in intelligence. Note the low foster-parent-to-child correlation and the larger own-parent-to-child correlation (the median here being almost exactly 0.50 as it would be expected to be on genetical grounds). Note the similarity of siblings and of DZ twins in median and in range of coefficients, and, as previously, the difference in degree of similarity between DZ twins and MZ twins. The survey "shows that mean intrapair differences on tests of mental abilities for dizygotic twins generally are between 1½ to 2 times as great as those between monozygotic twins reared together" (Erlenmeyer-Kimling and Jarvik, 1963). Finally we note again the great degree of similarity of members of MZ pairs, and the fact that rearing separately does, in many but not all cases, make some difference in attainment on tests.

PROBLEM

1. In their study of morphological variation, Osborne and De George obtained the following data on within-pair variance in male twins. The numbers represent mean variance in each case.
   (1) upper arm length: MZ = 0.316; DZ = 0.846
   (2) upper arm circumference: MZ = 1.120; DZ = 1.528
   What conclusions are warranted concerning relative genetic components in these two traits?

REFERENCES

Blewett, D. B., 1954. "An experimental study of the inheritance of intelligence," *Journal of Mental Science*, **100**:922–33.

Erlenmeyer-Kimling, L., and L. F. Jarvik, 1963. "Genetics and intelligence a review," *Science*, **142**:1477–79.

Gardner, I. C., and H. H. Newman, 1940. "Mental and physical traits o identical twins reared apart. Case XX. Twins Lois and Louise," *Journal o Heredity*, **40**:119–26.

Jarvik, L. F., 1962. "Biological differences in intellectual functioning," *Vita humana*, **5**:195–203.

Muller, H. J., 1925. "Mental traits and heredity," *Journal of Heredity*, **16**: 433–48.

Newman, H. H., 1940. *Multiple Human Births*. New York: Doubleday, Doran & Company, Inc.

Newman, H. H., F. N. Freeman, and K. J. Holzinger, 1937. *Twins: a Study of Heredity and Environment*. Chicago: University of Chicago Press.

Osborn, F., 1951. *Preface to Eugenics*, rev. ed. New York: Harper & Brothers.

Osborne, R. H., and F. V. De George, 1959. *Genetic Basis of Morphological Variation*. Cambridge, Mass.: Harvard University Press.

Shields, J., 1962. *Monozygotic Twins*. London: Oxford University Press.

Thurstone, T. G., L. L. Thurstone, and H. H. Strandskov, 1953. "A psychological study of twins. 1. Distributions of absolute twin differences for identical and fraternal twins," *Research Report No. 4, Psychometric Laboratory, University of North Carolina*, pp. 1–9.

Vandenberg, S. G., 1962. "The Hereditary Abilities Study: hereditary components in a psychological test battery," *American Journal of Human Genetics*, **14**:220–37.

Woodworth, R. S., 1941. "Heredity and environment," *Bulletin No. 47, Social Science Research Council, New York*.

22.

THE EUGENIC IDEAL
AND THE NATURE
OF SELECTION

The eugenics movement was started by Sir Francis Galton in the latter part of the nineteenth century. A cousin of the more widely known Charles Darwin, Galton was a pioneer in the study of human genetics, specializing in statistical studies of such quantitative traits as stature. As we noted in Chapter 11, these traits are now explained as the action of polygenes, but Galton, a contemporary of Mendel, yet unaware of his work, did not think in terms of genes.

Galton coined the name **eugenics**, which may be dissected into "eugenics" and translated as "true-born" or "well-born." Galton defined the term as follows: "Eugenics is the study of agencies under social control that may improve or impair the racial [i.e., hereditary] qualities of future generations, either physically or mentally" (Popenoe and Johnson, 1933). It is worthy of note that Galton referred to eugenics as a "study," and, indeed, investigation into human genetics has always been a primary factor in the movement. Following such studies, however, it is the idealistic hope of eugenists to *do* something about improving the human race. Man has worked wonders in improving cultivated plants and domestic animals. Could he not apply to his own improvement some of the methods that have been so successful with these lower forms?

Plant and animal breeders rely heavily on the complementary practices of hybridization and selection. Hybridization implies control of mating. This is not practicable in human relationships. True, there have been communities in which marriages have been arranged by a leader or by a committee of elders; this was the case in the early years of the Oneida Community in New York State. However, the transitoriness of such practices testifies to their unacceptability to most people in Western cultures.

Might not the other procedure, that of selection, be applied with profit to man himself? Mankind presents great heterogeneity, even without controlled hybridization. Might not selection, therefore, be employed for human improvement? That was the eugenic dream.

Traditionally, eugenics was divided into the aspects, *positive eugenics* and *negative eugenics*. Without going into detail, we may simply state that the goal of positive eugenics was to encourage people having superior genetic traits to have more children. The goal of negative eugenics was to discourage the production of children on the part of people having inferior genetic traits.

Positive eugenics as a separate entity always was a bit vague and uncertain. *Who* should be urged to have larger families? What qualities should one select as the ones to be encouraged? Because most eugenists were intellectuals, intelligence was strongly emphasized. However, life is not intellect alone. Who should decide? And how could "desirable" parents be encouraged to have more children than they naturally were inclined to have? (We shall ignore the perversion of eugenics by Hitler and his followers. That was not part of the main stream of eugenics.)

In point of fact, most of the emphasis was placed on negative eugenics. Actually, positive and negative eugenics are simply two sides of the same coin, for if one discourages reproduction among people having undesirable genetic traits, then *ipso facto* one is encouraging reproduction among people *lacking* these undesirable traits. In a sense, absence of undesirable traits is equivalent to presence of desirable traits.

Can we agree on what traits are undesirable? To some extent we are in the same dilemma as before, but only partly so, for there are some traits that are generally agreed to be undesirable. The eugenics movement concentrated heavily on insanity, epilepsy, and feeblemindedness (to use the older and more picturesque name for what we now call mental deficiency or retardation).

Hence an important aspect of the eugenic dream was this hope: If we can prevent, or reduce, reproduction on the part of people who are insane, epileptic, or feebleminded, can we not succeed in reducing greatly the number of such individuals in future generations? Clearly the ideal is a worthy one; from the standpoints of society as a whole and of individuals with their personal and family problems it *would* be a boon to have fewer people suffering from these sad defects.

There were two methods for effecting the reduction in reproduction. The first, termed *institutionalization,* simply meant keeping the sexes separate in institutions. Although this is necessary for people who are unable to be self-supporting or to care for themselves, it is undesirable for people who can be self-supporting members of society. For this latter group, *eugenic sterilization* was proposed as a means of preventing reproduction. (We shall consider eugenic sterilization later in connection with a discussion of genetic counseling.)

Whatever the methods employed, the key question remains, can the proportion of people suffering from mental deficiency, insanity, and epilepsy in future generations be reduced substantially by preventing mental defectives, the insane, and epileptics from reproducing? Earlier in the present century, this seemed to be a reasonable hope. What lessened that hope? To a considerable extent, hopes were dimmed when the principles of population genetics became generally understood. We turn now to a consideration of what selection can and cannot be expected to accomplish. We refer readers to Haller (1963) for more details of the history of the eugenics movement, and to Osborn (1951) for a summary of the principles of eugenics.

Total Negative Selection

Gene Dominant   Total negative selection means that possessors of a certain gene, or genotype, produce no offspring. Let us consider, first, total negative selection against a dominant gene, A; that is, possessors of gene A produce no offspring. Let us suppose that a population in one generation has the following constitution: 1 percent AA, 18 percent Aa, 81 percent aa. If the 19 percent who have an A gene either as homozygotes or as heterozygotes do not produce any offspring at all, the entire generation of offspring will have the genotype aa, having inherited solely from the aa parents. This statement is subject to one qualification: we may expect some mutation to occur—an occasional a gene mutating to its dominant allele, A. In general we may conclude that *total negative selection against a dominant gene will, in one generation, reduce the frequency of that gene to the low level maintained by recurrent mutation.*

In the case of a dominant gene, negative selection is very effective. When dominant genes are involved, cannot the eugenic dream be realized? Unfortunately, many human abnormalities are not determined by dominant genes. There is one notable exception: Huntington's chorea which, as noted earlier (pp. 73–75), gives evidence of simple dominant inheritance. In this case, it is safe to say that if every person who has the gene for Huntington's chorea did not produce children, Huntington's chorea would virtually disappear in one generation. However, the matter is not as simple as it sounds. Many potential parents who have the gene do not know it, because they do not develop choreic symptoms until after they have married and produced children. In the future, it may be possible through tests (pp. 381–383) to identify which child in a family having a choreic parent will later become choreic himself. If all these children were prevented from having children when they reached reproductive age, Huntington's chorea could be eliminated (except for that originating from a fresh mutation).

Even then it would be necessary to bear several things in mind. In the first place, practically every person who has Huntington's chorea is heterozygous, having had only one choreic parent. Thus, on the average, half of the children of choreic people are normal. If we prevent a choreic person from reproducing, we are preventing the birth of normal offspring as well as of choreic ones. Would this be right? There is a difficult value judgment here—and only one of several. Would a program that prevented the birth of both normal and abnormal children be worthwhile, or just? Perhaps the potential gain would be outweighed by the loss of valuable future citizens. Perhaps within another generation the symptoms of Huntington's chorea can be alleviated; we have the recent conquest of phenylketonuria (p. 216) as a cheering example of what medical science can accomplish in preventing genes from producing their harmful effects. We must remember that any program of eugenic control would have to be a large one, involving thousands of people, many of whom would not wish to cooperate. An extensive program of education would be necessary before even the smallest step could be taken, to say nothing of the complete control implied in the phrase "total negative selection." We can almost read the headlines now: "Desecrating the Sanctity of the Human Home"—"Invasion of Personal Rights"—"the God-Given Right to Have Children"!

When we say that Huntington's chorea *could* virtually be eliminated if every potential choreic could be identified and prevented from having children, we are not saying that this is likely to be done or even that it *should* be done. We have only hinted at a few of the complexities in the human problems of putting such a program into effect.

We should note here that although our subject is *total* negative selection, selection need not be total to contribute to the realization of eugenic ideals. This is not an all-or-none situation. Every time an individual with the gene for Huntington's chorea fails to pass on the gene to offspring, the proportion of choreic individuals in the next generation is decreased. Such a decrease, even though it is fractional rather than total, contributes to the genetic improvement of mankind, and hence is eugenic. We do not envision large compulsive programs, but rather a program of educating individuals as to what is best for themselves and for future generations, a matter of genetic counseling rather than of legislation (Chap. 25).

In theory it is true that prevention of reproduction by all people who possess a dominant trait will quickly reduce the frequency of the gene to the level maintained by recurrent mutation. What is the result if people who have a phenotype determined by a *recessive* gene do not reproduce?

Gene Recessive Let us consider a gene that is completely recessive; the only people showing the phenotype are the ones homozygous for the gene.

Let us suppose that we have a population with the following constitution: ¼ *AA*, 2/4 *Aa*, ¼ *aa*. As noted previously (pp. 91–92), in such a population p (frequency of the dominant allele) is ½, and q (frequency of the recessive allele) is ½. If there is no selection, the proportions as stated will remain indefinitely. However, let us suppose that there is selection, of such nature that none of the *aa* individuals produce offspring. What will be the nature of the next generation?

First, we must calculate the changed values of p and q. Let us call them p_1 and q_1 to distinguish them from the p and q of the first (original) generation. Now only the *AA* and *Aa* individuals reproduce, and we note that there are twice as many *Aa's* as there are *AA's*. Therefore, the effective breeding population is: ⅓ *AA*, ⅔ *Aa*. In this effective breeding population, the frequency, p_1, of the dominant gene is comprised of the entire contribution of the *AA* parents plus half the contribution of the *Aa* parents. q_1 is comprised entirely of the other half of the contribution of the *Aa* parents.

Thus:

$$p_1 = \tfrac{1}{3} + \tfrac{1}{2}\left(\tfrac{2}{3}\right) = \tfrac{1}{3} + \tfrac{1}{3} = \tfrac{2}{3}$$
$$q_1 = \tfrac{1}{2}\left(\tfrac{2}{3}\right) = \tfrac{1}{3}$$

Then:

$$p_1^2 + 2p_1q_1 + q_1^2$$
$$\left(\tfrac{2}{3}\right)^2 + 2\left(\tfrac{2}{3}\right)\left(\tfrac{1}{3}\right) + \left(\tfrac{1}{3}\right)^2$$
$$\tfrac{4}{9}\,AA + \tfrac{4}{9}\,Aa + \tfrac{1}{9}\,aa$$

Thus, one generation of total negative selection against *aa* individuals has reduced the frequency of such individuals from ¼ to 1/9 (from 25 percent to 11.1 percent), and the frequency of gene *a* in the gene pool from ½ to ⅓. In other words, the number of *aa* individuals has been reduced by 13.9 percent. This might be considered a substantial accomplishment even though it does not compare with the effectiveness of total negative selection against a dominant gene.

What will be the frequency of *aa* individuals in the third generation if *aa* members of the second generation do not reproduce? Because *AA* and *Aa* members of the second generation occur in equal numbers, the effective breeding population may be written: 2/4 *AA*, 2/4 *Aa*.

Then:

$$p_2 = \tfrac{2}{4} + \tfrac{1}{2}\,(\tfrac{2}{4}) = \tfrac{3}{4}$$
$$q_2 = \qquad \tfrac{1}{2}\,(\tfrac{2}{4}) = \tfrac{1}{4}$$
$$p_2^2 + 2p_2q_2 + q_2^2$$
$$(\tfrac{3}{4})^2 + 2(\tfrac{3}{4})\,(\tfrac{1}{4}) + (\tfrac{1}{4})^2$$
$$\tfrac{9}{16}\,AA + \tfrac{6}{16}\,Aa + \tfrac{1}{16}\,aa$$

Thus, two successive generations of total negative selection have reduced the frequency of *aa* individuals to $\tfrac{1}{16}$ or 6.2 percent. The reduction from the second to the third generation was from 11.1 percent to 6.2 percent, or 4.9 percent, considerably less than the reduction between the first and second generations (13.9 percent).

If total negative selection continues in the third generation, what will be the relative frequency of *aa* individuals? We already have a simple formula for solving this problem, the formula we derived in Chapter 7 to answer the question: What proportion of recessive-phenotype children is to be expected from matings in which both parents show the dominant phenotype? The formula is $\left(\dfrac{q}{1+q}\right)^2$ (p. 100).

Here we need only change the formula to recognize that the frequency of the recessive gene is changing from generation to generation. So we write:

$$q_3^2 = \left(\frac{q_2}{1+q_2}\right)^2$$

Then, since

$$q_2 = \tfrac{1}{4} \text{ (above):}$$

$$q_3^2 = \left(\frac{\tfrac{1}{4}}{1+\tfrac{1}{4}}\right)^2 = \left(\frac{\tfrac{1}{4}}{\tfrac{5}{4}}\right)^2 = (\tfrac{1}{4} \times \tfrac{4}{5})^2 = (\tfrac{1}{5})^2 = \tfrac{1}{25}$$

In the fourth generation the frequency of *aa* individuals is $\tfrac{1}{25}$ or 4.0 percent, the frequency of the recessive gene being $\tfrac{1}{5}$. Between the third and fourth generations, selection succeeded in achieving only a 2.2 percent reduction in the frequency of *aa* individuals.

What would be accomplished by total negative selection in the fourth generation?

Since

$$q_3^2 = (\tfrac{1}{5})^2; \; q_3 = \tfrac{1}{5}.$$

$$q_4^2 = \left(\frac{q_3}{1+q_3}\right)^2 = \left(\frac{\tfrac{1}{5}}{1+\tfrac{1}{5}}\right)^2 = (\tfrac{1}{5} \times \tfrac{5}{6})^2 = (\tfrac{1}{6})^2 = \tfrac{1}{36}$$

In the fifth generation, then, *aa* individuals will constitute $\tfrac{1}{36}$ or 2.8 percent of the population, a further reduction of only 1.2 percent. Apparently as generation follows generation, continued selection accomplishes less and less. Why is this?

Table 22.1 summarizes expectations for six generations. Note the simple progressions in the fractions, e.g., in the column headed "Frequency of recessive gene." What would be the gene frequency in the seventh generation? What then would be the frequency of *aa* individuals (fifth column)? The table shows the declining effectiveness of selection, and also the reason for it. Look at columns 4 and 5. In the first generation the ratio of *Aa* individuals to *aa* individuals is 2:1, in the second generation it is 4:1,

TABLE 22.1. Total negative selection against a recessive genotype (*aa*).

Generation	Frequency of recessive gene	Proportions of genotypes			Reduction in
		AA	Aa	*aa*	*aa*
1	1/2	1/4	2/4	1/4 = 25.0%	13.9%
2	1/3	4/9	4/9	1/9 = 11.1%	4.9%
3	1/4	9/16	6/16	1/16 = 6.2%	2.2%
4	1/5	16/25	8/25	1/25 = 4.0%	1.2%
5	1/6	25/36	10/36	1/36 = 2.8%	0.8%
6	1/7	36/49	12/49	1/49 = 2.0%	

in the third generation 6:1, in the fourth generation 8:1, and so on. As the gene decreases in frequency in the gene pool, *more and more of the genes that remain are found in heterozygotes, not in homozygotes.* This is the reason that selection against homozygous recessives declines in effectiveness.

The point is illustrated graphically in Figure 22.1, which begins with the same population as does Table 22.1, continues for ten generations, and then, in 10-generation jumps, continues on up to the 100th generation. Note here, as in the table, that the relative frequencies of both *Aa* and *aa* individuals decline, although at a steadily decreasing rate, but that the *Aa* individuals outnumber the *aa* individuals more and more as the generations pass. Hence, selection applied against *aa* individuals alone becomes less and less effective as the gene becomes more and more rare (see Dahlberg, 1948).

Total negative selection against a dominant gene will eliminate the gene entirely (down to the level of replacement by mutation) in one generation. How many generations will be required for elimination of a recessive gene if total negative selection is applied against homozygous recessives only? In theory the gene is *never* eliminated; it approaches zero asymptotically. However, as shown in Figure 22.1, it becomes vanishingly small by the

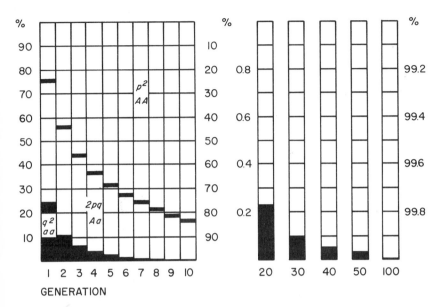

GENERATION

FIG. 22.1 Effect of total negative selection against homozygous recessives (*aa*). For the first ten generations the vertical scale is in percentage, for later generations in fractions of 1 percent. *AA*: homozygous
dominants. *Aa*: heterozygotes. In each vertical column the height of the
black portion at the base indicates the percentage of *aa* individuals,
the portion above this up to the heavy horizontal line represents the
percentage of *Aa* individuals, and portion at the top (above the heavy
horizontal line) represents the percentage of *AA* individuals. (Redrawn
from Dahlberg, G., 1948. *Mathematical Methods for Population
Genetics*. New York: Interscience Publishers. Used by permission of
the Institute for Medical Genetics, University of Uppsala, Sweden.)

100th generation (0.01 percent). How long is 100 generations? At least
2500 years. Can we imagine any program for human betterment being
continued consistently for so long?

Now we can see why the principles of population genetics have dimmed
the eugenic dream. For the most part, the genetic bases of disabilities in
which eugenists are interested are recessive in nature. This is true of
schizophrenia (pp. 301–303) and of the genetic component in most types
of mental deficiency that have such a component. The genes are relatively
rare. Our discussion has just demonstrated the relative ineffectiveness of
negative selection applied against rare recessive genes.

To add concreteness to our discussion, let us turn for a moment to a
trait with a simple mode of inheritance: albinism. Suppose that we should
be unwise enough to pass a law that albinos could not have children.
What effect would such a law, assuming perfect enforcement, have on the

number of albinos in the next generation? We mentioned earlier (pp. 96–97) that the form of albinism most commonly encountered depends on a recessive gene, and that about one person in 20,000 is an albino. Hence, $q^2 = \frac{1}{20,000}$, $q =$ approximately $\frac{1}{141}$. Now if albinos do not reproduce, how many albinos will there be in the next generation? Using the same formula applied above:

$$q_1^2 = \left(\frac{q}{1+q}\right)^2 = \left(\frac{\frac{1}{141}}{1 + \frac{1}{141}}\right)^2 = (\frac{1}{141} \times \frac{141}{142})^2 = (\frac{1}{142})^2 = \frac{1}{20,164}$$

To maximize the effect of selection, we will mention that the square of 141 is 19,881 (not 20,000). Hence, one generation of total negative selection against albinos would reduce the frequency from 1/19,881 to 1/20,164, or from 0.00502 percent to 0.00495 percent. Such tiny fractions of percentage are difficult to visualize, so we will convert them into number of people. The population of the United States is almost 200,000,-000; 0.00502 percent of 200,000,000 is 10,040; 0.00495 percent of 200,000,000 is 9900. A nationwide program of preventing albinos from having children could reduce the number of albinos by 140. Truly, in the words of Horace: "The mountains are in labor, and a ridiculous mouse will be born."

Again we emphasize the reason why selection against homozygous recessives accomplishes so little: under a system of random mating, the heterozygotes far outnumber the homozygous recessives, especially when the recessive gene is rare. We realize, therefore, that the effectiveness of selection would be increased by any factor that produced a relative increase in the number of homozygotes. As we noted in Chapter 7, assortative mating has this effect. If, instead of panmixis, we had a condition in which "like mates with like," selection would be expected to accomplish more than it would if mating were random.

To what extent is assortative mating actually encountered with respect to traits in which eugenists are interested? Perhaps the clearest evidence is that concerning mental ability. Many studies have indicated a tendency to assortative mating based on intelligence. Although exceptions are known to everyone, men and women tend to choose as mates individuals of about their own mental level. This tendency applies to the normal levels of intelligence and also to the subnormal levels (see Reed and Reed, 1965). Such a tendency to assortative mating would increase the effectiveness of selection applied to mentally retarded persons.

Let us see how this might work by considering the nonpathological or familial forms of mental deficiency. Under this term we include persons with an IQ lower than 70 who do not exhibit such pathological conditions as mongolism, phenylketonuria, cretinism, microcephaly, and many others. The commonly employed term "familial" suggests the observed fact that this form of mental retardation has a tendency to run in families. To a

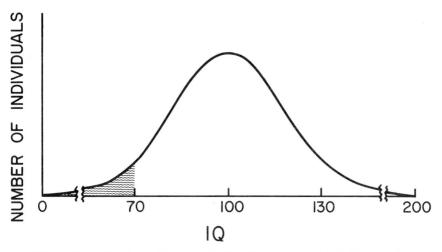

FIG. 22.2 Idealized diagram of the distribution of intelligence in a population. Shaded area: portion of the population regarded as mentally retarded.

large extent, such people form the "left end" of the normal frequency curve of intelligence (Fig. 22.2). As we noted in Chapter 21, such evidence as we have indicates that inheritance of intelligence is based on multiple genes (polygenes). Thus many if not most of these nonpathological mental retardates are those individuals who have been short-changed in the genes contributing to intelligence. Like the shorter plants in Figure 11.1 (p. 163), they do not have a sufficient number of effective alleles ("capital letter genes") to permit them to grow to greater size (mental capacity, in this case). In saying this, we are not overlooking the fact that normal mental development has environmental as well as genetic components. Achievement on intelligence tests is conditioned by environment as well as heredity, but at present we focus attention on the genetic component.

To an important extent, then, persons with an IQ below 70 have an unusually large proportion of those genes that do *not* make for superior intelligence. We may picture such people as having more than their share of "small letter genes" (*a, b, c,* etc.) and less than their share of the "capital letter genes" that contribute to intelligence. From our discussion of poly-genic inheritance (Chap. 11), we can readily understand that when these people choose to marry each other, some of their children will also have a high proportion of the "small letter genes" and be mentally retarded. In an extensive investigation not limited entirely to the nonpathological re-tardation we have used as an example, Reed and Reed (1965) found that "fifty-four fertile unions of two retarded persons in our unselected sample produced 215 surviving children, of whom 85 (39.5 percent) were re-tarded." That not all of the children born to a pair of retarded parents are retarded reflects the fact that the parents are heterozygous and that some of their children inherit genes for intelligence ("capital letter genes") from *both* of their parents and so have more of them than either parent has.

However, the point we wish to make here is that because retardates tend to choose each other as mates, and because a substantial proportion of the children of such matings are also retarded, eugenic measures to prevent reproduction by retardates could be more effective than they would be if assortative mating did not occur.

The eugenic measures referred to are the institutionalization and eugenic sterilization mentioned previously. In a democratic society, such measures are less likely to be employed with distant goals of genetic improvement in mind than they are with the more immediate goals of the welfare of the individuals concerned. Some of the higher grade mental retardates may become self-supporting members of society, but they are unlikely to attain incomes making possible an adequate standard of living for a large family. Is it not, therefore, to their advantage to avoid having such a family? Although some of the children may be of normal intelligence, is it best for normal children to be reared in the environment of a home in which the parents are retarded? These are some of the questions that suggest the value of eugenic measures to the individuals themselves (see Chap. 25). Emphasis on these immediate goals may lead to the adoption of measures that will also make possible the attainment of long-range goals for the improvement of mankind.

The occurrence of assortative mating, then, increases the effectiveness of selection against recessive genes. Are there ways in which the effectiveness could be increased still further? Because the genes with which we are concerned are relatively rare, with the result that most of them are carried by heterozygotes, we could increase the effectiveness of selection by including these heterozygotes. First, however, there is the problem of identification. How can we tell who is heterozygous and who is not? Sometimes this can be demonstrated by a study of the parents (e.g., if a normally pigmented person had an albino parent, we know that he must be heterozygous). Occasionally, tests can be applied to prove whether or not one is a carrier (pp. 385–386). However, in the majority of cases, people do not demonstrate that they are heterozygous until they have children who reveal the genotypes of the parents.

Suppose that we solve the problem of identification. What about the ethics of preventing phenotypically normal people from having children? The practice is especially doubtful when we recall that if a heterozygote marries a person who is not heterozygous (e.g., $Aa \times AA$), *all* the children will be normal. Even if two carriers marry each other (e.g., $Aa \times Aa$), three fourths of the children will be expected to be normal. Thus, we are not likely to see any programs to prevent reproduction by heterozygotes.

Again, we note that information concerning heterozygosity may be of vital importance in genetic counseling. Here the emphasis is on the *individual*, his best interests and those of potential children. If he carries a gene that results in severe abnormality, he may be advised, for example, not to marry a relative because of the increased chance of marrying another carrier if he does so (Chap. 8). We shall discuss genetic counseling further in Chapter 25.

PROBLEMS

1. A population has the following constitution: 3000 *AA*, 2000 *Aa*, 500 *aa*.
   (a) If no possessors of the gene *A* reproduce, how many members of the next generation will be *AA*? *Aa*? *aa*?
   (b) If the *aa* individuals do not reproduce, how many members of the next generation will be *AA*? *Aa*? *aa*? Assume that the population remains stationary in total size (5500).

2. The gene *e* is semilethal, homozygotes dying before puberty. In a certain community the child population has the following constitution: 98,010 *EE*, 1980 *Ee*, 10 *ee*. Thus, one child in 10,000 has the genotype *ee*. What fraction of the next generation will be expected to have the genotype *ee*?

3. In a certain panmictic population, 4 percent of the people are homozygous for a certain recessive gene. If they die before reaching reproductive age, what percentage of the next generation will be expected to be homozygous recessive?

4. In Population I the frequency, *q*, of a recessive gene is 0.01. In Population II the frequency of the gene is 0.1. What is the ratio of homozygous recessives to heterozygotes in each population? In which population will negative selection against homozygous recessives prove most effective in reducing the proportion of homozygous recessives in the next generation? Why?

REFERENCES

Dahlberg, G., 1948. *Mathematical Methods for Population Genetics.* New York: Interscience Publishers.

Haller, M. H., 1963. *Eugenics.* New Brunswick, N. J.: Rutgers University Press.

Osborn, F., 1951. *Preface to Eugenics*, rev. ed. New York: Harper & Brothers.

Popenoe, P., and R. H. Johnson, 1933. *Applied Eugenics.* New York: The Macmillan Company.

Reed, E. W., and S. C. Reed, 1965. *Mental Retardation: A Family Study.* Philadelphia: W. B. Saunders Company.

23.

DIFFERENTIAL FERTILITY
AND POPULATION PROBLEMS

The central idea of differential fertility is nothing more remarkable than the obvious fact that some people have more children than others. The point of interest is whether or not there are, on the average, significant differences between people who have many children and those who have few, or none.

It will be convenient to divide our discussion into two parts: (1) differential fertility among groups of people, and (2) individual differential fertility. The distinction is somewhat artificial since, of course, groups are composed of individuals, but it is convenient for emphasis.

Group Differences in Fertility

No subject in this book is in a greater state of flux and change than the one we are about to discuss. We shall therefore draw the picture as it existed in the past and trace trends observable at the time of writing, without trying to foresee whether or not these trends will continue.

The Inverse Ratio   For generations, even for centuries, students of mankind have been classifying people into groups and then observing differences among these groups in the number of children produced. The groupings may be based on income, social position, the occupation of the husband, or some other means of distinction. To have a general term for such groupings we call them **socioeconomic groups**, and at the risk of some snobbishness we classify them as "higher" and "lower." For generations, an inverse ratio, or negative correlation, existed, between the "height" of the group and number of children produced. The larger the income the fewer the children. The families of professional men were smaller than those of businessmen, which, in turn, were smaller than those of skilled artisans, which were smaller than those of unskilled laborers, and so on. The greater the amount of education of the parents, the smaller the families they produced.

This was the traditional picture for generations. We can see why it was a matter of concern to persons interested in the genetic future of mankind. *If* the differences between socioeconomic groups rest to a considerable extent on differences in ability, and *if* these differences in ability are at least in part determined by heredity, then the inverse ratio is **dysgenic**. Dysgenic is the opposite of eugenic; it means "detrimental to the future of mankind," especially to man's genetically determined nature. For example, *if* a man who earns $10,000 a year is genetically superior to a man who earns $1000 a year, then the fact that this second man was producing more children than the first would be dysgenic—more of the second man's than of the first man's genes would be present in the gene pool of the next generation. The prospect was not one a eugenist could regard with equanimity.

The "ifs" we have employed in the preceding sentences suggest at once that many questions are involved. Three of these merit particular attention: (1) To what extent are the differences between socioeconomic groups determined by differences in heredity? (2) If differential fertility continued, would it lead to decline in the intelligence of future generations? (3) Does the traditional inverse ratio apply to our modern society?

Are Socioeconomic Differences Determined by Differences in Heredity?
In attempting to answer the first question, we are at once confronted with the problem of measuring differences in ability. Does it take greater ability to be a college professor than it does to be a successful businessman (or vice versa)? Does a lawyer necessarily have greater natural ability than a skilled artisan? We lack objective yardsticks for measuring such differences. Naturally enough, then, we fall back on the use of intelligence tests. Many investigations through the years have given evidence that there is also an inverse ratio between the socioeconomic group and performance on intelligence tests. Children in the larger families produced on the average by the "lower" groups do less well than do children in the smaller families produced on the average by the "higher" groups. If, as we have seen (pp. 313–316), intelligence as measured by tests is in part gene-determined, this relationship between low ability and high fertility

is a matter of concern. Students of the subject have predicted that the relationship is sufficient to lead to a decline in average intelligence from generation to generation. Some investigators have even predicted the reduction in number of IQ points to be expected between two successive generations.

We are touching here on a subject of great interest to educators, psychologists, and sociologists, as well as to students of human genetics. The voluminous literature concerning differential fertility and intelligence is reviewed in Westoff (1954) and Anastasi (1956). We can only take space here to point out that things may not be entirely what they seem to be in these matters. To what extent is an intelligence test a yardstick that is equally applicable to children in all socioeconomic groups and in all sizes of family? The most widely used test is the Stanford-Binet. Psychologists at the University of Chicago (Eells *et al.*, 1951) have demonstrated that the choice of words employed in this test is such as to constitute "a definite bias against lower-class children in that the language and form in which the problems are couched are geared to the world of the upper and middle-class child" (Thompson, 1957). We do not pretend to be experts on testing intelligence, but we mention this point as indicative of the complex variables that must constantly be taken into account in attempting to draw conclusions from the data available.

Why do children of larger families perform less well on intelligence tests than do children from smaller families? This negative correlation between size of family and performance on the tests has been demonstrated many times. Anastasi (1956, 1959) has suggested three principal reasons. (1) Heredity—this applies to large families of which the parents have inferior intelligence for genetical reasons. The inferior genes of the parents are inherited by the children. (2) "Psychological differences in the environments provided by parents of varying intellectual levels." Here the children may be handicapped, not by poor genes but by the poor home environment. (3) Family size itself. This is allied to the second point in that it involves restriction of the environment. Usually a large family is subjected to financial stress that restricts the educational and cultural opportunities of each individual child. In particular, in a large family contact of the individual child with adults may be reduced, thereby slowing language development, and language plays a crucial role in success both on intelligence tests and in educational attainment in general.

We are particularly interested in the hereditary aspects of the problem. Here a difficulty arises: How can we distinguish poor performance based on genetic reasons from poor performance based on reasons that are essentially environmental? How much of the poorer showing on intelligence tests made by children in "lower" groups is caused by the fact that they do belong to such groups, how much to the fact that they belong on the average to large families? Although we cannot answer these ques-

FIG. 23.1 Heredity has done its part. What will be the effect of environment? (Photo by Tony Rollo. From *Newsweek*.)

tions, we can at least beware of drawing incautious conclusions. The environmental reasons for poor performance on the tests loom so large that we should not conclude that poor performers are necessarily, or perhaps even usually, genetically inferior to good performers (Fig. 23.1).

Thus, to our first question—to what extent are the differences between socioeconomic groups determined by differences in heredity—we can only answer that we do not know. Even when we restrict our attempts to measure differences in ability to measuring differences in performance on intelligence tests, we find so many variables that no certain conclusions are possible. Undoubtedly people do vary in genetically determined ability, but every socioeconomic group is a vast mixture of people, with many varying degrees of ability. One unskilled laborer is unskilled because he lacks the ability to be anything else; another is unskilled because he had no opportunity for education and training as a child, not because he could not have profited from them if he had had the opportunity. This second man's genes are all right and therefore his producing of a large family is not dysgenic. Whether or not his doing so is *socially* desirable depends on whether he, and society, can provide the children with education and opportunities commensurate with their abilities. That, however, is another question.

Our inability to give a definite answer to the question points up the fact that analyzing large, mixed groups of people is not a particularly good method of determining the hereditary component in intelligence. The twin method (Chaps. 20 and 21) is much better, and so is our old friend, the study of pedigrees. If high test scores were achieved by parents, we should find great interest in determining the test scores of the children, particularly if at the same time we analyzed the environment. "Thus, in an extreme case where all members of the family achieved high test scores, in spite of great social adversity of a kind normally associated with low scores in the rest of the population (crowding in the home, low socio-economic status, and so on), one might reasonably infer an exceedingly strong hereditary component for high intelligence in these particular parents" (Newcombe, 1963).

Will Average Intelligence Decline?   We turn now to our second question: If differential fertility continued, would it lead to a decline in the intelligence of future generations? The foregoing discussion suggests the answer. In the first place, we have noted that there is good reason to doubt that low-average performance on intelligence tests is indicative of low-average, gene-determined intelligence. We have also pointed out that great diversity of intelligence exists within each socioeconomic group. Indeed, some evidence exists that the more highly endowed members of a certain group may have a higher rate of reproduction than have the less highly endowed members. Such intragroup differentials might offset any intergroup differentials.

We referred above to the inverse ratio between family size and achievement on intelligence tests. Rather surprisingly, various investigations have shown that there is a similar negative correlation between family size and *stature*. On the average, families in which the children are short are larger than are families in which the children are tall. Unless we are cautious, this might lead us to prophesy that people will be getting shorter as generations pass. Actually, as is common knowledge, our population is growing taller on the average; the reasons for the increase in stature are probably nutritional (i.e., environmental). In all probability there is no significant change in the genetic structure of the population with regard to stature. However, this example warns us of the dangers (a) of drawing conclusions from correlations alone and (b) of concluding that inferior performance on intelligence tests by members of large families presages a decline in the intelligence of our descendants.

Furthermore, a variable is introduced by differences in the proportion of people who marry and produce children. Members of the Dight

Institute of Human Genetics of the University of Minnesota investigated 1016 families for whom IQ scores of both parents and one or more of their children were available (Higgins *et al.*, 1962). All tests were done when the individuals were children. One portion of the results of the study is summarized in Table 23.1. The average number of offspring was 2.75, but

TABLE 23.1. Relation between IQ of parents (taken singly) and the size of family they produced.

IQ of parent	Average number of children	No. of parents
70 and below	3.81	73
71–85	2.98	180
86–100	2.65	597
101–115	2.68	860
116–130	2.70	287
131 and up	2.94	35
Average	2.75	

(From Higgins, J. V., E. W. Reed, and S. C. Reed, 1962. "Intelligence and family size: a paradox resolved," *Eugenics Quarterly*, 9:84–90.)

parents with an IQ of 70 ("moron") and below averaged 3.81 children, an example of the inverse ratio we have been discussing. However, a study of the siblings of these "moron" parents revealed that this group had a low rate of marriage: "The higher reproductive rate of those in the lower IQ groups who are parents is offset by the larger proportion of their siblings who never marry or who fail to reproduce when married" (Higgins *et al.*, 1962). As a result, the group *as a whole* does not produce more children than do groups with higher intelligence. In general, previous analyses of differences between socioeconomic groups did not take sufficient account of the childless members of the groups.

A third reason for doubting that differential fertility leads to a decline in average intelligence is based on the probable genetic structure of the population. Many studies have indicated a strong tendency for assortative mating—a tendency of people of low intelligence to choose each other as mates and of people of higher intelligence to choose mates of approximately their own intellectual caliber. Penrose (1950, 1962) has suggested that if we added *heterosis* to assortative mating, a situation would occur that would explain maintenance of genetic equilibrium despite differences in fertility. As we have noted previously (pp. 272–273), heterosis is superiority of heterozygotes over homozygotes. In this case we visualize the superiority as manifesting itself in increased fertility. Differences in innate intelligence are probably to be explained on the basis of polygenic inheritance (Chapter 11)—many genes with additive effect. Perhaps persons with extremely high IQ's are relatively homozygous for genes for high intelligence, whereas the opposite is also true—people with very low intelligence are also relatively homozygous for their unfortunate genes. That leaves the bulk of people in between, with varying degrees of heterozygosity for genes concerned with intelligence. If there is assortative mating and *if* these heterozygotes produce more children on the average than do either of the extremes, an equilibrium will be established, the supply of the extremes in each generation being replenished by the matings of the heterozygotes.

Penrose (1950, 1962) illustrated the principle with a simple model (Table 23.2). Let us oversimplify by assuming that only one pair of genes

TABLE 23.2.   Imaginary population with completely assortative mating: intelligence level determined by a perfectly additive gene pair.

Types of mating	Frequency of mating pair	Relative birth rate per family	Offspring		
			AA (IQ 103) Superior	Aa (IQ 73) Inferior	aa (IQ 43) Sublethal
AA × AA	90	1.89	170	—	—
Aa × Aa	10	4.00	10	20	10
All types	100	2.10	180	20	10
Parental pairs in next generation			90	10	—

(From Penrose, L. S., 1962. *The Biology of Mental Defect,* 3rd ed. London: Sidgwick & Jackson Ltd.)

is involved, A and a. In setting up the model, Penrose postulated that AA people have an IQ of 103 and a birth rate not sufficient to replace themselves: 1.89 births per family. Aa people are postulated to have an IQ of 73 and elevated fertility—4.00 births per family, whereas aa people have an IQ of 43 and do not reproduce at all. He further postulated complete assortative mating and that 90 percent of the matings are AA × AA and 10 percent are Aa × Aa. Then, as shown in the table, the 90 AA × AA pairs will produce 170 children, all AA. The 10 Aa × Aa matings will produce children in a 1:2:1 ratio: 10 AA, 20 Aa, 10 aa. The 180 AA children and 20 Aa children will be the only fertile members of their generation. They will constitute 90 AA × AA pairs and 10 Aa × Aa pairs, as their parents did; therefore, the population is evidently in equilibrium. The average IQ of the children is the same as that of their parents.

This is an oversimplified model. Penrose has worked out more realistic hypotheses, using a greater number of gene pairs. However, the model illustrates the point that, given the factors of assortative mating and heterosis, maintenance of an equilibrium is to be expected despite failure of the extremes to produce "their share" of offspring. In point of fact, matings are not completely assortative as in the model. *AA* × *Aa* matings would occur and would increase the supply of superior children. Of the two factors postulated, assortative mating is observed to occur in human populations, and heterosis of the kind postulated is to be expected, in view of its wide occurrence in plants and lower animals which have been the subject of genetic experimentation.

In response to the question—if differential fertility continued, would it lead to a decline in the intelligence of future generations?—we can reply that various lines of evidence lead us to think that such an outcome would not be likely.

Do we have any direct evidence of changing intelligence with the passage of time? We may mention three investigations bearing on this question. In 1932, over 87,000 11-year-old Scottish children were given an intelligence test; they achieved a mean score of 34.5 points. In 1947, nearly 71,000 11-year-old Scottish children were given the same test; their mean score was 36.7 points. A random sample of the children in the two surveys was given the Binet test, with no appreciable change in scores being noted (Scottish Council for Research in Education, 1949).

Again, investigation of intelligence test scores of military personnel in World War I and in World War II showed better performance by the personnel of the second war. This paralleled an increase in the amount of education the men had received (Tuddenham, 1948).

The third investigation was an analysis of mental test scores achieved by some 130,000 American high school pupils over a period of 26 years (Finch, 1946). The results indicated that the average mental ability of the pupils in more recent years was equal, or slightly superior, to the mental ability of the pupils who had been in high school during the earlier years. This was true despite the fact that the proportion of children going to high school had increased substantially in the meantime.

To say the least, then, decline in intelligence does not seem to characterize our population.

What of the Present?   We turn now to our third question (p. 337): Does the traditional inverse ratio apply to our modern society?

For many years students of the subject have pointed out that the differences in fertility between socioeconomic groups seemed to be diminishing. Up until about the time of World War II the diminishing difference was caused largely by a decrease in the fertility of the more fertile groups, whereas the fertility of the less fertile groups remained unchanged. This trend caused the groups to become more alike in fertility. What was the basis of this change?

In answering this question we first ask another: What was the underlying reason for the differential fertility between groups in the first place? There is general agreement that the differential depended on differences in voluntary control of family size—in other words, in the use of contraception or birth control. The more successful, better educated people practiced birth control more, and more effectively, than did their less well-endowed contemporaries. However, as time went on, effective use of birth control increased in lower groups, with the result that their originally high birth rate decreased until the rate approached that of the higher groups.

This line of reasoning implies that some people, indeed whole groups of people, have more children than they want to have. No one doubts the truth of this in individual cases. A systematic investigation of the matter has been made by Freedman, Whelpton, and Campbell (1959), as part of a large study of family planning and fertility in 2713 white married women between the ages of 18 and 39, inclusive, selected to represent a scientific probability sample of wives of that age in the national population. They were asked many questions about their families, the size of family they regarded as desirable for themselves, their use of contraceptive measures, and so on. From the voluminous report, we extract one bit of data: the correlation of success in family planning with the amount of education. This part of the study is based on 1454 married women who were *fecund*, meaning that they were capable of having children. They were asked: Before your last pregnancy began did you really want another child at some time in the future or would you just as soon not have had one? Mothers who indicated that they or their husbands did not want the last pregnancy were classed as exhibiting "excess fertility" (Table 23.3). These

TABLE 23.3. Percentage of cases in which the most recent pregnancy was undesired, classified according to the education of the couple.

Education of parents	No. of women	Percentage of excess fertility
Both college	210	7
One high school, other college	272	10
Both high school, 4 years	310	9
One high school, 1–3 years; other high school, 4 years	234	14
Both high school, 1–3 years	118	14
One grade school, other more	235	20
Both grade school	75	33

(From *Family Planning, Sterility, and Population Growth* by R. Freedman, P. K. Whelpton, and A. A. Campbell. Copyright © 1959, McGraw-Hill Book Co., Inc. Used by permission of McGraw-Hill Book Company.)

data give some indication of degree of success in voluntary control of family size. We note that success was greatest when both parents had a college education, least when the education of the parents was limited to grade school. We may anticipate that this differential will be reduced, and perhaps will disappear, if and when birth control methods become more effective and simple enough to be used effectively by relatively uneducated people. However, we must remember that birth control methods are intended for the *voluntary* control of fertility. Some people want to have large families. Thus, with the spread of birth control, differential fertility between socioeconomic groups will disappear only if the *desired* family size is the same for all groups (and if fecundity—ability to produce children—does not vary between groups).

This introduces the second reason for the decrease in the differential fertility among socioeconomic groups. Since World War II, the fertility of the "highest" groups has increased. Although no one knows the reason for this trend, it is related to a change in the desires of the most favored groups in our population. Formerly the people with larger incomes and better education wanted few children; now they want to have larger families.

At this point, we are tempted to include reams of tables from the 1960 United States Census; we shall be satisfied with including two short tables. The data presented in Table 23.4 relate to white wives 35 to 44 years old, married between the ages of 14 and 21 to "professional, technical, and kindred workers" who had one year or more of college education. The numbers in the table give the number of children ever born per 1000 married women (including childless wives) and per 1000 mothers. The differences between the groups are relatively small—typical of the diminishing differentials we have mentioned. The greatest fertility lies at the two ends: among those with lowest income and among those with highest income. If the level of income gives some measure of success, evidently the most successful college-educated people are having more children than their less successful fellows. This same relationship prevails in groups in which the husband is a farmer or farm manager, businessman, or craftsman. Interestingly, high income combined with high school education did not seem to have the same effect in elevating fertility. One gains the impression in looking at the tables that college-educated people, financially able to provide good educational and cultural opportunities for their children, are producing larger numbers of children to enjoy those advantages. The effect is most noticeable at the "$10,000 or over" income level. In this connection, we may note that Dice *et al.* (1964), in a study of 545 male inhabitants of Ann Arbor, Michigan, found that men with yearly incomes of $10,000 or more were more fertile than were men with smaller incomes.

A bimodal relationship (high at the two "ends") of the type shown in

TABLE 23.4. U. S. Census of 1960. Number of children ever born to white wives aged 35 to 44, married at ages 14 to 21 to "professional, technical and kindred workers" who had 1 year or more of college education, classified by income of husband for 1959.

Income of husband	Children per 1000 wives	Children per 1000 mothers
$1 to $1999, or loss	2792	3060
$2000 to $3999	2583	2755
$4000 to $6999	2614	2806
$7000 to $9999	2667	2846
$10,000 or over	2780	2937

(Data from U. S. Bureau of the Census. 1964. *U. S. Census of Population: 1960. Subject Reports. Women by Number of Children Ever Born.* Final Report PC(2)-3A, Table 39, p. 199. U. S. Government Printing Office, Washington, D. C.)

Table 23.4 has been observed previously. Referring back to Table 23.1, we note that parents with an IQ of "131 and up" had more children than did parents with lower IQ's (until the IQ level of 71–85 points was reached). Similarly, a study of 979 people born in 1916 or 1917, and given intelligence tests at 11 years of age, showed that the ones with the highest IQ's eventually had more children than did the ones with lower IQ's (until the 80 to 94 level was reached; Bajema, 1963).

Much has been written about the fact that, traditionally, the greater the number of years of education a woman had, the smaller the number of children she produced. In times past this inverse relationship was striking. Is it as marked today as it was previously? Table 23.5 presents data for two age groups of women reported in the U. S. Census of 1960: those who were between 35 and 44 years of age in that year, and those who were between 45 and 54 years of age. As we look at the data concerning the older women, we note that the inverse ratio is shown in typical fashion, most strikingly in the column headed "Children per 1000 women," which refers to all women of that age, married or not. The same trend, although less marked, is shown in the column headed "Children per 1000 wives," which refers only to married women (marital fertility).

Turning to the younger women (35 to 44 years old), we note that the inverse relationship is much less striking. The least educated among them had slightly more children than did the least educated older women, but the fertility of women with more education was much greater than that of the older women with comparable amounts of education. Also, the percentage of childlessness was much lower. We may note that the youngest of these younger women were 20 years of age at the end of World

War II and, hence, may have participated in the "baby boom" of the postwar years.

TABLE 23.5. U. S. Census of 1960: Fertility of women related to amount of education they have received.

Education of women	35–44 years old			45–54 years old		
	Child-less percent	Children per 1000 women	Children per 1000 wives	Child-less percent	Children per 1000 women	Children per 1000 wives
Elementary, less than 8 years	18.3	3101	3796	20.3	3007	3773
Elementary, 8 years	15.7	2686	3186	20.5	2454	3089
High school, 1–3 years	13.9	2511	2915	21.8	2173	2780
High school, 4 years	16.6	2244	2691	26.3	1800	2443
College, 1–3 years	17.9	2219	2703	27.8	1723	2385
College, 4 or more years	26.4	1952	2652	39.4	1371	2261

Figures relate to the United States as a whole. (Data from *U.S. Census of Population: 1960. Subject Reports. Women by Number of Children Ever Born.* Final Report PC (2)-3A, Table 28, pp. 117–18. U. S. Government Printing Office, Washington, D.C.)

The Bureau of Census has estimated that, at the death rates prevailing in 1959, 2140 births per 1000 women are necessary for replacement. A group is said to be replacing itself if the number of adults of reproductive age remains constant from generation to generation. We note from the table that with one exception all groups of the younger women exceeded this replacement level. The exception was formed by women who had four or more years of college; they produced 1952 children per 1000 women. Even this number is not far below the replacement level. Various causes contributed to this lower birth rate. A chief cause was probably an increase in the number of women who did not marry, as compared to groups of women with less education. From census data not shown in the table, we learn that whereas only 4.8 percent of women in the "Elementary, 8 years" category, and only 5.4 percent of the women in the "High school, 4 years" group remained unmarried, 14.2 percent of the women in the "College, 4 or more years" group did not marry. Parenthetically, we may note that among the older women, 19.1 percent of the "College, 4 or more years" group did not marry.

Turning to marital fertility (children per 1000 wives), we note that the younger wives with high school and college educations differed little in the number of children and that they had already produced more children than had the older wives with comparable amounts of education. (Moreover, many of the families of the younger wives were probably not completed, as the women were still of reproductive age.) The fact that these younger wives had married at an earlier age doubtless influenced this result. Moreover, in the past, if a woman married, her educational career was almost always terminated; this is no longer true.

Thus, for various reasons, differences in fertility related to education have decreased. Although low innate ability is only one reason that girls end their schooling, the tendency among women who have high school and college educations to have increased numbers of children will no doubt be beneficial to the average intelligence of future generations.

We can see that at present (a) differences in fertility between socioeconomic groups are small and (b) there is a tendency to increased fertility on the part of the "highest" groups. Insofar as members of these groups differ genetically from members of "lower" groups, this trend is definitely eugenic. Insofar as members of these groups are people best able to provide their children with educational and cultural advantages, this trend is socially desirable. From the standpoints of both "nature and nurture" we may rejoice in the trend.

This trend is by no means confined to North America. Investigations have revealed its existence in England, France, Sweden, and West Germany (Carter, 1962). Doubtless it is found elsewhere, as well. Is the trend a permanent one, or is it merely a passing phase in the long history of populational change? Only the future will disclose the answer. Already there are students of the subject who believe they see signs that the trend has run its course and that the increase in number of births among "the white-collar groups" will not continue into the future (Osborn, 1963). We shall wait and see.

The Population Explosion

Strictly speaking, eugenics is concerned more with *quality* of population than with its quantity, yet the two aspects are so indissolubly associated that some consideration of population size, as such, is appropriate here.

The much-discussed "population explosion" is a recent phenomenon in human history. Prior to World War II, most of the countries of western Europe had relatively stable populations, or populations slowly declining in size. For some countries the decline was a matter of national concern, and measures were taken to encourage increase in the birth rate so that it might at least attain a replacement level. Such measures included economic aid to families and assistance with the costs of childbirth and the care of children. In the United States, the population was growing steadily but at a decreasing *rate* of growth, as census followed census. Hence attainment of a stable population was visualized for the not-distant future, at least by the end of the century. As I write, I have before me an "authoritative" estimate made in 1940; it predicted that by 1965 the population would be somewhat over 149 million, and that this would have increased to 153 million by 1980. In point of fact, our population reached 190 million in 1963. What happened?

As everyone knows, there was a sudden increase in the birth rate following World War II. The increase on the part of higher socioeconomic groups discussed above was part of a larger picture. What caused the increase? Many factors were involved. In part, it was a catching up on family production, which had been disrupted by the war. In part, it reflected improved economic conditions; more people were able to afford the expense of rearing and educating large families than in the preceding generation. In part, it was the pattern of younger marriage than had been the custom in the recent past. Marriage while husband or wife, or both, were in college, coupled with the production of babies while one or both parents were acquiring an education meant that child-bearing began sooner, during the couple's most fertile years. Some observers at the time felt that a change in timing was all that was involved—that young people were starting their families sooner but that they would also stop sooner, with one or two children. The young people confounded these prophets by producing third and fourth children, or more. Evidently a psychological change had occurred as well, manifested by a desire for larger families

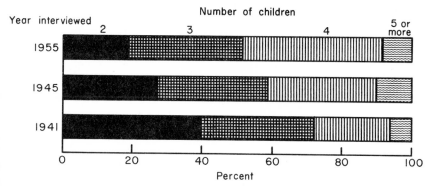

FIG. 23.2 Sizes of family considered ideal by women questioned in surveys conducted in 1941, in 1945, and in 1955. The scale along the base line gives the percentages of women responding, respectively, that they considered 2, 3, 4, and 5 or more children the ideal number. (Redrawn from *Family Planning, Sterility, and Population Growth* by R. Freedman, P. K. Whelpton, and A. A. Campbell. Copyright © 1959, McGraw-Hill Book Co., Inc. Used by permission of McGraw-Hill Book Company.)

than generations in the immediate past had wanted.

Changing ideals with regard to family size are reflected in Figure 23.2, based on data from three surveys of the opinion of women concerning what they considered the "ideal" family size to be (Freedman *et al.*, 1959). We note that in 1941, about 40 percent of the women interviewed considered two children ideal, whereas only 21 percent considered four to be the ideal number. By 1955, the proportions were almost exactly reversed: 19 percent of the women regarded two children as the ideal family, whereas 41 percent considered four ideal. Interestingly, none of the women in any of the surveys regarded a childless marriage as ideal. A one-child family was regarded as ideal by 1 percent of the women in 1941 and 1945 (not shown on the graph), but by none of the women in 1955. The average size of ideal family in the 1955 survey was 3.4 (if we are bothered by "fractional children," we may translate that as 34 children for each 10 families), but let us hasten to add that the actual size of family *expected* by these women (all married) was less than this: about 3.0 (Freedman *et al.*, 1959). Of course, not all of them had as many children as they said they expected to have when interviewed.

Mr. Frederick Osborn, one of America's most distinguished eugenists, has estimated on the basis of data from the study by Freedman *et al.* (1959), and others, that if American women had the number of children they wished to have, that number would be from 2.34 to 2.39 (Osborn, 1963). This number is somewhat lower than the ones quoted above, primarily because a reduction is made for "subfecundity" (the fact that some women cannot have as many children as they wish to have). Estimating that the size of family necessary for replacement is about 2.17, Mr. Osborn concluded: "A reduction of births to the number wanted by the parents would bring the birth rate close to replacement and would slow the rate of population growth. If a reduction of the rate needed for replacement were attained within 10 years, our population would grow to reach about 300 million in the year 2020 and be about stationary thereafter. We would have more time to adjust our political, educational, and social institutions to our great growth in size and to the urbanization of our people. There would be less pressure on our natural resources and less danger of ultimate overpopulation."

What is the significance of Mr. Osborn's estimate of 300 million people in the United States by the year 2020? A large population is neither intrinsically good nor intrinsically bad. It is good or bad depending on whether or not it is accompanied by sufficient economic and technological progress so that the members of the large population can enjoy a satisfactory standard of living. Hence the problems lie in the realms of economics and technology rather than in the field of human genetics. Will there be enough food, housing, and other goods? Will educational and cultural opportunities keep pace? Will the country's water supply prove adequate? Can sufficient electrical energy be generated? These are only a few of the questions.

By the time this book is in print our population may well be 200 million. Mr. Osborn suggests that less than 60 years from now the population may be half again as large as it is now. Will this country be able to provide that number of people with "the good life"? Perhaps we are not being too optimistic if we prophesy that it can do so. At the same time we may well wonder how much *beyond* that we can go without detriment to our standard of living. Freedman *et al.* (1959) estimated that if the average family had three children, our population would reach 312 million by the year 2000, and 600 million by 2050. Note that this latter figure is three times our present population. We may hope that family size remains nearer the replacement level than this, and that Mr. Osborn is correct in his prophecy that the population size will remain stationary soon after reaching 300 million. If, as he thinks, this can be accomplished under a system in which parents have as many children as they want and are able to have, we have real cause for optimism concerning the future.

The goal seems attainable, for, as we noted previously, size of family is coming more and more under voluntary control. We may be sure that in the near future, parents in all socioeconomic groups will control their fertility so that they have only as many children as they wish to have. There is evidence that the concept of ideal family size does not differ greatly among the different groups. Population stability without destruction of our standard of living seems an attainable goal. (See National Academy of Sciences, 1965, for discussion of problems of high fertility in the United States.)

World Population

When we turn from the United States with its advanced industrial civilization to the rest of the world, we encounter a much more chaotic situation. Population was small for a long time, then it increased slowly for a long time, and like compound interest, it has been increasing at an accelerating rate (Fig. 23.3). It is estimated that the population doubled in the nearly 200 years from 1650 to 1840, doubled again in the 90 years from 1840 to 1930, "and is now increasing at a rate that would cause doubling every 35 to 40 years" (Coale, 1961). This is the population explosion the authors of the article entitled, "Doomsday: Friday, 13 November, A.D. 2026" had in mind (von Foerster *et al.*, 1960). "At this date human population will approach infinity if it grows as it has grown in the last two millennia." On the basis of their statistical predictions the authors stated, no doubt with tongue in cheek: "Our great-great-grandchildren will not starve to death.

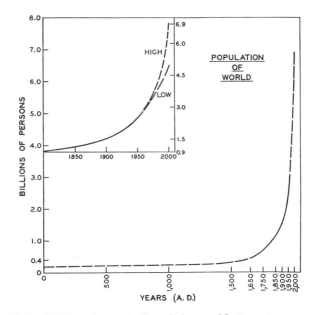

FIG. 23.3 Estimated population of the world, (A.D. 1 to A.D. 2000. (From Dorn, H. F., 1962. "World population growth: an international dilemma," *Science*, **135**:283–90. Copyright 1962 by the American Association for the Advancement of Science.

They will be squeezed to death."

This is not going to happen. There will be changes between now and 2026 A.D. Some of the changes are already visible. Reduction in rate of growth is theoretically possible in three ways: "external migration, a decline in the birth rate, or a deliberate increase in the death rate" (Nortman, 1964). Here we might note parenthetically that some people deny the need for any reduction in rate at all, maintaining that economic and technological development will always be able to keep pace with growth of population. Carried to extremes, however, this point of view seems highly untenable. The size of the earth is limited, and possibilities of increasing supplies of food and energy are not boundless. Fortunately much can be accomplished along these lines, thus giving us needed time to work out longer-range solutions.

External migration is a limited solution. At present, there are large areas of the earth that could support much larger populations than they now have. With much effort, even the Arctic tundra could be made habitable. However, there are definite limits, and whatever may be the future of space exploration, we can hardly imagine that emigration to other planets will do much to relieve population pressure on earth.

"Deliberate increase in the death rate" is a humanly unthinkable solution. Much of our present problem is created by the fact that medical science has decreased the death rate in many parts of the world where it was formerly high. Under primitive conditions, a high death rate helps to control population size by compensating for a high birth rate. Much of the problem arises because death (before birth, in infancy, and in childhood, especially) is being reduced so that more people live to adulthood and become parents themselves. We cannot, and would not wish to, turn back the clock in this respect.

This leaves us the third choice: a decline in the birth rate. This is inevitably the long-range solution to the problem. It is difficult to put into effect for many reasons. For one thing, means of birth control are far from perfect. However, great strides are being made in their improvement, and, in the very near future, means will be perfected that can be used effectively even by uneducated people, granted the will to do so. The problem of educating primitive people so that they will understand why they should limit births, as well as how to do so, is staggering but not impossible. The matter is a delicate one, affecting the most intimate and personal aspects of one's life, and it must be presented to each group and nationality in such a way as to avoid offense to religion, customs, and folkways.

Fortunately, many countries are alive to their own population problems. National interest has been spurred by the fact that governmental leaders have come to realize that uncontrolled increase in population delays the *economic* growth of a nation (Stycos, 1964). Three countries with acute problems already have national population policies: India, Pakistan, and Korea (Nortman, 1964). Dr. Nortman listed as "countries with limited involvement in family planning" Malaysia, Hong Kong, Ceylon, Puerto Rico, and Barbados, and "countries with experimental or pilot projects" Taiwan, Tunisia, Turkey, United Arab Republic. Other countries are exhibiting an "emerging interest" in their population problems. All this is only a beginning; to date the effects have not altered the escalating birth rate, but they give promise of doing so in the future.

To be successful, a national policy for reducing the birth rate must depend on voluntary cooperation of the citizens. Coercive measures would be undesirable and ineffective. To what extent do people want to limit the number of children they produce?

Earlier, we mentioned the ideals of American couples concerning family size (p. 350). An interesting comparison is afforded by a pilot study of 241 couples in Taiwan (Freedman, 1963). Despite their different cultural background, the size of family these people considered ideal was close to that in the American study, the extremes being 4.3 and 3.5, and the ideal stated varied little with the education of the parents. There was, however, a strong inverse relationship between the amount of education and the percentage of parents who actually practiced some form of family planning. Less than 10 percent of parents with no formal education practiced such voluntary control, whereas from 62 to 71 percent of the best-educated parents did so. Similar studies are being made or have been made in many other countries: "13 countries of the Western Hemisphere, 3 African, 3 Middle Eastern, 5 European, and 7 Oriental nations" (Stycos, 1964). Dr. Stycos concluded: "The ideal in most countries tends to be a family of three or four children."

How is limitation of family size to be achieved? Although it is repugnant to Americans for moral and religious reasons, legalized abortion is practiced in many countries as a means of population control. "The remarkable decline in birth rates in Japan can be attributed largely to the utilization of this method" (Stycos, 1964). Sterilization will be discussed in Chapter 25. It is of particular value as a means of population control for parents who already have as many children as they want.

Less drastic methods of family limitation are the various techniques of contraception. Traditionally these have consisted of various methods of preventing sperm and ova from coming into contact. Recently, research has brought forward other possibilities: use of hormones or drugs to prevent ovulation by women, or formation of sperm by men; prevention of a zygote, once it is formed, from becoming implanted in the wall of the uterus so that embryonic development may ensue; use of various intra-uterine devices which, in ways not now understood, have proved effective in preventing pregnancy (for a more extensive summary, see National Academy of Sciences, 1963). We mention these matters primarily to indicate that there are many possibilities, some of which are sure to result in simple, effective, and acceptable methods of controlling family size.

We may conclude with Dr. Nortman (1964): "Hope lies in the fact that latent among all people—in Asia, Africa, and Latin America, as well as in the Western World—is the desire to limit births to the number that can be adequately cared for and raised. Public opinion polls in various parts of the world indicate that large proportions of all people have some concept of an ideal number of children. Not all know that they can restrict their births to this ideal, but there is sufficient evidence to indicate that people in the emerging countries can acquire and apply the necessary knowledge."

As we stated at the outset, as eugenists we are more concerned with *quality* than we are with quantity of people. In the future as quantity is gradually brought under control, we wish to be sure that quality does not suffer. If only the genetically best-endowed portions of the population practiced voluntary control of births, the effect could be dysgenic. However, such evidence as we have indicates that almost all people have the desire to control the size of their families. Hence we may expect that when the means of doing this become more generally and easily available, the population may stabilize with much the same genetic constitution it has at present (although breaking down of isolates and intermarriage between races may alter the *distribution* of the genes; see pp. 120–123). Because of the great heterozygosity of the population, the marriages of average people will continue to produce, in addition to average children, gifted individuals and, less fortunately, defective ones (pp. 331–334). Therefore, voluntary control of births is not likely to lead to deterioration of the population. Indeed, it may have the reverse effect if the genetically best-endowed individuals choose to have more children on the average than do their less well-endowed contemporaries.

Individual Differential Fertility

The gene pool of one generation is not necessarily a random sample of the gene pool of the parents. Not all the genes in the parental generation are passed on to offspring. Some members of the parental generation do not marry. Some who do marry do not have children. Some who have children have fewer of them than do others. This is what we mean by individual differential fertility.

A striking example is afforded by data collected many years ago by Powys on the fertility of married women, primarily of British ancestry, in New South Wales, Australia (Powys, 1905). These women had died after the age of 46, i.e., after their child-bearing years were over. Hence the data represent completed families. From Table 23.6 we note that of the 10,276 women, the more fertile 50 percent produced 76.4 percent of the children. The data are noteworthy for a few families of rather spectacular size; even if we omitted these, a strong differential fertility would still be evident.

The data illustrate a trend common to both advanced and primitive cultures. Neel (1958) summarized data showing that in a certain township on the Gold Coast of Africa the more fertile 50 percent of the women produced 69.7 percent of the children. A survey in Liberia showed that 50 percent of the women produced 78.5 percent of the children. In two villages in Pakistan, 50 percent of the women produced 69 percent of the children. In the United States, as revealed by the 1940 Census, 50 percent of the women produced 88 percent of the children (Neel, 1958).

This tendency for a descendant generation to be produced by only a portion of the parental generation was noted long ago by Karl Pearson, the eminent British biometrician. He wrote: "It is a point which seems to me of the utmost significance that, allowing for the porportion of unmarried in the population, about ⅕ to ⅙ only of the adults produce quite one-half of the next generation, and any correlation between inheritable (physical or social) characteristics and fertility must thus sensibly in-

TABLE 23.6.   Differential fertility of married women in New South Wales, Australia. (The women had died after the completion of the reproductive period, i.e., after 46 years of age.)

Size of family	No. of married women	No. of children	
0	1110	0	
1	533	533	
2	581	1162	15,030
3	644	1932	children
4	702	2808	= 23.6%
5	813	4065	
6	755	4530	
6	100	600	
7	976	6832	
8	963	7704	
9	847	7623	
10	786	7860	
11	568	6248	
12	422	5064	
13	226	2938	
14	129	1806	48,623
15	57	855	children
16	39	624	= 76.4%
17	12	204	
18	5	90	
19	2	38	
20	2	40	
21	1	21	
22	1	22	
24	1	24	
30	1	30	
	10,276	63,653	

5138 women = 50% (upper group); 5138 women = 50% (lower group)

Data from Powys, A. O., 1905. "Data for the problem of evolution in man. On fertility, duration of life and reproductive selection," *Biometrika*, 4:233–85.

fluence that next generation" (Neel, 1958).

What is the significance of such differential fertility? Pearson and others since his time have been concerned that the more fertile portion of the population might be inferior to the less fertile portion. Insofar as the superiority had a genetic basis, lessened fertility on the part of superior individuals would be dysgenic. We have discussed this question as it relates to *group* differences in fertility, and as groups are only assemblages of individuals we need not repeat the discussion here. At any rate, differentials of this type may well be decreasing, as we have noted.

Turning the question around, we ask: Why do some parents have fewer children than do others, or have no children at all? In part, reduced fertility is a matter of voluntary control, as we have seen, but to an important extent it is involuntary. Sterility and lowered fecundity may have physical bases, or the difficulties may be primarily psychological. Penrose (1962) has concluded that the extremely low birth rate of low-grade mental defectives has a psychological basis rather than being a matter of physical inability to bear children.

Multiple neurofibromatosis is a disfiguring defect in which the skin is covered with unsightly nodules formed of benign tumors growing at the ends of peripheral nerves. The trait seems to be inherited as a simple autosomal dominant. Studies at the University of Michigan reveal that the fertility of affected individuals is only 52.7 percent that of their normal siblings (Neel, 1958). Only 32 percent of affected males marry, whereas 58 percent of affected females do so; but among those who do marry, the fertility is only 79.5 percent that of unaffected siblings. Here we have an example of differential fertility that is *eugenic* in the sense that reduced fertility decreases the number of members of the next generation who will have the deleterious gene.

Differential fertility in multiple neurofibromatosis is also an example of natural selection in action. In Chapter 17 we discussed natural selection as it relates to mutations. Its role in producing human diversity will receive attention in Chapter 24. At this time, we emphasize again that the very basis of natural selection is differential fertility. When possessors of one genotype produce fewer offspring on the average than do possessors of another genotype, natural selection is operating. Because the reasons that some people have more children than others are determined at least in part by genes (manifesting themselves physically or psychologically, or both), individual differential fertility results in a change in the gene pool of the subsequent generation. Some genes present in the gene pool of the parental generation are not represented at all in the gene pool of the offspring (e.g., if the gene is dominant and lethal, or produces sterility). More commonly, deleterious genes of the parents are transmitted to offspring, but with decreased frequency. This is natural selection working for the good of future generations.

REFERENCES

Anastasi, A., 1956. "Intelligence and family size," *Psychological Bulletin,* 53:187–209.

Anastasi, A., 1959. "Differentiating effect of intelligence and social status," *Eugenics Quarterly,* 6:84–91.

Bajema, C. J., 1963. "Estimation of the direction and intensity of natural selection in relation to human intelligence by means of the intrinsic rate of natural increase," *Eugenics Quarterly,* 10:175–87.

Carter, C. O., 1962. "Changing patterns of differential fertility in northwest Europe and in North America," *Eugenics Quarterly*, 9:147–50.

Coale, A. J., 1961. "Population growth," *Science*, 134:827–29.

Dice, L. R., P. J. Clark, and R. I. Gilbert, 1964. "Relation of fertility to occupation and to income in the male population of Ann Arbor, Michigan, 1951–54," *Eugenics Quarterly*, 11:154–67.

Eells, K. W., A. Davis, R. J. Havighurst, V. E. Herrick, and R. Tyler, 1951. *Intelligence and Cultural Differences.* Chicago: University of Chicago Press.

Finch, F. H., 1946. "Enrollment increases and changes in the mental level of the high school population," *Applied Psychology Monographs*, 10:1–75.

Freedman, R., 1963. "Changing fertility in Taiwan." In R. O. Greep (ed.). *Human Fertility and Population Problems.* Cambridge, Mass.: Schenkman Publishing Company, Inc. Pp. 106–31.

Freedman, R., P. K. Whelpton, and A. A. Campbell, 1959. *Family Planning, Sterility, and Population Growth.* New York: McGraw-Hill Book Company, Inc.

Higgins, J. V., E. W. Reed, and S. C. Reed, 1962. "Intelligence and family size: a paradox resolved," *Eugenics Quarterly*, 9:84–90.

National Academy of Sciences, 1963. *The Growth of World Population.* Publication 1091, National Academy of Sciences–National Research Council, Washington, D. C.

National Academy of Sciences, 1965. *The Growth of U. S. Population.* Publication 1279, National Academy of Sciences–National Research Council, Washington, D. C.

Neel, J. V., 1958. "The study of natural selection in primitive and civilized human populations," *Human Biology*, 30:43–72.

Newcombe, H. B., 1963. "I.Q. scores and genetic trends," *Science*, 142:1621.

Nortman, D., 1964. "Population policies in developing countries and related international attitudes," *Eugenics Quarterly*, 11:11–29.

Osborn, F., 1963. "Excess and unwanted fertility," *Eugenics Quarterly*, 10:59–72.

Penrose, L. S., 1950. "Genetical influences on the intelligence level of the population," *British Journal of Psychology*, 40:128–36.

Penrose, L. S., 1962. *The Biology of Mental Defect*, 3rd ed. London: Sidgwick & Jackson Ltd.

Powys, A. O., 1905. "Data for the problem of evolution in man. On fertility, duration of life and reproductive selection," *Biometrika*, 4:233–85.

Scottish Council for Research in Education, 1949. *The Trend of Scottish Intelligence.* London: University of London Press.

Stycos, J. M., 1964. "The outlook for world population," *Science*, 146:1435–40.

Thompson, W. R., 1957. "The significance of personality and intelligence tests in evaluation of population characteristics." In *The Nature and Transmission of the Genetic and Cultural Characteristics of Human Populations.* New York: Milbank Memorial Fund.

Tuddenham, R. D., 1948. "Soldier intelligence in World Wars I and II," *American Psychologist*, 3:54–56.

von Foerster, H., P. M. Mora, and L. W. Amiot, 1960. "Doomsday: Friday, 13 November, A. D. 2026," *Science*, 132:1291–95.

Westoff, C. F., 1954. "Differential fertility in the United States: 1900 to 1952," *American Sociological Review*, 19:549–61.

24.

HUMAN DIVERSITY
AND ITS ORIGIN

No one needs to be convinced that human beings show great diversity. We differ from each other in eye color, hair color, stature, blood groups, and in almost countless other ways. We say that man is *polymorphic* (many-formed). When we think of the diversity among races we sometimes use the term *polytypic* (many-typed), but the distinction is principally one of degree.

The polymorphism that we see or detect by serological and biochemical tests is, of course, phenotypic. It is the outward expression of the *genetic* polymorphism previously mentioned (p. 157). In saying so, we must never forget that most traits are the product of the interaction of heredity and environment. Blood groups may be an exception, being wholly gene-determined, but environment contributes to most phenotypic traits. We may have genes for the production of sufficient melanin in our skins to cause us to be brunets, but the actual shade of our skins will depend in part on how much time we spend sunbathing.

The question we are interested in now is: How did human diversity arise? How does the gene pool of a population attain such variety? How do the gene pools of different populations come to differ from one another?

As we recall our previous discussions, we readily recognize that the basic process responsible for genetic diversity is the process of mutation, using the term in its most general sense to include changes in chromosomal material, both those that are, and those that are not, visible with the microscope (p. 246). Mutations are the raw materials of change. Even if a gene pool were uniform at one stage in its existence, mutations would occur to introduce diversity.

What happens to mutations once they occur? In the first place, we recall from our discussion in Chapter 7 the underlying tendency of populations to remain in equilibrium. Suppose that with respect to a certain chromosomal locus, a gene pool contains 90 percent A genes and 10 percent a. We will also suppose that the a genes arose from the A genes by mutation, although this need not have occurred in the immediate past. Then if random mating occurs among the possessors of these genes, we will expect that 81 percent of the offspring will be AA, 18 percent will be Aa, and 1 percent will be aa (see Hardy-Weinberg formula, p. 92). If the offspring when mature also mate at random, their offspring in turn will also occur in approximately the same proportions. This Hardy-Weinberg equilibrium is predicated on the assumption that the gene pool does not change. Obviously every time an A gene mutates to form an a gene, the pool *is* changed by just that much. This tendency of genes to mutate, at a low but rather constant rate, is called **mutation pressure**. In itself, it forms one means by which diversity is introduced into a gene pool. There is, however, a tendency to *reverse* mutation (of gene a to mutate back to gene A), so that these opposing mutation pressures will be expected to balance each other and produce an equilibrium of their own. Without recourse to the customary mathematics, we can understand that an equilibrium will be attained when the number of newly formed A genes in each generation equals the number of newly formed a genes. The point we wish to make here is that although mutations are the raw materials for evolutionary change, mutation pressure by itself is not a very potent force for making such change.

Indeed, the term "polymorphism" is frequently restricted to the diversity present in a population in excess of the amount introduced by mutation pressure. A widely accepted definition is that of Ford (1964): "Genetic polymorphism is the occurrence together in the same locality of two or more discontinuous forms of a species in such proportions that the rarest of them cannot be maintained merely by recurrent mutation." What, then, are the forces that lead to polymorphism by producing changes in populations and their gene pools? We shall emphasize two: genetic drift and natural selection.

Genetic Drift

This term refers to chance occurrences in small populations. The Hardy-Weinberg formula assumes large populations in which breeding is at random. However, the equilibrium predicted by the formula may be upset if the population is small. By way of illustration, let us take the smallest possible "population," one male and one female. Let us suppose that one is *Aa*, the other *aa*. Here the frequency, *p*, of *A* is ¼ or 25 percent, the frequency, *q*, of *a* is ¾ or 75 percent. We cannot use the Hardy-Weinberg formula because we cannot have random mating. However, because this formula is only one aspect of Mendelian thinking, we state the simpler expectation that in such a mating half the offspring are expected to be *Aa*, half to be *aa*. As we have emphasized repeatedly, such a 1:1 ratio is only expected on the average. Suppose that the two parents produce only two offspring. What is the chance that one child will be *Aa*, the other *aa*? Because such a family can arise in two ways (older child *Aa*, younger child *aa*, *or* older child *aa*, younger child *Aa*), the chance is 2 × ½ × ½ = ¾. Only two fourths of the time will the family of two be expected to fit the 1:1 ratio exactly. What will happen the remaining two fourths of the time? One fourth of such families of two will be *Aa* and *Aa*. If this occurs, the frequency of the gene *A* has been *doubled*; *p* is now 50 percent. Alternatively, one fourth of the families of two will be expected to be *aa* and *aa*. If this occurs, the gene *A* is lost, *p* = 0. So merely by chance, with no regard for usefulness, a gene may increase in frequency in the gene pool, or it may decrease in frequency, down to the point of being completely lost. These chance fluctuations in gene frequencies are what we mean by drift.

Our example of two parents replacing themselves by producing two children is hardly a population, although it does illustrate the fact of chance fluctuations. Similar fluctuations may occur when numbers of individuals are large enough to be considered populations, even though they are small ones. Starting with the gene frequencies just employed (*p* = 0.25; *q* = 0.75), we may imagine a population of 16 people constituted as follows: 1 *AA*; 6 *Aa*; 9 *aa*. In theory this is a population in Hardy-Weinberg equilibrium, as a moment with pencil and paper will convince us. If the population were 100 *AA*, 600 *Aa*, and 900 *aa*, we could feel reasonably confident that the offspring would occur in about the same proportions as the parents, the gene pool remaining unchanged. However, we have only 16 people, not 1600. How will these 16 people marry each other (we will assume that they are equally divided as to sex)? We can imagine many combinations, but let us suppose that the matings actually occur as follows: (1) *AA* × *aa*; (2) *Aa* × *Aa*; (3) *Aa* × *aa*; (4) *Aa* × *aa*; (5) *aa* × *aa*; (6) *aa* × *aa*; (7) *Aa* × *Aa*; (8) *aa* × *aa*. We will next suppose that this population replaces itself, the 16 parents being represented in the next generation by 16 offspring who lived to reproductive age in their turn. Each mating produces two such offspring. What will be the nature of these offspring? Here the laws of chance will enter in, but let us suppose that the outcome is as follows:

Mating	Offspring
1. $AA \times aa$	Aa, Aa (this is necessarily so)
2. $Aa \times Aa$	aa, aa (other combinations are possible)
3. $Aa \times aa$	aa, aa (other combinations are possible)
4. $Aa \times aa$	Aa, Aa (other combinations are possible)
5. $aa \times aa$	aa, aa (this is necessarily so)
6. $aa \times aa$	aa, aa (this is necessarily so)
7. $Aa \times Aa$	Aa, aa (other combinations are possible)
8. $aa \times aa$	aa, aa (this is necessarily so)

Although the outcome might have been different, this is what actually did happen. As a result there has been a change in the population:

Parents: 1 AA, 6 Aa, 9 aa
Offspring, 0 AA, 5 Aa, 11 aa

What is the nature of the gene pool of these offspring?

$$p = {}^5\!/_{32} = 15.6\%$$
$$q = {}^{27}\!/_{32} = 84.4\%$$

Thus we see that the frequency of the dominant gene has "drifted" downward, whereas the frequency of the recessive gene has "drifted" upward correspondingly (from the 25 percent and 75 percent, respectively, of the parental generation). In a third generation this drift might continue, or it might be reversed. If it continued, gene A might disappear from the population completely in a generation or two. In that event we would say that gene a had attained "fixation." If the direction of drift were reversed, gene A would increase in frequency and this trend might continue until gene a was eliminated and gene A had reached fixation.

Anything could happen. The point we wish to make is that genetic drift is a matter of random fluctuations in small populations, entirely without regard to the usefulness of the genes concerned.

It is possible to simulate the conditions leading to genetic drift by employing simple models composed of marbles, or of colored beads, representing the genes. For a description of such models see Moody (1962).

Can we demonstrate instances of genetic drift in actual human populations? An apparent instance of it has been studied by Dr. Bentley Glass and his students at Johns Hopkins University (1952; 1953; 1956). The population consisted of an Old Order Dunker (Old German Baptist Brethren) community in Pennsylvania. The community has existed for over two centuries, ever since the ancestors migrated from Germany. The average size has remained between 250 and 300 persons, with less than 100 parents present in any given generation. Fecundity is high, but the total size remains fairly constant because of emigration from the group. "The maintenance of the group as a genetic isolate has thus depended not so much on the failure of marriages with outsiders to occur, as rather upon the characteristic exclusion from the group of those who do marry outside" (Glass *et al.*, 1952).

Dr. Glass and his associates studied a variety of genetic traits, comparing their frequency of occurrence with frequencies in (a) West Germany, whence the ancestors came, and (b) the United States in general. For our purposes we shall consider only one example: the MN blood groups (pp. 56–59). The findings were as follows:

	M	MN	N
West Germany	29.85%	49.9%	20.2%
Dunker isolate	44.5%	41.9%	13.5%
United States	29.16%	49.58%	21.26%

(From B. Glass *et al.*, *The American Naturalist.*)

We note that the figures for West Germany and for the general population of the United States agree closely in the frequencies of the three types, but in the Dunker community the proportion of type M people is considerably elevated. There is apparently no advantage to be gained by being of type M (certainly no advantage that would apply to Dunkers more than to other people), so that the higher frequency of type M Dunkers may be ascribed to chance, i.e., to genetic drift.

Similar evidence of drift was found in the distribution of the ABO blood groups and of some, but not all, of the other traits studied.

The MN groups are of interest, in that drift seems to be demonstrable within the lifetime of people still living. If we let p represent the frequency of gene *M*, and q the frequency of gene *N*, in the United States in general the frequencies are approximately as follows: $p = 0.54$, $q = 0.46$.

The investigators divided their Dunker population into three age groups, representing roughly three generations: (a) 56 years old or older, (b) 28 to 55 years old, (c) 2 to 27 years of age (Glass 1953, 1956). Among people of the oldest generation the gene frequencies were approximately those of the surrounding population, just given; among people of the second generation: $p = 0.66$, $q = 0.34$; and among the young people of the third generation, $p = 0.74$, $q = 0.26$. Dr. Glass commented: "these genes were apparently caught in the act of drifting." We note at once the similarity to our hypothetical example above.

Another example of genetic drift may be provided by the high percentage of blood group A people in the Blackfoot and Blood tribes of Indians in Montana. Approximtaely 80 percent of these people belong to group A, in contrast to the 2 to 22 percent found in other tribes of North American Indians. Because there seems to be no reason why being of group A should be of more advantage to Blackfeet and to Bloods than it is to other tribes of Indians, we ascribe the occurrence of this high percentage to genetic drift.

A related consideration has been called the **founder principle** by Dr. Ernst Mayr of Harvard (Mayr, 1942). Suppose that the population of a country has this distribution of the MN blood groups: 29 percent M; 50 percent MN; 21 percent N. We will also suppose that a group of 100 people emigrate from this country to some previously uninhabited region, to form a colony. The emigrants may consist of a random sample of the original population, or they may not. As an extreme example we may take the possible, albeit improbable, case in which all 100 emigrants belong to type M. Then in future generations all the people in the colony will be found to be of type M, instead of having the distribution of groups that characterized the ancestral population "back in the Old Country." Less extreme deviations from the original proportions are more likely, of course. The point is that by chance the founders of a new colony may differ in gene frequencies from the population from which the founders come. Thus, by chance, the colony may differ from the ancestral population.

We see, then, that chance may cause populations to differ from one another. By itself chance seems to operate most effectively when populations are small and isolated. Without doubt some of the differences between small, isolated groups of people can be attributed to this cause. Of how much importance is genetic drift in producing the diversity found in human popultaions on a larger scale? What, if any, role has it played in human evolution?

Here we encounter considerable differences of opinion. Theoretical considerations and observations and experiments with plants and animals indicate that most rapid evolutionary change occurs in small populations, although not in populations so small as to be in danger of extinction. It is in such small populations that drift is likely to occur. Hence it is argued that in the past a small population may by chance have become characterized by a high frequency of a certain gene-determined trait. Perhaps that trait proved to be a valuable one, better fitting its possessors to live in their environment, or permitting them to enter a new environment and exploit its possibilities. When this occurred, the "lucky" population would flourish, and perhaps expand at the expense of less well-endowed contemporaries. Thus evolutionary progress toward more perfect adaptation to the old, or a new, environment would be made.

Note that this progress involved two steps: (a) a small population becoming possessed of a trait by chance, i.e., through genetic drift; (b) natural selection operating on the trait, in terms of its value to the population. The first step is important only insofar as it leads to the second. "Nonadaptive differentiation is obviously significant only as it ultimately creates adaptive differences" (Wright, 1948). The words are those of Dr. Sewall Wright, long identified with the idea of genetic drift—so much so that it is sometimes termed "the Sewall Wright effect." Even he sees it only as a first step, providing a small population with something that natural selection can then utilize.

Is genetic drift really necessary as a first step? A number of students of the subject answer in the negative (cf., Ford, 1949). They argue that genetic drift only occurs in populations having less than 1000 breeding individuals in any given generation, and that such small populations have no evolutionary future. They may continue to exist as they are for a long time, but they are not "going anywhere." Furthermore, proponents of this view maintain that natural selection itself operates right from the start on every significant genetic change that occurs. Hence there is no need to invoke a first step in the form of a random occurrence like genetic drift. Probably, as usual, both views have validity. In some instances, random drift may be a contributing factor, in other instances not. At any rate, all agree that the ultimate arbiter is natural selection.

Before leaving the subject of genetic drift, we may note that it has sometimes been invoked to explain the occurrence in a population of what are called **nonadaptive traits**. Nonadaptive traits are *neutral*; they confer no benefit, and neither are they disadvantageous. Since natural selection can act only on traits that are not neutral, how can we explain nonadaptive traits? Why is it that various populations have an MN blood group distribution of around 29 percent M, 50 percent MN, 21 percent N? Here we are regarding the MN blood groups as nonadaptive traits. We are free to do so until someone finds that they have some significance in human life. Frankly, we cannot answer the question; but chance may have been involved. Perhaps as a result of genetic drift in a small ancestral population the 29:50:21 ratio came into existence, and it has persisted ever since in the multitudinous descendants of those ancestors. Perhaps the founder principle was operative. Under stringent conditions, populations go through "bottlenecks." Famine, natural catastrophes, and epidemics cause great loss of life, leaving small numbers of survivors to become the parents of the next generation. The collection of genes that the survivors chance to have will then determine the genetic constitution of future generations.

The foregoing comment about regarding the MN blood groups as nonadaptive traits is indicative of the fact that our list of such traits is steadily dwindling with advancing knowledge. Had this book been written a few years ago, the ABO blood groups would have been mentioned as being nonadaptive. However, in our discussion of these groups (pp. 156–157), we noted that they may be connected to susceptibility to disease and so may not be neutral at all. Many if not most genes are *pleiotropic*, having two or more effects on their possessors. Some of these effects may be noticeable but insignificant; others, perhaps not so noticeable, may be of real significance in the lives of their possessors. The noticeable effects may be anatomical; the significant effects may be biochemical or physiological. If so, natural selection will act on the significant effects, and the insignificant ones will simply "tag along."

Imagine, for example, a red-eyed insect living in the Temperate Zone.

In this insect a dominant mutation occurs, which changes the eye color to black *and* alters the physiology so that the insect can live in extreme cold. Eventually biologists might find a black-eyed race of this insect living in the Arctic. This would occur, not because black eyes were advantageous for arctic living but because of the physiological accompaniment that made it possible for the insect to survive in extreme cold. The example is hypothetical but undoubtedly true to life, and it explains why, as our knowledge of biochemistry, physiology, and pathology increases, our list of nonadaptive traits becomes smaller and smaller. In other words, there remain fewer and fewer traits to be explained merely on the basis of chance. More and more of what we had previously regarded as nonadaptive traits we now see to be subject to the action of natural selection.

Natural Selection

We have seen that some genetic diversity, particularly in small populations, may be produced by the operation of chance, but by far the most potent force for change in a gene pool is natural selection.

In Chapter 17 we discussed natural selection as a force determining the significance, and ultimate fate, of mutations. We noted that its essential idea is that individuals or populations possessing certain traits succeed better than do individuals or populations possessing other traits, and they leave larger numbers of offspring. As we emphasized again in Chapter 23, natural selection is the equivalent of differential fertility. Possessors of one phenotype leave more offspring than do possessors of another one, and hence the gene pool of the next generation contains a disproportionate number of the genes of the successful individuals.

This equating of natural selection to differential fertility may seem strange to some readers who are more used to thinking of natural selection as "the survival of the fittest," a term that Darwin himself used in his classic (1859) entitled, *The Origin of Species by Means of Natural Selection, or the Preservation of Favored Races in the Struggle for Life,* to quote the full title as we seldom do. Darwin emphasized survival although he recognized full well that unless the individuals who survived also reproduced, nothing significant for future generations would ensue.

And who are the "fittest"? They are the individuals who leave the largest numbers of offspring. "The 'fittest' is nothing more remarkable than the producers of the greatest number of children and grandchildren" (Sinnott, Dunn, and Dobzhansky, 1958). This concept of Darwinian fitness has not always been recognized and, indeed, will seem strange to some readers today. In times past, the fittest have been thought of as the strongest and most belligerent—the best fighters. Sadly, this misconception has been used to justify all manner of social injustices: "to the victor belongs the spoils," "the devil take the hindmost," "might makes right," and the like. Cutthroat competition and the exploitation of less fortunate peoples have been justified on grounds connected with this misconception. Some of the saddest events of world history during the past century have evolved from mistaken ideas concerning what constitutes fitness and what are the privileges and prerogatives of those who can demonstrate their fitness by becoming "top dog." No wonder that Darwinism (i.e., natural selection) fell into disrepute among sensitive and thoughtful people.

Now we see that strong and belligerent fighters are only "the Fittest" if they leave more offspring than do their less bellicose fellows. On the other hand, it may well happen that the strong fighters kill each other, leaving their less warlike compatriots to father the next generation.

Therefore, fitness in the Darwinian sense is contributed to by any aspect of body and mind that leads to the production of large numbers of offspring. Obviously, individuals must survive, at least to reproductive age, to do this, but survival in itself is not enough. A strong, healthy, intelligent person may survive, but if he does not pass on genes to offspring the genetical constitution of the future is not improved by his having lived.

Please note that we did not say society is not improved by his having lived. Man has two kinds of inheritance: genetic and cultural. Cultural inheritance is the accumulated wisdom of generations, transmitted by the spoken and written word, by art, music, etc. People who have no children may make great contributions to this type of inheritance. However, cultural inheritance is a strictly human phenomenon. Among plants and animals, and even in at least the earlier stages of the evolution of man, an individual's greatest contribution to posterity was his genes. Consequently, those who contributed their genes most copiously had the most influence on the future.

How does natural selection operate to produce the genetic diversity we have been discussing? When mutations occur, they will increase in frequency in the gene pool if possessors of the altered genotype leave more offspring than do individuals lacking the altered genotype.

Let us consider first the situation in which a normally occurring recessive gene, *a*, mutates to form a dominant allele, *A*. As noted in Chapter 22, selection will operate rapidly on such a new allele. At first all individuals possessing the gene will be heterozygous, *Aa*. If the gene contributes to survival and fertility, such *Aa* individuals will leave a disproportionate share of offspring, and hence the gene *A* will increase in frequency in the gene pool. Eventually, homozygous *AA* individuals will arise (offspring in the first instance of *Aa* × *Aa* matings). If they are as viable and fertile as are *Aa* individuals, they also will contribute to the increase of gene *A* in the gene pool. On the other hand, they may be less viable or fertile, in which case every time homozygotes are produced, genes will be lost through failure of the homozygotes to reproduce. This situation will lead to an equilibrium, the decreased fertility of *AA* individuals counteracting the increased fertility of *Aa* individuals. The result is the production of a balanced polymorphism (pp. 272–274). We noted, for example, that in an environment containing malaria, heterozygotes for the sickle-cell gene have an advantage. Hence, although homozygotes for the gene have severe anemia and produce few offspring, the gene is kept in the gene pool at a substantial frequency. This is because heterozygotes survive malaria better than do homozygotes who do not have the gene at all, and therefore leave more than "their share" of offspring.

Alternatively, the new allele *A* may decrease the viability or fertility of its possessors. In this case it will be eliminated rapidly, leaving the field to the normal *aa* individuals (Chap. 22).

We turn next to the situation in which a normally occurring dominant gene, *A*, mutates to form a recessive allele, *a*. If recessivity is complete, *Aa* individuals will be exactly like *AA* individuals in viability and fertility. Hence the gene will accumulate in the gene pool until heterozygotes become common enough so that they chance to mate together and produce homozygous recessive, *aa*. If these individuals enjoy some advantage involving viability or fertility, the frequency of the gene will increase in the gene pool. If, however, they suffer some disadvantage, the frequency of the gene will decrease. However, as we noted in Chapter 22, as long as selection operates on homozygous recessives only, change in gene frequency, be it upward or downward, will occur very slowly. Much more rapid change will occur if recessivity is not complete, if *Aa* individuals differ from *AA* individuals. If both *Aa* and *aa* individuals are inferior in viability or fertility, gene *a* will be eliminated much more rapidly than it will be if *aa* individuals alone are deficient. If both *Aa* and *aa* individuals are superior to *AA* individuals, gene *A* will tend to disappear from the gene pool. If *Aa* individuals are superior to both *aa* and *AA* individuals, a state of balanced polymorphism will arise, as just described.

In sum, we see that the fate of any given new mutation will depend on the answer to several questions. Does it produce an effect in heterozygotes or does it not? If it does, are homozygotes superior or inferior to heterozygotes? Are homozygotes for the new mutation superior or inferior to homozygotes for the "old" (unmutated) gene? For the sake of simplicity, we have confined our discussion and questions to a single pair of alleles, *A* and *a*. When multiple alleles, polygenes, or other complexes of genes are involved, as they frequently are, the genetic situation becomes much more complex, but, of course, natural selection acts on gene complexes as well as on single genes.

In stating the above questions we have used the terms "superior" and "inferior." In the present context these terms refer to relative ability to contribute genes to future generations. It is important to emphasize that natural selection always operates in an environmental setting. A gene may be superior in one environment but inferior in another one. In the case of the sickle-cell gene, for example, we note that heterozygotes for it are only superior in an environment containing malaria. In America, where malaria is almost absent, heterozygotes enjoy no advantage. Therefore, because homozygotes always suffer a severe disadvantage, we may expect that the gene brought to this country by immigrants from Africa will gradually disappear in their descendants.

Natural selection is constantly tending to cause organisms to become better adapted to the environments in which they live. To the extent that two populations live in differing environments, placing different demands on their inhabitants, natural selection will cause those populations to differ from each other. In this way, natural selection promotes diversity.

Origin of Races Let us imagine a large population of animals that is thriving and growing in size so that it spreads over more and more territory. As it extends its range in this manner, portions of the population become separated from each other by distance and perhaps also by geographic barriers. Perhaps the animals spread from the lowlands up into neighboring mountain valleys, so that the inhabitants of each valley are no longer in contact with the inhabitants of other valleys. Such isolated portions of a large population we frequently call subpopulations. What will happen in each of these subpopulations?

If a subpopulation is small, genetic drift may operate. By chance some genes may become common in one subpopulation, not in another. This will introduce diversity, so that in time one subpopulation will come to differ from another in various ways.

In addition, natural selection will operate on each subpopulation to cause it to become adapted to its particular mountain valley. Perhaps one valley is wooded, another one covered with sagebrush. One valley may be well watered, another one dry and barren. All manner of differences may be found. In each valley a premium will be placed on ability to adapt to specific conditions. As time goes by, the inhabitants of the wooded valley will come to differ in various ways from the inhabitants of the unwooded valley; the inhabitants of the well-watered valley will have developed some traits not possessed by the inhabitants of the barren valley, and vice versa.

As a result of the combined action of genetic drift and natural selection, the subpopulations have become different from each other and from their ancestors. Now if an inquiring biologist comes along and studies them, he will probably wish to recognize the differences by designating each subpopulation a **microgeographic race**. By this he will mean that each subpopulation has some distinguishing features and occupies a small unit of territory. Examples are numerous in biological literature. As one instance, Dr. Lee R. Dice of the University of Michigan studied small populations of whitefooted mice (*Peromyscus leucopus*) inhabiting woodlots in the neighborhood of Ann Arbor (Dice, 1937). The woodlots were separated from each other by open fields which the woodland inhabitants seldom crossed. Thus they formed subpopulations of the sort we have been discussing. Although separated from each other by only three or four miles, the subpopulations showed statistically significant differences in a variety of bodily and skeletal measurements and in hair color.

If the territory inhabited by a race is larger, the "micro-" is dropped and the term **geographic race** or **subspecies** is employed. Usually, the physical differences between one geographic race and another are more marked than are the differences between microgeographic races. In many if not most instances the geographic races probably arose from microgeographic races that, although small and isolated, developed traits that fitted them for a larger territory. In cases in which this larger territory was available and unoccupied by animals of similar kind, the microgeographic race could expand to become a geographic race.

Aside from its territoriality, what are the attributes of a geographic race? In general, two are important. Geographic races usually differ from each other in a variety of bodily traits although the differences are small compared to the basic similarities. Members of different geographic races are usually entirely interfertile if and when they do come into contact. They have not developed what we call **reproductive isolation**; they will interbreed freely when the opportunity is offered.

Races usually differ from each other in the *frequencies* with which genes occur rather than in the presence of a gene in one race and its absence from another. For example, at one time I studied the distribution of blood group antigens in some populations of deer mice (*Peromyscus*) from the Columbia River Valley (Moody, 1948). These antigens were similar in many ways to the human A, B, M, N, etc., we have discussed. The different populations, which were in part representatives of different geographic races, differed from each other in the percentages of mice possessing each of the antigens. This situation exactly parallels that found in human races. The four blood groups, A, B, AB, and O, are represented in every race, but the percentages of people who belong to each one differ from race to race. In Chapter 9 we discussed the differing percentage of antigen B possessed by inhabitants of England and China. A high percentage of antigen B is characteristic of Mongolian peoples, exemplified by the Chinese. Interestingly enough, some peoples who are not Mongolian also have a high proportion of B, e.g., Abyssinians, and Pygmies in the Congo. Eskimos, Portuguese, and Australian aborigines, members of three different races, resemble one another in blood group distributions.

This illustrates a very important point about races: *The differences between races are of the same kind as the differences between groups of people within races.* Race differs from race in frequencies of genes concerned with blood antigens, ability to taste PTC and other chemicals, production of melanin in the skin, and all manner of anatomical, physiological, and biochemical traits. Populations *within* one race differ in these ways, too; members within one family may differ in them. Thus, races are merely "constellations of characters" (Boyd, 1950). The "characters" are traits by which people within races also differ. The genetic bases of some of the characters have been analyzed. We are still ignorant of the genetics involved in the others although we have no reason to doubt that principles learned from the genetically analyzed traits apply to them as well.

It is no accident that anthropologists have difficulty in classifying races. To a degree, like students of races in plants and lower animals, they are attempting to draw lines where no lines exist. We find no difficulty in distinguishing Scandinavians from Japanese, or either of these from Congolese, and we may say that they belong to white (Caucasoid), Mongolian, and Negroid races, respectively (although some anthropologists will quarrel with the names chosen). So far everything has been easy. "It will, however, be far from easy to delimit these races if one observes also the inhabitants of the countries geographically intermediate between Scandinavia, Japan, and Congo, respectively. Intermediate countries have intermediate populations, or populations which differ in some characteristic from all previously outlined races" (Dobzhansky, 1963). Thus one "constellation of characters" differs from another, but only in part, and this other constellation differs to some extent, but not completely, from a third, and so on. No wonder anthropologists have difficulty in deciding where one race begins and another leaves off. Biologists are faced with the same problem. As we are now in a position to understand, the problem arises from the very nature of the origin of races: small isolated populations acted on by drift and natural selection, with interbreeding (hybridization) whenever the populations come into contact through migration, conquest, or other means of expanding the originally small territories.

Origin of Human Races   We shall never know the history of the races of man, but from our knowledge of race formation in general we can draw some probable conclusions.

The evidence suggests that before the development of civilization, even before the advent of agriculture, our remote ancestors were hunters and food gatherers. Judging from modern peoples who have retained this means of livelihood, they were joined together into rather small family groups or tribes. Because a hunting tribe must have a considerable area available to it as a source of food, the population cannot be of the density possible to an agricultural society. Hence each tribe defends its own territory from encroachment and so keeps itself comparatively isolated from its neighbors. "The requirements of hunting and collecting keep the number of people who live near enough to one another to breed as a unit within about 500 or 600 individuals" (Coon, 1962). Dr. Carleton Coon estimated that of this number only about a third would at any one time be of childbearing age. Hence each such group would constitute a subpopulation of the type we discussed above. To a considerable extent, also, each would be a genetic isolate although the isolation would break down at times through migration, conquest, wife-stealing, and so forth.

Insofar as each of these small groups retained its identity, it constituted a subpopulation within which genetic drift and natural selection could operate, as we have discussed. In part by chance, in part in response to differing environmental needs, the subpopulations came to differ from one another in a manner comparable to the formation of the microgeographic races we discussed above. Most of these groups existed for a time and then disappeared, or were incorporated into other groups. Some of them, especially ones well separated from each other for thousands of years, persisted and became the ancestors of today's major races.

If we are correct, then, the differences between races may be explained largely as a result of the action of genetic drift and natural selection. Ancestral populations would have been small enough so that drift could have occurred. This would have been especially true at times when a tribe was small as an aftermath of famine, war, or disease. The survivors, and hence "founders" (p. 363) of the future population, might by chance have had gene frequencies quite unlike those that prevailed before the tribal catastrophe. Consequently, future generations might have differed quite strikingly from previous ones, and the differences might have been transmitted down to the present time. In this manner, genetic drift in small ancestral populations can account for racial differences that are neutral or nonadaptive. At present we do not know what proportion of racial traits falls into this category. It is often assumed that most of them do. Yet, as we noted previously, the more our knowledge of the body's physiology and biochemistry increases the more we realize that many traits previously thought to have no significance are, in fact, of importance to their possessors, and thus subject to the action of natural selection.

The analysis of racial differences in physiology and biochemistry is in its infancy, and therefore any conclusions drawn at the present time must be extremely tentative. Let us consider, as our example, the trait that everyone thinks of first when race is mentioned: skin color. The distribution of people with much melanin in their skin suggests that a dark skin is an adaptation for living in open country with strong sunlight. Such people are found in open regions of Africa south of the Sahara Desert, in Melanesia, New Guinea, southern India, and Australia—thus this is an adaptation common to different races. It seems likely that the dark skin is a protection against damage by ultraviolet radiation and also a protection against skin cancer. Turning the matter around, we ask: What advantages are there in having a light skin, as forest dwellers the world over and the peoples who originated in northern Europe have? Here we are hard-pressed for an answer. The answer is sometimes given that lighter pigmentation is of advantage in weaker light, for it permits ultraviolet rays to penetrate into skin cells which can then synthesize vitamin D. The importance of this is doubtful, however, especially in nothern Europe where the inhospitable climate forced ancestral tribes to cover their skin with clothing.

We have cited this example partly to show that we do not know enough human biochemistry to understand the most important reasons for differences in skin color. Melanin, the pigment itself, is contained in cells called melanocytes located between the two layers of the skin, the dermis and epidermis. These cells are produced by embryonic nervous tissue. People of all races have the same number of these cells; the difference is in the amount of melanin the cells contain. The amount of pigmentation is controlled by at least three hormones, two from the pituitary gland, one from the pineal gland (Lerner, 1961). Hence we see here a complex contributed to by the nervous system and the endocrine glands. Dr. Lerner suggested (1961): "The color-regulating hormones may have even more important functions as members of the mysterious group of neurohormones, which mediate the interplay between the endocrine and nervous systems in the regulation of the body." If this proves to be correct, color differences may be a more or less unimportant by-product of physiological differences that were important at the time the races originated. As in so many aspects of human genetics, we await the results of future research with great interest.

World War II stimulated interest in physiological differences between races because "the global nature of modern warfare stimulated the interest of several nations in man's ability to live in all climates, particularly the arctic" (Coon, 1962). Of the researches summarized by Coon, we shall mention only adaptation for living in the cold. Investigations demonstrated that Mongolian peoples, such as Indians in Alaska and in Tierra del Fuego, compensate for heat lost from their bodies by having an elevated basal metabolism. In the case of the Canoe Indians of Tierra del Fuego the "basal metabolism is 160 per cent higher than the norm for whites of the same age and stature" (Coon, 1962). When their hands are placed in cold water, the blood flow to the hands is increased to twice that of white men tested under the same conditions. By contrast, such increased flow of blood to hands placed in cold water is an adaptation not possessed by

Lapp reindeer hunters, who live under similar stringent conditions, or by white Norwegian fishermen living above the Arctic Circle.

On the other hand, Australian aborigines who sleep naked on the desert where temperatures may go below freezing have a different adaptation. The hands and feet become chilled (with temperature as low as 54° to 59° F.), but the internal body temperature remains normal. A complex arrangement of blood vessels makes this possible.

Going from cold to heat we may mention that Negroes have been found to have a greater tolerance for humid, hot conditions than have whites (Dobzhansky, 1962).

Various anatomical characteristics have their physiological concomitants. Peoples who live in a dry atmosphere tend to have noses with narrower openings than do peoples who live in a damp atmosphere. In the narrower nose the air inhaled is humidified more efficiently. People who live in cold climates tend to be stockier, with shorter limbs, than do people who live in warm climates. The nearer the body form approaches a sphere the less the heat lost through the surface. These are only a few of the adaptive differences between peoples. (For more complete discussion see Coon, 1962, and Dobzhansky, 1962.)

Unfortunately, in examples like those cited we do not know to what extent the differences are genetic, to what extent they depend on the ability of the body to become acclimatized to extreme conditions. Yet even this ability to adjust to a variety of environmental conditions has a hereditary basis. One's genotype produces a "norm of reaction," an ability to adjust to a range of conditions. The range may be broad or it may be narrow. One genotype may make possible accommodation to a range of high temperatures, another to a range of lower ones. Hence, in one form or another, genetic differences are certainly involved.

"Identity versus Equality"   This heading, borrowed from Mayr (1963), suggests that equality and identicalness or sameness are two different things. Some people are disturbed by the thought that there *are* any differences between races. In their devotion to race equality they may even deny the evidences that such differences exist. In our discussion we have tried to introduce the matter in such a way as to emphasize the fact that race formation in man is part and parcel with race formation throughout the living world. Drift and natural selection in virtually all organisms cause populations to develop differences in the frequencies of genes, and such differing populations we call races (in plant, insect, bird, lower mammal, or man). These differences have nothing to do with *equality*. This is an ethical concept, not a biological one. When the framers of our Declaration of Independence stated that "all men were created equal" they did not mean that all men were created identical. They knew better than that. In the words of Dr. Mayr: "Simply stated, equality means equal status before the law and equal status in human social relations in spite of genetic difference." It means that skin color, form of hair, shape of nose, blood groups, and all manner of other racial differences are irrelevant in determining legal and social status.

Intelligence and Educability   Do races differ in intelligence? This question has been answered in various ways.

One point of view is that of those who deny that intelligence is to any degree gene-determined. If that were true, any genetic differences between the races would have no effect on intelligence, which presumably would be determined entirely by environment. Such a point of view totally ignores the results of twin studies and other evidence of a genetic component in intelligence (Chap. 21).

Another viewpoint is that of those who recognize that genes are important in determining intelligence, and who recognize that genetic differences exist between races. If races differ in the frequencies of genes controlling such things as skin color and blood groups, should we not also expect them to differ in the frequencies of genes controlling intelligence? The small ancestral groups from which the races sprang differed in physical and social environments. Might not these differences have led to differences in the distribution of genes controlling intelligence?

At least two answers have been given to these questions. Some people have answered the questions in the affirmative and in some cases have presented what they regard as evidence that such differences do in fact exist. The evidence usually consists of results of intelligence tests given to children of different races. In Chapter 21 we noted the results of studies indicating that intelligence tests are constructed in such a manner that they are not equally fair to children of all socioeconomic groups (within one race). The subject matter is more likely to be familiar to children of the "upper" groups than it is to children of the "lower" groups. If this is true *within* one race, how much more bias will be introduced by using one and the same test for children from different racial and cultural backgrounds, who usually differ in socioeconomic rank as well. Unless it is possible to devise a truly culture-free intelligence test, no conclusive results can ever be obtained.

Let us suppose for the moment that the difficulties are overcome, and that an investigation does afford conclusive evidence that two races differ in average intelligence. As every schoolchild knows, when large numbers of people are tested, the scores tend to approximate the familiar bell-shaped normal frequency curve. The largest numbers of individuals group around a midpoint or median, small numbers attaining higher or lower scores, respectively. Figure 24.1 presents a hypothetical situation of

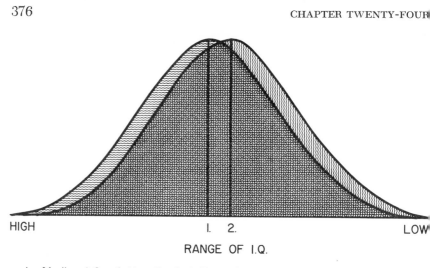

HIGH   I.   2.   LOW

RANGE OF I.Q.

I. = Median I.Q. of Hypothetical Race A

2.= Median I.Q. of Hypothetical Race B

FIG. 24.1 A suppositious case: two hypothetical races differing from each other in average IQ. Each race is represented by a normal frequency curve, one curve shaded vertically, the other horizontally.

this kind. Here we have two overlapping bell-curves with slightly differing medians. The median of Race A differs from the median of Race B by a few IQ points, but note the huge area of overlap. Large numbers of people in Race B are more intelligent than are large numbers of people in Race A. The curves illustrate a most important point about racial differences: the differences found *within* races are greater than the differences *between* races. This is observably true and can be documented abundantly. Applied to our hypothetical races it means that great contributions may be expected from members of both races, and it means that programs for education and environmental improvement in general must consider each individual as an individual without regard to race. Gifted children of both races must be accorded similar opportunities. Mental defectives of both races must be similarly cared for. What we are saying, then, is that even if an ideal investigation does reveal average differences in intelligence between races, that finding will have no real significance for the managing of human affairs.

Figure 24.1 oversimplifies in representing "intelligence" as a unit. As we noted in Chapter 21, there are many component parts to intelligence, and heredity seems not to be equally important in all of them. It may well be that Race B will be superior to Race A in some components, and vice versa. In our present state of knowledge concerning intelligence we can merely suggest a not-improbable possibility.

Thus far we have been discussing the first answer to our question as to whether racial differences in intelligence are to be expected—the affirmative answer. Other writers consider that differences of this kind are unlikely to have arisen in human evolution (Dobzhansky and Montagu, 1947; Montagu, 1959; Dobzhansky, 1962). Man's greatest superiority over lower animals is his ability to control his environment, instead of being controlled by it. Other organisms become adapted to live in one environment, or at most a restricted number of environments. Man can and does live in all environments, from the Tropics to the Arctic, from the desert to the rain forest, from sea level to the high Andes and Himalayas. This plasticity or adaptability (as opposed to narrow adaptation) is man's most distinctive attribute. At its base, lies the ability to learn by experience, educability. At all times and in all societies, so the argument runs, natural selection will have placed a high premium on educability, which undoubtedly is a gene-controlled trait, at least in part. We have a tendency to underestimate the complexity of the lives and social structures of people we regard as "primitives." We do this largely from ignorance. As we learn more of the demands placed on them for survival, the more we respect their abilities, much as they may differ from ours. An American capable of contributing to the space program might well die of thirst in the Australian desert where an aborigine could easily locate a subterranean water supply. "Life at any level of social development in human societies is a pretty complex business, and is met and handled most efficiently by those who exhibit the greatest capacity for adaptability, plasticity" (Dobzhansky and Montagu, 1947). Hence it may well be that natural selection has produced the same degree of educability in all races. If there are differences in averages, they are likely to be small and of no real practical significance, as noted above.

Race Mixture We mentioned earlier the fact that when previously isolated populations come into contact, through migration, conquest, or expansion of territory, they interbreed. In this way, gene frequencies acquired by the populations during their period of isolation are altered, and traits are combined through hybridization to form new "constellations." This interfertility of all peoples has contributed to the problems of classification faced by anthropologists.

At this point we may appropriately note the death of an old idea. This was the theory that in the beginning there were "pure" races (e.g., pure Caucasoids, pure Mongolians, pure Negroids), and that the present great diversity of peoples arose through intermarriage between these original pure races. The more we learn about prehistoric peoples, including the "fossil men," the more we realize that mankind has always been characterized by great diversity. The pure races are a myth.

As far as evidence is available it indicates that race mixture has always been characteristic of mankind. Biologically, then, it is entirely normal. All peoples share so many fundamental similarities, despite superficial dissimilarities, that hybrids are normal and healthy. This, of course, assumes that in each case the specific parents and ancestries were such as to provide the genes for health. Indeed, we might well have mentioned hybridization, along with natural selection and drift, as a force in the production of new races. For example, some anthropologists consider that a new race is now arising in Hawaii. Called "Neo-Hawaiian" by Coon, Garn, and Birdsell (1950), the new race represents an amalgam of genes from many other peoples, notably Polynesian, European, Japanese, and Chinese (see also Garn, 1961; Dobzhansky, 1962). These writers also suggest that a new race is emerging in our own country: "North American Colored." Here the genes are derived mainly from African, European, and American Indian sources. Just so, new races with their internal variabilities and fluctuating gene frequencies have doubtless been arising from time immemorial.

Because race mixture is biologically normal, is it therefore desirable? Biologically, yes. The problems involved are *sociological.* However they are very real and difficult problems. They stem principally from the fact that "half-castes have been more often than not treated as outcasts by society" (Montagu, 1959). In those societies in which this is not true, as apparently in Hawaii, race mixture is normal and without disadvantage. When will this attitude be true of all societies? Prejudices die hard, and usually only with the deaths of the holders thereof, but I think we are not being too optimistic if we foresee a future in which race mixture will seem normal and matter-of-course.

REFERENCES

Boyd, W. C., 1950. *Genetics and the Races of Man.* Boston: Little, Brown & Company.

Coon, C. S., 1962. *The Origin of Races.* New York: Alfred A. Knopf.

Coon, C. S., S. M. Garn, and J. B. Birdsell, 1950. *Races.* Springfield, Ill.: Charles C Thomas.

Darwin, C., 1859. *The Origin of Species by Means of Natural Selection.* (Available in many reprint editions, e.g.—Collier Books series, The Crowell-Collier Publishing Company, New York; Mentor Books series, New American Library, New York; Modern Library series, Random House, New York.)

Dice, L. R., 1937. "Variation in the wood-mouse, *Peromyscus leucopus novebor-acensis,* in the northeastern United States," *Occasional Papers of the Museum of Zoology, University of Michigan,* 352:1–32.

Dobzhansky, T., 1962. *Mankind Evolving.* New Haven: Yale University Press.

Dobzhansky, T., 1963. "Genetics of race equality," *Eugenics Quarterly,* **10**: 151–60.

Dobzhansky, T., and M. F. Ashley Montagu, 1947. "Natural selection and the mental capacities of mankind," *Science,* 105:587–90.

Ford, E. B., 1949. "Early stages in allopatric speciation." In G. L. Jepsen, E. Mayr, and G. G. Simpson (eds.). *Genetics, Paleontology, and Evolution.* Princeton, N. J.: Princeton University Press. Pp. 309–14.

Ford, E. B., 1964. *Ecological Genetics.* New York: John Wiley & Sons, Inc.

Garn, S. M., 1961. *Human Races.* Springfield, Ill.: Charles C Thomas.

Glass, H. B., 1953. "The genetics of the Dunkers," *Scientific American,* 189: 76–81.

Glass, H. B., 1956. "On the evidence of random genetic drift in human populations," *American Journal of Physical Anthropology,* 14:541–55.

Glass, H. B., M. S. Sacks, E. F. Jahn, and C. Hess, 1952. "Genetic drift in a religious isolate: an analysis of the causes of variation in blood group and other gene frequencies in a small population," *American Naturalist,* 86: 145–59.

Lerner, A. B., 1961. "Hormones and skin color," *Scientific American,* 205:98–108.

Mayr, E., 1942. *Systematics and the Origin of Species.* New York: Columbia University Press.

Mayr, E., 1963. *Animal Species and Evolution.* Cambridge, Mass.: Harvard University Press.

Montagu, Ashley, 1959 *Human Heredity.* Cleveland: The World Publishing Company.

Moody, P. A., 1948. "Cellular antigens in three stocks of *Peromyscus maniculatus* from the Columbia River valley," *Contributions from the Laboratory of Vertebrate Biology, University of Michigan,* 39:1–16.

Moody, P. A., 1962. *Introduction to Evolution,* 2nd ed. New York: Harper & Brothers.

Sinnott, E. W., L. C. Dunn, and T. Dobzhansky, 1958. *Principles of Genetics,* 5th ed. New York: McGraw-Hill Book Company, Inc.

Wright, S., 1948. "On the roles of directed and random changes in gene frequency in the genetics of populations," *Evolution,* 2:279–94.

25.

GENETIC COUNSELING

We may well conclude our discussion with the question: What can be *done*? To what practical use can we put our ever-increasing knowledge of human inheritance?

As we mentioned at the outset (Chap. 1), the most important justification for the study of human genetics is the desire to *know*, to understand ourselves. Our greatest distinction from the rest of the organic world is the ability to acquire knowledge, to pass it on from generation to generation, and to modify our behavior in the light of accumulated wisdom. Any significant contribution to this social or cultural inheritance is important, and in itself affords ample justification for the effort involved.

Now we ask the "practical" question: Of what use is human genetics in the management of human affairs, in the business of everyday life?

Genetics is most immediately useful to the medical profession as it seeks to keep us healthy and to help us order our lives so that we shall be as happy and successful as possible. Knowledge of human genetics may frequently aid a physician in diagnosing a pathological condition. In their early stages many disorders have symptoms that are very much alike. If a physician knows that a certain disorder is in the family, he has a clue as to what the early symptoms are likely to portend and can begin treatment accordingly. For example, various deficiencies result in failure of the blood to clot normally. Knowledge of a patient's ancestry may help the physician to decide whether the symptoms are those of hemophilia (pp. 195–198), afibrinogenemia (pp. 117–118), or some other disorder. Serological tests will then confirm or refute the suspicions. Information about inheritance will aid the physician in selecting those tests that are most likely to be informative.

Although testing all newborn babies for phenylketonuria (p. 216)

s becoming increasingly common, a physician who knows that PKU is
n a mother's family will be especially careful to have the blood test performed at once so that treatment may be started as soon as possible should
the baby prove to have the deficiency. If a phenylketonuric baby is born,
relatives should be warned to have their babies tested, too, for "the incidence of phenylketonuria in cousins is about twenty times higher than
n the general population" (Centerwall *et al.*, 1963). Knowledge of the
hereditary nature of a disease thus aids in its control.

As the new science of human cytogenetics develops, analysis of a
patient's chromosomes will also aid in the diagnosis and in the decision
as to wisest treatment (see McKay, 1964).

Dominant Traits

Sometimes disorders having a genetic basis do not manifest themselves
at birth—the symptoms appear later, during childhood, adolescence, or the
adult years. We have discussed a notable example of this, Huntington's
chorea (pp. 73–75). Symptoms usually do not appear until at least the
third decade of life although they may appear earlier. We recall that the
gene for the disease is dominant. Usually, if not always, people who have
the disease are heterozygous, having inherited the gene from one parent,
the normal allele from the other. Because heterozygotes are most likely to
marry homozygous normals, their marriages may be indicated as $Hh \times hh$.
On the average, half the children from such a mating are expected to be
choreic (later in life), half to be normal. However, such a statistical
prophecy is of small comfort to the individuals concerned. If we imagine
ourselves in the position of children of a choreic parent, our most pressing
question would be: "Will *I* become insane as I grow older?" No statement of mathematical probabilities can answer that question. What we
need is some means of identifying possessors of the gene when they are
young, before they develop the symptoms of the disorder.

A most interesting study was made as a cooperative investigation of the
Neuropsychiatric Institute and the Heredity Clinic of the University of
Michigan (Patterson *et al.*, 1948). Persons with Huntington's chorea have
abnormal electroencephalograms (EEGs), "brain waves." The investigators studied the EEGs of 26 individuals, each of whom had a choreic
parent. Eighteen of the 26 were under 20 years of age. The brain waves
of 12 of the 26 were so abnormal that the investigators concluded that
they were likely to develop Huntington's chorea. (Note that this fits the
1:1 expectation almost perfectly.) Of the remaining 14, 7 had slightly
abnormal EEGs and it was considered a "bare possibility" that they would
develop chorea. The other 7 "probably will never develop the disease."

Doubtless follow-up studies of this group of people will be made to determine whether subsequent changes occur in the EEG patterns and especially to find out whether prophecies come true as to who will develop the disease and who will not.

More recently, Falek and Glanville (1962) employed a test that records the muscular tremors made by the hand. By means of electronic equipment such tremors can be recorded as a tracing on a strip of paper. The hand tremors of a normal person produce a characteristic pattern, those of a person with Huntington's chorea a very different pattern. In the one family group tested to date, the mother was choreic and had two sons, aged 19 and 14 years, respectively. The sons showed none of the symptoms of the disease, as was to be expected at their age. The hand tremors of the older boy produced a normal tracing, but the tremors of the younger son produced an abnormal tracing like that of his mother. Will this younger son develop Huntington's chorea in later life? Only time will tell.

The point we are interested in is the possibility that eventually tests (either physical or biochemical) may be perfected so that it will be possible to test a small child and predict with certainty that Huntington's chorea is or is not in store for him. When that day comes, happy the child for whom the prediction is negative! But what about the child for whom the prediction is positive?

Here we are brought face to face with a delicate human problem. Should the child be told? What would be the effect on one's emotional and psychological health of knowing for certain that muscular incoordination accompanied by severe mental deterioration would strike in one's 30's or 40's? It would seem to be best for a young person not to know of such an impending fate unless, and until, remedial measures are possible. As long as nothing can be done to avert the fatal outcome, informing the person constitutes needless mental cruelty, and may lead to neurotic and psychotic disturbances quite unrelated to the chorea itself. The hope is, of course, that remedial measures may be discovered, as they have been in the case of phenylketonuria. It seems most probable that deterioration of enzyme-controlled reactions in the body, probably in the central nervous system, underlies the development of the symptoms. We may hope that the biochemical reactions will be identified, and that means will then be evolved to prevent the retrogressive changes. If and when this becomes possible, it will be valuable to identify potential choreics, so that preventive measures can be instituted. That day has not arrived as yet, but we may hope that it is not far distant.

Thus, we see the value of developing tests that will enable us to identify individuals with genotypes that will cause disorders in later life. Another means of accomplishing this result would be to discover a marker gene closely linked to the gene for the pathological trait (see p. 215). If, for example, we could discover a gene for a red blood cell antigen closely linked to the gene for Huntington's chorea, then in *some* families the children found to possess the antigen would be almost certain to become choreic in later years, whereas the children lacking the antigen would also lack the gene for chorea. We stress that this would be true in some families because of the phenomena of crossing-over and of coupling and repulsion linkage discussed previously. Undoubtedly a direct EEG or biochemical test would be more precise than would a marker-gene test, useful as this could be.

Thus far, our discussion has been centered on the individual himself, on the values, and in some instances the potential dangers, of early diagnosis of hereditary conditions that may not develop their untoward symptoms until later in life. Now we turn our attention to the individual's children, actual or contemplated.

A large proportion of the questions addressed to genetic counselors concern the matter of having children. "If I have children, will they be normal or abnormal?" Here, unfortunately, the counselor can seldom answer with the certainty hoped for by the inquirer. He must deal largely in probabilities. Again, Huntington's chorea will serve as a useful example. As we have noted, persons who will eventually develop chorea are heterozygous, *Hh*, but may not develop symptoms until late in life. This means that most of them live through their reproductive years without knowing for sure that they are carriers (heterozygous). They may know that one of their parents became choreic in later life, and they may have been told that there is a 50:50 chance that they have the gene, but they can always hope that they are in the 50 percent who do not have it. In the absence of some means of early diagnosis they cannot be sure, however. Here is another reason to develop tests making possible a diagnosis early in life: they will help young people considering marriage to decide about the wisdom of having children. If the (future) tests are negative, the offspring of a choreic parent need have no fear of producing choreic children in his turn (barring the extremely small possibility that a new mutation will occur). If the tests are positive, he will know that half of his children, on the average, may be expected to develop chorea.

We have, then, two advantages to be gained from the hoped-for tests. They will enable a young person to know whether or not he will later become choreic, and whether or not he will produce choreic children if he marries in the meantime. Again we must note the psychological hazards of a young person's possessing such information.

All this is in the future. At present, what can a counselor tell the son or daughter of a choreic parent? Substantially this: there is a 50 percent chance that you will eventually become choreic; if you do not become choreic, none of your children ever will either; if you do become choreic, 50 percent of any children you have produced in the meantime will be likely to become choreic in their turn. Not very comforting information.

However, **Dr. F. C. Fraser** of McGill University wrote of a physician who was so skillful in giving counsel that he managed to convey to the son of a choreic mother the dangers of his having choreic children "without revealing to him the fact that he was a candidate for the disease" (Fraser, 1956). In this particular case the man and his wife decided to adopt children instead of having any of their own.

This case illustrates another aspect of genetic counseling. The wise counselor does not tell people what to do. Insofar as he is able, he lays before them the probabilities of producing abnormal children; examples have been noted frequently in earlier chapters. However, the decision as to whether or not to take the risk must always be made by the potential parents. Thus, on the basis of the probabilities one couple, like the one just mentioned, will decide to refrain from having children, another couple will decide to take the chance in the hope that the "dice of destiny" (Rife, 1947) will roll in their favor.

By no means do all dominant genes produce their phenotypic effects only after a lapse of years. The effects of many are evident at birth or soon after. Thus, retinoblastoma (pp. 75–76) is caused by a dominant gene with high penetrance. The condition develops in childhood and is almost always fatal unless the affected eye or eyes are immediately removed. Before surgical treatment was developed, carriers of the gene died young and so did not transmit the gene to offspring. This is an example of natural selection in operation (Chap. 17). Today, however, people who have the gene are surviving (although half or totally blind), marrying, and having children who in turn inherit the condition (Fig. 6.2, p. 76). To the extent that this occurs, the frequency of the gene will increase in future generations.

Wise genetic counseling could have a eugenic effect here. After all, no one really wants to have children who will be doomed to blindness. A survivor of retinoblastoma can expect that half of his children may be so afflicted (but see also p. 390). Many persons so advised would conclude that they had best refrain from parenthood.

Recessive Traits

Large numbers of hereditary defects are recessive in the sense that heterozygotes suffer little or no disadvantage. In many cases the heterozygotes are not distinguishable from homozygous normals, and that poses a problem.

In preceding chapters we have frequently used albinism as an example. Although albinism is not as serious as Huntington's chorea and retinoblastoma, many people would nevertheless prefer not to have albino children. Genetic counselors are frequently asked by young couples, who greatly to their surprise have produced an albino child, whether or not their next child will be an albino, too. The parents are of normal pigmentation, so they must both be heterozygous, $Cc \times Cc$. Thus, as we understand fully from earlier discussions, the chance that each child will be of normal pigmentation is ¾; the chance that he will be an albino is ¼. This is explained to the parents, and then they make the decision as to whether or not to take the chance.

In a most useful book on the subject of counseling, Dr. Sheldon C. Reed (1963) told of such a couple who came to the Dight Institute for Human Genetics of the University of Minnesota. This couple produced an albino boy. After the probabilities had been explained, they decided to take the chance, and "by intention, produced a normal boy who has been a tremendous pleasure to them." The albino older brother has succeeded well in school and in other activities.

At the present time, this is the pattern of most cases involving recessive genes. A couple produces an abnormal child, usually to everyone's great surprise, for as we know recessive genes may be carried along unobserved for many generations. The couple then wants to know their chances of having another abnormal child. The more serious the abnormality the more urgent the question.

As Dr. Reed has emphasized in the book just mentioned, ideally genetic counseling should be premarital, especially when serious disorders are involved. It would be a tremendous advantage to be able to tell a young person exactly what deleterious genes he is carrying, so that he can avoid marrying someone who has those same genes, or producing children if he does marry such a person. The problem is: How to determine who is heterozygous for a given gene and who is not. If it so happens that an individual has a parent who is homozygous recessive, we know that the individual is heterozygous. Thus the normally pigmented son of an albino parent must be heterozygous and he can be advised not to have children should he marry the daughter of an albino parent. However, sons and daughters of albino parents are so rare that they constitute only a minute fraction of the heterozygotes for albinism. Most heterozygotes receive the gene from a heterozygous parent.

What we need is a test for heterozygosity. Despite his normal phenotype, is there some test we can give a heterozygote to identify him as different from the homozygous normal? In the case of albinism, the defect involves an enzyme in the chain of reactions by which tyrosine is converted to melanin (see p. 84). Although a heterozygote has enough of the enzyme for pigment production, delicate tests perhaps might show a quantitative difference in the enzyme, as compared to homozygotes for the dominant allele. Such a test is within the realm of possibility, or a test of an entirely different nature may be found. Some evidence indicates that heterozygosity for albinism can be detected by examining the eyes with suitable instruments (Falls and Neel, 1954).

With some other traits, carriers can be identified with more or less accuracy, and the search for new and more accurate tests is proceeding. Lists of traits in which the carrier state can, or may be, identified are given by Neel (1949), Neel and Schull (1954, Table 8.1), and Falls and Neel (1954). From earlier discussions we are already familiar with one example. Heterozygotes for the sickle-cell anemia gene can be recognized by testing their red blood cells. When deprived of oxygen, the cells assume bizarre shapes; they "sickle," (Fig. 4.5, p. 50).

We have made frequent reference to phenylketonuria. At least two tests are being employed to identify heterozygotes: a phenylalanine tolerance test, and a determination of phenylalanine level in blood plasma (Knox and Messinger, 1958). Not all individuals can be classified accurately by either test, but greater accuracy will doubtless be attained in the near future.

In general, women who are heterozygous for the sex-linked hemophilia gene have blood with a longer clotting time than normal. The test has not been perfected so that it will identify all carriers, but we may expect progress in the future.

Another condition somewhat similar to sickle-cell anemia is *thalassemia* or *Cooley's anemia*. Homozygotes suffer a severe anemia called thalassemia major, whereas heterozygotes have a milder condition called thalassemia minor or microcythemia. If they have no outward symptoms, they can be identified serologically. In the province of Ferrara, Italy, one person in ten is heterozygous (in some townships, one in five) (Roberts, 1962). Dr. Roberts pointed out that with random mating in these townships one child in every hundred has the severe anemia. In some regions, tests are made and registers posted so that heterozygotes may avoid marrying each other. Dr. Roberts commented: "Of course, it is a little late when the banns have been published and the wedding arrangements made, but this knowledge may well prevent those early approaches which ultimately lead to courtship and marriage."

Our few examples illustrate sufficiently the principles involved. As knowledge, particularly of biochemistry, grows we may expect a steady increase in ability to identify heterozygotes for all manner of recessive defects. We can easily understand how much these new tools will increase the accuracy and certitude of genetic counseling.

The list of hereditary defects is a long one. Interested readers will find tables of them in Dobzhansky (1962, Table 8; four-and-a-half pages in length), in Montagu (1959), Appendix A; nineteen pages), and in Reed (1963, Appendix; twenty-three pages). In some of the tables, the traits are designated as dominant or recessive, but readers should beware of placing too much emphasis on these terms. In the cases of rare traits the data are usually few, one or two families in some cases. If a trait seems to skip a generation, it is called recessive; if not, it is called dominant. In only a comparatively few instances have the rigorous analyses we have discussed in previous chapters been made. In any event, the distinction between dominant and recessive is more or less artificial. If a recessive gene affects the heterozygote *in any way*, then to that extent the gene is not truly recessive (pp. 271–274).

In Dr. Reed's list the type of inheritance is not designated. Rather, the reader is referred to a recent, or most significant, paper on each trait.

Control of Parenthood

In our discussion so far we have spoken rather glibly of married couples deciding not to have children. Obviously, having children or not having them is not always a matter of voluntary decision. Even couples who attempt to control conceptions are not always successful in doing so. Nevertheless improvements in contraceptive methods are making voluntary control over parenthood increasingly effective. The time is not far distant when control will be virtually complete for those who desire it so.

New methods of birth control are being developed, and old methods are being improved. Not all methods are equally acceptable to all people. For example, of the methods now available, only the rhythm method has the official sanction of the Roman Catholic Church. At the present time much research is being devoted to improving this somewhat uncertain method.

The objective of most contraceptive techniques is to prevent ova from coming into contact with sperm, with ensuing fertilization (recall, however, that other approaches to the problem are possible, p. 354). The prevention may be of a more or less mechanical nature, or it may be a matter of timing: ova not present when the sperm cells are. The latter is the basis of the rhythm method and of methods that employ hormonal extracts to suppress ovulation.

Of the mechanical methods, the surest is a surgical operation by which sperm cells are prevented from leaving the testes, or ova are prevented from passing down the oviducts. We have referred to such operations previously as eugenic sterilization (p. 326). They should be clearly distinguished from *castration*, in which the testis or ovary is *removed*. Testis and ovary are glands of double function. They produce sperm and ova, respectively, but they also produce the sex hormones, which in a very real sense cause females to be female and males to be male, physiologically and emotionally. These sex hormones pass from the testis or ovary into the blood, which transports them throughout the body.

However, in eugenic sterilization the testis or ovary remains in place to manufacture its hormones and pass them into the blood stream. Only the ducts through which sperm or ova usually pass are interfered with. This simply means in the male that the semen, produced by the prostate and other glands, contains no sperm cells. Because of the nature of the male anatomy, the operation is simplest in a man, not involving an opening of the body cavity. In women the operation has been compared to an uncomplicated appendectomy. Obviously, if the wife is not promiscuous, the simple operation on the husband is all that is required to prevent the production of children.

Surgical control of conception is commoner than we realize, and probably is increasing in frequency. In our discussion of differential fertility (Chap. 23), we mentioned some of the results obtained by Freedman, Whelpton, and Campbell (1959) from a survey of 2713 white American wives between the ages of 18 and 39 years. Apparently to their surprise, the investigators found that in 9 percent of these families an operation to prevent further reproducion had been performed on either the wife or the husband. In some cases the operation had been performed for contraceptive reasons; in some cases the reasons were therapeutic (but note that the survey did not include older women in whom hysterectomies for health reasons are fairly common).

Sterilization for contraceptive reasons is increasing more rapidly in some other countries than in our own. Thus, for India, Nortman (1964) stated that up to February, 1963, 334,000 sterilizations had been reported, almost two thirds of them on males. "The State of Maharashtra has initiated sterilization camps and some States provide financial compensation of from 10 to 30 rupees per sterilization in addition to free transportation and time off from work" (Nortman, 1964). Pakistan is initiating a somewhat similar program. These and some other countries as well are using this technique in the battle against the "population explosion." Of the various methods of contraception available to an American couple, the one that is most acceptable and desirable will be determined by many rather intangible but personally important considerations.

Sterilization is the contraceptive method of choice in one situation: that in which the intelligence of the couple is so low that they cannot use other contraceptive methods effectively. Despite a few glaring exceptions which used to excite an older generation of eugenists, mentally retarded persons do not have a high birth rate. Thus the Eugenics Survey of Vermont (1929) reported that "the average number of children per inadequate family (one or both parents feebleminded or insane) is 3.5. This average excludes those children who died in infancy, stillbirths, and sex unknown." The Survey compared this figure with a family size of 3.04 for parents not known to be feebleminded or insane. In their extensive survey, Reed and Reed (1965) found that "when infant deaths are excluded, the effective family size for male retardates is 4.2, and that for female retardates is 3.5 children." Thus we need not worry, as some eugenists have, that normal portions of our population are in danger of being submerged by a sea of offspring produced by mental retardates. Nevertheless, there is serious question as to the wisdom of parenthood for persons of subnormal intelligence. Many mentally retarded men may be trained to be self-supporting. The income of such a man may be adequate to support himself and his wife, but inadequate to support several children without disastrous lowering of the standard of living. A mentally retarded mother is unlikely to provide a stimulating home environment for the rearing of children, whether they are mentally retarded or not. Moreover, as we have seen, some types of mental defect are inherited, so some of the children are likely to be retarded. Thus, both from the environmental and genetic standpoints, control of fertility is best for the individuals concerned. Many people of quite low intelligence can be made to understand the desirability of controlling births, but they simply do not know how to do it effectively. For them, eugenic sterilization is frequently a welcome answer.

Some Problems of Genetic Counseling

Thus far we have discussed cases in which the mode of inheritance is relatively simple. This results in easily calculated expectations: as 1:1 for offspring of a heterozygote for a dominant trait, or 3:1 for the offspring of two heterozygotes when the abnormal gene is recessive. When inheritance does not have a single-gene-pair basis, prediction cannot be so clear-cut. When systems of polygenes (Chap. 11) or of interacting genes are concerned, geneticists must compile results from many families in order to estimate the probability of having affected children. We have seen, for example, that schizophrenia has a definite genetic component (pp. 301–303), but we do not know how many genes are involved or how they interact with each other. By studying many families in which at least one child becomes schizophrenic, or in which one or both parents have schizophrenia, we can gain an idea of the average risk of producing schizophrenic offspring. Altshuler (1957), who compiled results from many studies, concluded that when one child is schizophrenic, there is about a 10 percent chance that if the parents produce another child that child will be affected too. This is to be compared with the 0.85 percent chance that any child taken at random in the population will develop schizophrenia. When one parent has schizophrenia, from 8 to 16 percent of the children will develop the disorder, and when both parents are schizophrenic the risk rises to from 53 to 68 percent. Turning to mental retardation, we find that the data compiled by Reed and Reed (1965) led these investigators to conclude that when a normal person who has a retarded sibling marries a retarded person there is a 23.8 percent chance that the first child will be retarded. If a normal person with one or more retarded siblings marries a normal person the chance that the first child will be retarded is 2.5 percent. These percentages are to be compared with 0.53 percent, the chance that a first child born to normal parents without retarded siblings will be retarded. Although this type of genetic information is not as satisfactory as are the probabilities based on simpler modes of inheritance, it is useful in genetic counseling.

Because data are not so numerous for many traits as they are for schizophrenia and mental retardation, predictions as to the risk of producing affected offspring must be still more tentative. Dr. F. C. Fraser of McGill University (1956) stressed two other sources of uncertainty in genetic counseling: (1) "two clinically similar cases may be genetically different," and (2) "a single gene may have widely different manifestations in different persons." The first problem is one of diagnosis, the second is one of variable expressivity (pp. 80–81). Dr. Fraser also mentioned the uncertainty introduced by the occurrence of **phenocopies**. At times environmental factors can combine to produce a phenotype in one individual that closely resembles a phenotype produced in another individual by his genes. Such an environmentally induced "copy" is not inherited, nor is the trait passed on to offspring. The production of phenocopies is a well-known phenomenon in experimental organisms, and it may well occur in man, too, although we have little actual information on the subject. It is suspected, for example, that retinoblastoma sometimes appears as a phenocopy, in the absence of the dominant gene discussed previously (Fraser, 1956). As we noted, if the survivor of retinoblastoma has the condition because of possession of the dominant gene, half of his children will be expected to be affected. However, if he has the condition because it arose in him as a phenocopy, no children he produces will be affected. This poses a real problem for the counselor. As Dr. Fraser recognized, what we need is a means of distinguishing phenocopies from genetic cases.

Another source of uncertainty lies in the fact that in some family lines a trait may be inherited in one way, whereas in other families the inheritance may be of a different type. This is one reason for not adhering too rigidly to the idea that a given trait is dominant, or recessive, or X-linked. In some families it may be one, in some families another. *Pseudohypertrophic muscular dystrophy* (Duchenne type) will afford an example. This is usually listed as an X-linked trait, for in most families only boys are affected. Boys with this disorder are normal during childhood, but when they reach their early teens the muscles waste away; they become more and more helpless, and die before attaining maturity. Because the boys in such lineages never live to produce children, affected females do not occur (Chap. 12). However, families are known in which affected girls are produced and in which inheritance seems to be of the autosomal recessive type (Kloepfer and Talley, 1957–1958). Assuming that this is not a case of confusion of two very similar disorders (Dr. Fraser's first point, above), we may ask how this can be. We may mention two possibilities. A gene usually present on the X-chromosome may, by translocation, have become transferred to an autosome (Chap. 16), or different genes affecting the final outcome may have mutated in different lineages.

The normal phenotype (absence of muscular dystrophy) is the result of the interaction of the genotype as a whole. We have seen that long chains of gene-controlled enzymatic reactions are involved in production of even "simple" traits, and attainment of normal nervous and muscular development is far from simple. Many genes are doubtless involved, some of them in the X-chromosome, some in the autosomes. If any one of these genes fails to do its part, normal development is impossible and the symptoms of dystrophy arise. A chain may be broken by failure of any one of its numerous links. In the case of Duchenne type of muscular dystrophy, failure of a gene in the X chromosome usually constitutes the broken link. At other times, failure of an autosomal gene to do its job may give the same disastrous result.

We have stressed this matter in order to emphasize two points. (1) There are genetic reasons for expecting that a given trait will show different modes of inheritance in different family lines. (2) A genetic counselor should obtain as much information as possible on the ancestry of his clients so that his predictions may apply as precisely as possible to the specific case. In the case of a given couple is the trait dominant or recessive or X-linked? Does it have a more complex genetic basis? Is it a phenocopy?

This recital of the uncertainties involved in genetic counseling may seem discouraging. It is not intended to be so. Much useful counseling is being done despite the uncertainties, but they do constitute a challenge for much further research in human genetics.

Sometimes the question posed is so general or indefinite that a meaningful answer is difficult. Such a query was the one mentioned in the first chapter: "A friend of mine is desirous of marrying his half-sister's daughter, would such a relationship be too close, relative to 'blood-lines,' for normal healthy children?"

In this case we know nothing about the individuals or their ancestry. Probably they are all "normal," but it is also probable that each one of them, or each one of us, is heterozygous for one or more recessive genes that would be harmful to a homozygote. Therefore we might proceed to answer the question in terms of such a gene. If the parent shared in common by the man and his half-sister had such a gene, what are the chances that a child born to the man and his half-sister's daughter would

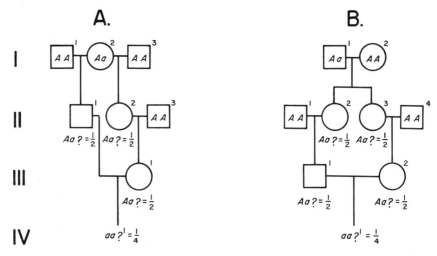

FIG. 25.1 Relative probabilities of producing a child homozygous for a recessive gene possessed by a common ancestor if, A, a man marries his half-sister's daughter, and if, B, a man marries his first cousin. Known or postulated genotypes are written inside squares and circles. "Aa? = ½" written outside such a symbol indicates that the probability is one half that the individual carries the gene *a*.

be homozygous for the gene?

In Figure 25.1, A, we have represented the parent shared by the man and his half-sister as being a mother, I-2, who married twice. (Whether this parent was the father or the mother makes no difference unless we postulate an X-linked trait.) If I-2 has a certain recessive gene, *a*, what are the chances that the man, II-1, and his half-sister, II-2, will also possess it (i.e., be *Aa*)? In answering, we shall assume that the gene is rare enough so that I-1, I-3, and II-3 are very unlikely to possess it (i.e., they are *AA*). Hence the chance that II-1 will be *Aa* is ½, and the chance that his half-sister, II-2, will be *Aa* is also ½. If II-2 is *Aa*, what are the chances that her daughter, III-1, will be *Aa*, also? Again the chance is ½. If II-1 is *Aa* and III-1 is *Aa*, what are the chances that a given child born to them will be *aa*? This chance is ¼. The total chance of producing a child homozygous for a recessive gene possessed by the common parent is ½ × ½ × ½ × ¼ = ¹⁄₃₂.

With what shall we compare this fraction? If, as we assume, gene *a* is rare, the chances of producing an *aa* child in the absence of consanguinity would be very small indeed, far smaller than one chance in 32. A more meaningful comparison might be that with the commoner type of consanguinity: first cousin marriage. Figure 25.1, B, presents such a family.

Again the gene a is assumed to be present in one grandparent, I-1. Following through the pedigree as before, we find that the chance that the cousins, III-1 and III-2, will produce an aa child is $\frac{1}{2} \times \frac{1}{2} \times \frac{1}{2} \times \frac{1}{2} \times \frac{1}{4}$ $= \frac{1}{64}$. On this basis we can state that, other things being equal, the marriage of a man to his half-sister's daughter is twice as dangerous as is the marriage of first cousins: twice as likely to result in an unfavorable homozygous condition.

How "dangerous" is first-cousin marriage itself? Dr. Sheldon Reed (1963), basing his judgment on many studies, stated: "It is clear that the risk of a congenital abnormality in the child from a first-cousin marriage is about twice that expected for children from a marriage of nonrelatives." If the latter chance is small, twice it is also small, but the increased probability is there. Dr. Reed headed the chapter from which the sentence was quoted: "Don't Marry a Relative!"

In the chapter mentioned, Dr. Reed told of a case involving closer inbreeding than does first-cousin marriage: brother-sister mating. A teenage brother and sister "had been so carefully shielded from the viciousness of the outside world that they were completely innocent of any sex education whatever. At least, they were able to convince the social worker that they had no idea that a baby might result from their sexual intercourse" (Reed, 1963). The child had a mildly deformed clubfoot, which could be corrected, but was otherwise apparently normal. Her IQ was only 95 (low normal). This rather low IQ may or may not have been connected with the close inbreeding; more information would be necessary for a decision on that point.

The genetic counselor deals not only with science but also with people, with all their foibles. They seek his advice for many reasons. Most commonly, perhaps, a husband and wife want to have more children but are fearful of doing so. At times, however, one spouse desires a larger family but the other does not; each hopes that the counselor will provide ammunition for his side of the argument. In other cases both husband and wife wish to have no more children and they therefore hope that the counselor will advise them that having more children would be dangerous or unwise. A very different situation was reported by Dr. Fraser (1956). In this case, the man, an albino, hoped that the counselor would aid him to escape from the clutches of a designing woman to whom he was engaged, by telling him that it would be dangerous for him to marry. Any counselor can add to the list, for no two cases are alike. A counselor's role is not easy, but neither is it dull.

Sometimes parents of an abnormal child come to a counselor seeking to fix the "blame" for the child's abnormality. "Whose fault was it, mine or my husband's?" This idea of someone being at fault is an unfortunate one, and can lead to a serious rift in the marriage. In point of fact, if the abnormality results from homozygosity for a recessive gene, both parents have contributed to the defect. If the abnormality is caused by a dominant gene, the child is usually heterozygous, having received the gene from one parent only. However, that parent is in no sense "to blame" for having the gene or for passing it on. These are matters over which he has no control, short of refraining from having any children whatsoever. This should be abundantly evident to readers of this book, who therefore will not fall into this error if in the future they seek the advice of a genetic counselor.

REFERENCES

Altshuler, K. Z., 1957. "Genetic elements in schizophrenia. A review of the literature and résumé of unsolved problems," *Eugenics Quarterly*, 4:92–98.

Centerwall, W. R., H. K. Berry, and L. I. Woolf, 1963. "Detection." In F. L. Lyman (ed.) *Phenylketonuria*. Springfield, Ill.: Charles C Thomas. Pp. 114–35.

Dobzhansky, T. 1962. *Mankind Evolving*. New Haven: Yale University Press.

Eugenics Survey of Vermont, 1929. *Third Annual Report*. Burlington, Vt.: University of Vermont.

Falek, A., and E. V. Glanville, 1962. "Investigation of genetic carriers." In Kallmann, F. J. (ed.). *Expanding Goals of Genetics in Psychiatry*. New York: Grune & Stratton, Inc., Pp. 136–48.

Falls, H. F., and J. V. Neel, 1954. "The detection of carriers of 'recessive' genes," *Eugenics Quarterly*, 1:166–70.

Fraser, F. C., 1956. "Heredity counseling. The darker side," *Eugenics Quarterly*, 3:45–51.

Freedman, R., P. K. Whelpton, and A. A. Campbell, 1959. *Family Planning, Sterility, and Population Growth*. New York: McGraw-Hill Book Company, Inc.

Kloepfer, H. W., and C. Talley, 1957–1958. "Autosomal recessive inheritance of Duchenne-type muscular dystrophy," *Annals of Human Genetics*, 22:138–43.

Knox, W. E., and E. C. Messinger, 1958. "The detection in the heterozygote of the metabolic effect of the recessive gene for phenylketonuria," *American Journal of Human Genetics*, 10:53–60.

McKay, R. J., 1964. "Practical application of current knowledge concerning human chromosomes," *The Pediatric Clinics of North America*, 11:171–82.

Montagu, Ashley, 1959. *Human Heredity*. Cleveland: The World Publishing Company.

Neel, J. V., 1949. "The detection of the genetic carriers of hereditary disease," *American Journal of Human Genetics*, 1:19–36.

Neel, J. V., and W. J. Schull, 1954. *Human Heredity*. Chicago: University of Chicago Press.

Nortman, D., 1964. "Population policies in developing countries and related international attitudes," *Eugenics Quarterly*, 11:11–29.

Patterson, R. M., B. K. Bagchi, and A. Test, 1948. "The prediction of Huntington's chorea: An electroencephalographic and genetic study," *American Journal of Psychiatry*, 104:786–97.

Pearson, J. S., 1965. *Huntington's Chorea and Your Family.* Rochester, Minnesota: Minnesota Department of Public Welfare. (A pamphet obtainable without cost from the Dight Institute for Human Genetics, Zoology Building, University of Minnesota, Minneapolis, Minnesota, 55455.)

Reed, E. W., and S. C. Reed, 1965. *Mental Retardation: A Family Study.* Philadelphia: W. B. Saunders Company.

Reed, S. C., 1963. *Counseling in Medical Genetics,* 2nd ed. Philadelphia: W. B. Saunders Company. Also available in paperback under the title: *Parenthood and Heredity.* New York: John Wiley & Sons, Inc. (Science Editions, 1964).

Rife, D. C., 1947. *Dice of Destiny,* 2nd ed. Columbus, Ohio: Long's College Book Company.

Roberts, J. A. F., 1962. "Genetic prognosis," *British Medical Journal,* 1:587–92.

APPENDICES

APPENDIX A

Derivation of the formula expressing the probability that a child of first cousins will be homozygous for a recessive gene at a certain locus in an autosome.

In Figure A.1 the fact that II-2, II-3, III-2 and IV-1 are represented as female is arbitrary and immaterial, as sex linkage is not involved.

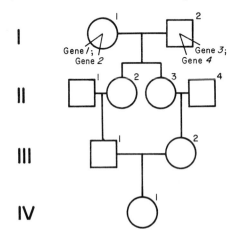

Fig. A.1   Marriage of first cousins.

What are the chances that IV-1 will be homozygous for a recessive gene at a certain locus? The allelic pairs at this locus in the great grandparents, I-1 and I-2, are designated, as "Gene 1" and "Gene 2," and "Gene 3" and "Gene 4," respectively. Any one of the four genes may be dominant or recessive.

What are the chances that IV-1 will inherit "Gene 1" *from her father* (III-1)? The chance that I-1 will pass "Gene 1" on to her daughter, II-2, is ½. The chance that if II-2 has the gene she will pass it on to her son III-1 is ½. The chance that if III-1 has the gene he will pass it on to IV-1 is ½. Thus the chance that IV-1 will receive "Gene 1" *from her father* is ½ × ½ × ½ = ⅛.

Similarly, what are the chances that IV-1 will inherit "Gene 1" *from her mother* (III-2)? The chance that I-1 will pass the gene on to II-3 is ½. The chance that if II-3 has the gene she will pass it on to III-2 is ½. The chance that if III-2 has the gene she will pass it on to IV-1 is ½ .So the chance that IV-1 will receive "Gene 1" *from her mother* is also ½ × ½ × ½ = ⅛.

Hence, the chance that IV-1 will inherit "Gene 1" from *both* parents (i.e., be homozygous for it) is ⅛ × ⅛ = ⅟₆₄.

By the same reasoning, we see that the chance that IV-1 will be homozygous for "Gene 2" is also ⅟₆₄. And the same reasoning applies to "Gene 3" and "Gene 4."

Thus the chance that IV-1 will be homozygous for *any one* of the four genes from her great grandparents, I-1 and I-2, is ⅟₆₄ + ⅟₆₄ + ⅟₆₄ + ⅟₆₄ = ⁴⁄₆₄ or ⅟₁₆. Note that we *add* the fractions because they represent mutually exclusive events. By this, we mean that IV-1 cannot be homozygous for more than one of the four genes. If she is a "Gene 1–Gene 1" homozygote she cannot also be a "Gene 2–Gene 2" homozygote, and so on.

What are the chances that the gene IV-1 is homozygous for is a recessive gene? The answer depends on the frequency of the gene in the population of which this kindred is a part. As usual we designate this frequency of the recessive gene by q. Therefore, the chance that IV-1 will be homozygous for a recessive gene inherited from the great grandparents shown in the pedigree is ⅟₁₆ q. It follows that the chance that IV-1 will *not* be homozygous for a recessive gene inherited from the great grandparents shown in the pedigree is ¹⁵⁄₁₆ q (⅟₁₆ q subtracted from unity, the totality of cases).

Thus far we have neglected the husbands of II-2 and II-3. These husbands, II-1 and II-4, of course, had parents in their turn although the parents are not shown in the diagram. There is some chance that the recessive gene we are interested in may have come from them. This chance is represented by the frequency of the gene, q. Hence the chance that homozygosity for the gene may arise in IV-1 from these "outside sources" (*not* from the great grandparents shown in the diagram) is

$$\tfrac{15}{16}\, q \times q = \tfrac{15}{16}\, q^2.$$

Thus the total chance that IV-1 will be homozygous for a recessive gene is the chance that she will be homozygous because of inheritance from the great grandparents shown (⅟₁₆ q) plus the chance that she will be homozygous because of inheritance from other ancestors (¹⁵⁄₁₆ q^2).

$$\tfrac{1}{16}\, q + \tfrac{15}{16}\, q^2 = q/16\,(1 + 15\,q)$$

See Dahlberg, G., 1948. *Mathematical Methods for Population Genetics*. New York: Interscience Publishers. Pp. 53–54. Stern, C., 1960. *Principles of Human Genetics*, 2nd ed. San Francisco: W. H. Freeman & Co. Pp. 374–75.

APPENDIX B

The von Dungern-Hirschfeld hypothesis of ABO inheritance. The basis of the statement by Bernstein (1925) that if the hypothesis were valid the following equation should be correct:

$$\overline{(A + \overline{AB})} \bullet \overline{(B + \overline{AB})} = \overline{AB} \quad \text{(p. 129)}$$

Let s = relative frequency of gene a
$(1 - s)$ = relative frequency of gene A (see p. 128)
t = relative frequency of gene b
$(1 - t)$ = relative frequency of gene B

Then taking the gene pairs separately we find that:

Frequency of $AA = (1 - s)^2$
Frequency of $Aa = 2(1 - s)s$
Frequency of $aa = s^2$

(Note here the similarity to the Hardy-Weinberg formulation.)

Frequency of $BB = (1 - t)^2$
Frequency of $Bb = 2(1 - t)t$
Frequency of $bb = t^2$

GROUP O.   Persons in this group would have the genotype *aabb*. Their expected frequency would be $s^2 t^2$.
GROUP A.   Persons in this group would have one of two genotypes:

AAbb, with a frequency of $(1 - s)^2 \times t^2$
Aabb, with a frequency of $2(1 - s)s \times t^2$

Total frequency for the group would be:

$$(1 - s)^2 t^2 + 2(1 - s)s \times t^2$$

which may be simplified as follows:

$$t^2[(1 - s)^2 + 2(1 - s)s]$$
$$t^2[(1 - s)^2 + 2s - 2s^2]$$
$$t^2[1 - 2s + s^2 + 2s - 2s^2]$$
$$t^2[1 - s^2]$$

In sum, the expected frequency of group A people would be $t^2 (1 - s^2)$.
GROUP B.   The two genotypes would be:

aaBB, with a frequency of $s^2 \times (1 - t)^2$
aaBb, with a frequency of $s^2 \times 2(1 - t)t$

The total, $s^2 [(1 - t)^2 + 2(1 - t)t]$, simplifies to $s^2 (1 - t^2)$ in the manner indicated for group A.

401

GROUP AB.

Genotypes	Frequencies
AABB	$(1 - s)^2 \times (1 - t)^2$
AaBB	$2(1 - s)s \times (1 - t)^2$
AABb	$(1 - s)^2 \times 2(1 - t)t$
AaBb	$2(1 - s)s \times 2(1 - t)t$

The total of these frequencies simplifies to $(1 - s^2)(1 - t^2)$.

IN SUMMARY:

Group O, $\overline{O}$, would have a frequency of $s^2 t^2$
Group A, $\overline{A}$, would have a frequency of $t^2 (1 - s^2)$
Group B, $\overline{B}$, would have a frequency of $s^2 (1 - t^2)$
Group AB, $\overline{AB}$, would have a frequency of $(1 - s^2)(1 - t^2)$

It follows that $\overline{A} + \overline{AB} = 1 - s^2$, calculated as follows:

$$t^2 (1 - s^2) + (1 - s^2)(1 - t^2) = t^2 - t^2 s^2 + 1 - s^2 - t^2 + t^2 s^2 = 1 - s^2$$

In the same manner:

$$\overline{B} + \overline{AB} = 1 - t^2$$

Therefore

$$(\overline{A} + \overline{AB}) \cdot (\overline{B} + \overline{AB}) = \overline{AB}$$

since

$$(1 - s^2)(1 - t^2) = (1 - s^2)(1 - t^2)$$

(Recall that this equation does not in fact fit the data, p. 130.)

Bernstein, F., 1925. "Zusammenfassende Betrachtungen über die erblichen Blutstrukturen des Menschen," *Zeitschrift für induktive Abstammungs- und Vererbungslehre*, **37**:237–70.

APPENDIX C

Chi-square test and its application to data concerning offspring of secretor parents (pp. 140–142).

The chi-square test is sometimes called a test of "goodness of fit." How well do actual data fit expectation based on theory? In the specific example (p. 141), 105 families in which both parents were secretors produced 241 secretor children and 33 nonsecretor children. Use of the formula

$$\left(\frac{q}{1+q}\right)^2$$

indicates that 28.6 nonsecretor children were to be expected. In using this formula, we are advancing the hypothesis that nonsecretion depends on a recessive gene, secretion on its dominant allele. Is the observed deviation in numbers significant evidence against the hypothesis?

Table C.1 shows the application of the chi-square test to this question. In the first column, headed o for "observed," we find the number of secretor and nonsecretor children counted in the investigation. In the second column, headed e for "expected," we find the numbers expected on the basis of the formula. Note that columns o and e must have the same total number. (The 245.4 is obtained by subtracting 28.6 from 274, the total number of children.)

In the column headed $o - e$ we find the *deviations*, obtained by subtracting the expected values from the observed ones. Note that the plus deviations must equal the minus deviations and hence the total of the $o - e$ column must be zero.

The deviations are then squared and the squares are divided by the respective expected values: column headed $\frac{(o - e)^2}{e}$. Each fraction is then divided out to form a decimal, and these decimals are added to give a total, which is called the *chi-square value,* χ^2.

TABLE C.1. An example of the chi-square test.

o	e	o — e	$\frac{(o-e)^2}{e}$	
241	245.4	—4.4	$\frac{19.36}{245.4}$	$= 0.079$
33	28.6	+4.4	$\frac{19.36}{28.6}$	$= 0.677$
Totals 274	274.0	0		$0.756 = \chi^2$

We may summarize this computation of chi-square by the formula:

$$\chi^2 = \frac{\Sigma (o - e)^2}{e}$$

(The chi-square value equals the sum of the squared deviations divided by the expected values.)

Reference is then made to the Table of Chi-Square (Table C.2). The body of the table is composed of chi-square values. The column headings are percentages expressed as decimal fractions, the values of P. The percentage in each case is the probability that the amounts of deviation represented by the chi-square values below will be exceeded *by chance.* If the probability is great that chance alone will produce a given amount of deviation, the occurrence of that amount of deviation is not considered significant evidence against the hypothesis being tested.

The horizontal rows in the table are numbered at the left to indicate the respective "degrees of freedom." To illustrate the idea of degrees of freedom, let us imagine a bag containing three marbles—one red, one white, one black. If, without looking, we reach into the bag and pick up a marble, we may pick up any one of the three; freedom of chance is complete. Suppose that by chance we remove the white marble on the first trial. On a second trial chance can still operate because the marble we pick up may be the red one or the black one. Suppose that by chance we remove the black marble on this second trial. Now if we reach in our hand a third time, chance can no longer operate; the marble we pick up *must* be the red one. So with three marbles we have *two* "degrees of freedom," two trials in which chance can operate. In general, there is one less degree of freedom than there are classes or categories. In the present example, when we first encounter a child we do not know whether he is a secretor or a nonsecretor. However, if by tests we find that he is a secretor, we have removed the chance that he might be a nonsecretor, and vice versa. Thus with the two categories, "secretor" and "nonsecretor," there is only one degree of freedom.

TABLE C.2. Table of chi-square.

Degrees of freedom	Probability, P						
	0.90	0.70	0.50	0.20	0.10	0.05	0.01
1	0.0158	0.148	0.455	1.642	2.706	3.841	6.635
2	0.211	0.713	1.386	3.219	4.605	5.991	9.210
3	0.584	1.424	2.366	4.642	6.251	7.815	11.341
4	1.064	2.195	3.357	5.989	7.779	9.488	13.277
5	1.610	3.000	4.351	7.289	9.236	11.070	15.086

Abridged from Table IV of Fisher and Yates, *Statistical Tables for Biological, Agricultural, and Medical Research,* published by Oliver & Boyd Ltd., Edinburgh, and by permission of the authors and publishers. See the book for a more complete table.

Accordingly, we enter the table on the first row and look for the chi-square value closest to the one we have obtained (0.756). We see that the chi-square value in the 50 percent column is 0.455, that in the 20 percent column is 1.642. The 0.756 is between these two, nearest to 0.455. This means that approximately 40 percent of the time the amount of deviation represented by our chi-square value would be exceeded by random chance. Because this probability is so great, we conclude that obtaining the deviation expressed by a chi-square value of 0.756 is not significant evidence *against* the hypothesis that the nonsecretor trait depends on a recessive gene (p. 142).

Where shall the line of significance be drawn? Usage differs, but many biologists draw the line at 5 percent. This means that if the probability of obtaining the observed deviation by random chance is less than 5 percent, the data probably do not fit the hypothesis being tested. The investigator should then obtain more data or formulate a hypothesis that fits the present data more closely.

APPENDIX D

Where to look for additional information.
The list of references at the end of each chapter will enable readers to find additional information concerning the subjects discussed in that chapter. However, in an elementary book of this kind, devoted to the discussion of principles rather than to the presentation of detailed information, many inherited traits in which readers may be interested are not even mentioned. This is especially true of the vast medical literature devoted to pathological traits.

Therefore we list below some of the most available sources of information. The list is representative but by no means complete. For the most part only recently published books have been included; references to other published material may be obtained from them.

BOOKS

Becker, P. E. (ed.), 1964. *Humangenetik. Ein kurzes Handbuch in fünf Bänden.* Stuttgart: Georg Thieme Verlag. (For those who read German.)

Boyer, S. H., IV (ed.), 1963. *Papers on Human Genetics.* Englewood Cliffs, N. J.: Prentice-Hall, Inc. (Reprinting of many important pioneer papers in the field.)

Burdette, W. J. (ed.), 1962. *Methodology in Human Genetics.* San Francisco: Holden-Day, Inc.

Cold Spring Harbor Symposia on Quantitative Biology
   Vol. 20, 1955: "Population genetics: the nature and causes of genetic variability in populations."
   Vol. 29, 1965: "Human genetics."
   Cold Spring Harbor, N. Y.: The Biological Laboratory.

Gates, R. R., 1946. *Human Genetics,* Vol. I, II. New York: The Macmillan Company. (Encyclopedic introduction to the older literature. The index for both volumes is at the end of Vol. II.)

Lenz, W., 1963. *Medical Genetics.* Chicago: The University of Chicago Press.

Li, C. C., 1961. *Human Genetics: Principles and Methods.* New York: McGraw-Hill Book Company, Inc. (Skillful exposition of mathematical principles involved.)

McKusick, V. A., 1961. *Medical Genetics 1958–1960: An Annotated Review.* St. Louis: The C. V. Mosby Company.

McKusick, V. A., 1964. *Human Genetics.* Englewood Cliffs, N. J.: Prentice-Hall, Inc.

Montagu, Ashley, 1959. *Human Heredity.* Cleveland: The World Publishing Company.

Neel, J. V., and W. J. Schull, 1954. *Human Heredity.* Chicago: The University of Chicago Press.

Pearson, J. S., 1965. *Huntington's Chorea and Your Family*. Rochester, Minnesota: Minnesota Department of Public Welfare. (A pamphlet obtainable without cost from the Dight Institute for Human Genetics, Zoology Building, University of Minnesota, Minneapolis, Minnesota, 55455.)

Penrose, L. S. (ed.), 1961. *Recent Advances in Human Genetics*. Boston: Little, Brown and Company.

Reed, S. C., 1964. *Parenthood and Heredity*, 2nd ed. New York: John Wiley & Sons, Inc. (Science Editions, paperback).

Roberts, J. A. F., 1963. *An Introduction to Medical Genetics*, 3rd ed. London: Oxford University Press.

Steinberg, A. G. (ed.), 1961 & ff. *Progress in Medical Genetics*, Vol. 1, 2, 3, 4. New York: Grune & Stratton, Inc. (Other volumes are to follow.)

Stern, C., 1960. *Principles of Human Genetics*, 2nd ed. San Francisco: W. H. Freeman & Company.

Sutton, H. E., 1965. *An Introduction to Human Genetics*. New York: Holt, Rinehart and Winston.

Whittinghill, M., 1965. *Human Genetics and Its Foundations*. New York: Reinhold Publishing Corporation.

Wolstenholme, G. E. W., and C. M. O'Connor (eds.), 1959. *Biochemistry of Human Genetics*. Boston: Little, Brown & Company. (Ciba Foundation Symposium).

PERIODICALS

Acta Genetica et Statistica Medica
American Journal of Human Genetics
Annals of Human Genetics
Eugenics Quarterly
Humangenetik
Journal de Génétique Humaine
Journal of Heredity
Journal of Medical Genetics

These are the leading journals in the field, but many others, especially the multitude of medical journals, contain papers on various aspects of human genetics. Furthermore, the scientific weeklies frequently contain important papers in this field. See, for example, *Nature, Science,* and *The Lancet.*

GLOSSARY

GLOSSARY

ABO blood groups. Classification of people on the basis of the presence or absence of the red blood cell antigens A and B.

ABO incompatibility. Refers to a marriage in which the husband has antigen A and/or B, which his wife lacks.

Acrocentric. Refers to chromosomes having the centromere located very near one end.

Acute radiation. A given amount of radiation received quickly within a brief span of time.

Adenine. One of the organic bases (purines) found in DNA and RNA.

Afibrinogenemia. An abnormality in which the blood does not clot normally due to lack of the serum constituent called fibrinogen.

Agglutinins. Antibodies that react with, for example, red blood cells containing the corresponding antigen (agglutinogen), causing the cells to clump together (agglutinate).

Agglutinogen. An antigen in, for example, red blood cells that will react with the corresponding antibodies (agglutinins), causing the cells to clump together (agglutinate).

Albinism. Lack of pigment in skin, hair, eyes, etc.

Alkaptonuria. A metabolic abnormality in the chain of reactions by which amino acids are broken down into simpler compounds for excretion. An intermediate product, homogentisic acid, collects in the urine, causing it to darken.

Allele (Allelomorph). One of two or more alternative genes which may be present at a given locus in a chromosome; e.g., A is the allele of a, and vice versa.

Amaurotic idiocy. *see* Infantile amaurotic idiocy.

Amino acids. Complex organic compounds from which proteins are formed.

Amnion. The inner membrane which encloses the embryo and its surrounding fluid (amniotic fluid) (see Fig. 20.1).

Anaphase. A stage in mitosis (see Fig. 3.2).

Anaphase lag. Said to occur when, following metaphase in mitosis, a chromosome fails to move normally toward the pole of the spindle (see Fig. 3.2). As a result, the chromosome is not included in either daughter nucleus; it is "lost" and later resorbed.

Anastomosis. Joining together of blood vessels so that blood flows from one into the other.

411

Aneuploidy. Chromosomal aberration in which the number of chromosomes is increased by less than the haploid number.

Angstrom unit. 1/10,000,000 of a millimeter.

Anthocyanin. A pigment found in flowers.

Antibodies. Proteins synthesized by the human or animal body in response to antigens such as viruses, bacteria, or proteins foreign to the body. The antibodies can react with the antigens that stimulated their formation.

Antigen. A substance that will stimulate the production of antibodies and react with them.

Antihemophilic globulin. A plasma protein forming part of the blood-clotting mechanism; people having hemophilia A are deficient in this globulin.

Antimutagenic agent. Any material or technique that might protect cells and their contents against the mutation-inducing effects of radiation.

Antiserum. Blood serum containing antibodies.

a priori **method** (of correcting pooled data). A means of compensating for the fact that when families of two heterozygous parents are identified only by virtue of having at least one child with the presumed recessive trait, more than one fourth of the children will be expected to show that trait.

Artificial insemination. Use of instruments to introduce sperm cells into the uterus of a female.

Ascertainment. In this context, the method by which an investigator learns of individuals or matings—the method of sampling.

Assortative mating. Mating based on choice or preference relative to the genetic trait being investigated, as opposed to random mating.

Autosomes. Chromosomes other than the sex chromosomes X and Y.

Back cross. Mating of a heterozygote to a homozygote, especially to the homozygote for a recessive gene; e.g., $Aa \times aa$.

Balanced polymorphism. A condition of equilibruim in a population having individuals of two or more forms (phenotypes). The relative frequencies of the two phenotypes remain constant from generation to generation.

"Balance hypothesis" (concerning the gene pool). The hypothesis that mankind has a high degree of heterozygosity and that, in general, heterozygosity produces normal phenotypes.

Barr bodies. Sex-chromatin bodies; deeply staining particles found attached to the inner surfaces of the nuclear membranes of the cells of females (see Fig. 15.5, A).

"Bleeder." A person who has hemophilia.

Blending inheritance. Inheritance in which F_1 offspring are intermediate between their parents with respect to some quantitative trait, and F_2 offspring vary widely, usually approximating a normal frequency curve. *see* Polygenes.

Brachydactyly. A hereditary trait characterized by markedly shortened fingers.

Brachyphalangy. *see* Brachydactyly.

Buccal smear. A stained preparation of cells scraped from the lining of the mouth.

Carbon-14. Radioactive isotope of carbon.

Carrier. A heterozygote; a person who has a certain gene but does not show the effects of it himself.

Castration. Surgical removal of ovaries or testes.

Cataract. An abnormality of the eye in which the lens becomes opaque.

Centriole. A tiny body outside the nucleus of a cell, concerned with formation of the spindle in mitosis and meiosis (see Fig. 3.2).

Centromere. A nonstaining body forming part of a chromosome. Chromosomes vary as to its location. It is important in causing separation of chromatids following metaphase in mitosis and meiosis (see Fig. 3.1; 3.2).

Chiasma (*plural:* **Chiasmata**). Crosslike pattern formed when two chromatids which have undergone crossing over start to separate following synapsis (see Fig. 3.6).

Chimera. *see* Mosaic.

Chi-square test. A test of "goodness of fit"—of the likelihood that deviation between observed data and values expected on the basis of some hypothesis is due to chance and hence does not constitute significant evidence against the hypothesis (see Appendix C).

Chorion. The outer embryonic membrane surrounding the amnion and its contents (see Fig. 20.1; 20.2).

Christmas disease. Hemophilia B.

Chromatid. When a chromosome has duplicated itself but the original and newly formed elements are still united by a centromere, each element is called a chromatid (see Fig. 3.1).

Chromatin. A term for the material of which chromosomes are composed, rich in nucleoproteins and especially the nucleic acid DNA.

Chromatin negative. Having no Barr bodies in the cell nuclei.

Chromatin positive. Having Barr bodies in the cell nuclei.

Chromatography. In this context, a means of separating into its component parts a mixture of peptide fragments obtained by digestion of a protein with trypsin. It depends on the fact that different peptides migrate along a strip of filter paper to different distances from the starting point (paper chromatography).

Chromomeres. Irregularly spaced, nodule-like enlargements on chromonemata or chromosomes (see Fig. 3.4).

Chromonema (*plural:* **Chromonemata**). A chromosome in a very attenuated, threadlike form (see Fig. 3.1).

Chromosomal aberration or mutation. Alteration in number or structure of chromosomes, visible with a microscope (*see:* Aneuploidy; Deletion; Duplication; Inversion; Isochromosome; Polyploidy; Translocation).

Chromosomes. Deeply staining bodies in the nuclei of cells, rich in nucleoproteins and especially the nucleic acid DNA.

Chronic radiation. A given amount of radiation received slowly over an extended period of time.

cis phase (of linkage). *see* Coupling linkage.

Cistron. The gene as a functional unit of heredity—having a significant effect on the phenotype.

"Classical hypothesis" (concerning the gene pool). The hypothesis that mankind has a high degree of homozygosity for genes that make for normal phenotypes.

Codominant genes. Alleles each of which produces an independent phenotypic effect in heterozygotes.

Codon. A nucleotide triplet in the genetic code, designating a certain amino acid; a "code word."

Colchicine. A drug used on living cells to cause the arrest of mitosis at the metaphase stage.

Color blindness. (1) **Complete.** Virtually total inability to distinguish colors; rare. (2) **Partial.** *see* Deuteranopia; Protanopia.

Complementary genes. Two (or more) dominant genes, not alleles of each other, that interact to produce a phenotype although neither gene produces a phenotypic effect by itself.

Concordance (of twins). Members of a pair of twins are alike with respect to a certain trait.

Consanguinity. Marriage between relatives.

Cooley's anemia. *see* Thalassemia.

Copying error. Production of a mutation by failure of a gene to duplicate itself precisely in preparation for mitosis or meiosis.

Correlation coefficient. In this context, a statistic expressing the degree of similarity between the attainment of one individual and that of another in the performance of some test.

Cosmic rays. Radiations originating in outer space.

Cotyledon. Embryonic leaf within a plant seed.

Coupling linkage. With reference to two pairs of genes: the dominant members of both pairs are located in the same chromosome, and the recessive members of both pairs are located in the same chromosome; e.g., (AB) (ab).

Cretinism. Mental deficiency arising from lack of adequate thyroid secretion during infancy and early childhood.

Crossing over. Exchange of material between one chromatid and another at the time of synapsis in meiosis (see Fig. 3.6; 13.1).

Cultural or social inheritance. The accumulated wisdom of mankind, transmitted by the written and spoken word, by art, music, etc.

Cytogenetics. Study of the contributions to heredity of structures and phenomena within the cells, especially of changes in chromosomes.

Cytoplasm. The portion of a cell lying outside the nucleus.

Cytosine. One of the organic bases (pyrimidines) found in DNA and RNA.

Daltonism. Partial color blindness. *see* Deuteranopia; Protanopia.

Darwinism. *see* Natural selection.

Deficiency. *see* Deletion; Mental deficiency.

Deletion. Chromosomal aberration in which a portion is lost from the chromosome (see Fig. 16.2).

Deuteranopia. A type of partial color blindness in which there is no marked reduction of sensitivity to any color but there is confusion in distinguishing red, yellow, and green (cf., Protanopia).

Diabetes mellitus. A disease in which the body lacks the normal ability to utilize sugar; the excretion of sugar in the urine is one symptom.

Differential fertility. Differences among individuals or groups in the number of offspring produced.

Diploid number ($2n$). The number of chromosomes in a somatic cell or in a germ cell before meiosis. The chromosomes occur in homologous pairs.

Discordance (of twins). Members of a pair of twins are not alike with respect to a certain trait.

Disjunction. Normal separation of chromosomes in mitosis and meiosis.

Distal hyperextensibility (of the thumb). Ability to bend the thumb sharply backward (dorsally) (see Fig. 7.1; 7.2).

Dizygotic or **DZ.** Literally, two zygotes; refers to twins that develop from separate ova; "fraternal twins."

DNA (deoxyribonucleic acid). Nucleic acid characteristic of chromosomes; its sugar component is deoxyribose.

Dominant. (1) A gene that produces a phenotypic effect in a heterozygote; (2) A trait that is shown phenotypically by both homozygotes and heterozygotes.

Double crossing over. Simultaneous breakage and recombination of synapsing chromatids at two points (see Fig. 13.3).

Down's syndrome. *see* Mongolism.

Drift. *see* Genetic drift.

Drosophila. The genus of fruit flies or "vinegar flies" widely used in genetical research.

"Drumstick." A lobelike appendage to the nucleus in white blood cells of females (see Fig. 15.5, B).

Duchenne type (of muscular dystrophy). *see* Pseudohypertrophic muscular dystrophy.

Duodenum. The portion of the small intestine attached to the stomach.

Duplication. Chromosomal aberration in which a portion of a chromosome is repeated within the same chromosome (see Fig. 16.2).

Dyad. A chromosome composed of two chromatids united by a centromere; usually applied to chromosomes in the secondary spermatocyte or secondary oöcyte stage of meiosis (see Fig. 3.5; 3.8).

Dysgenic. Adjective applied to any force or trend that contributes to genetic deterioration of mankind; opposite of Eugenic.

DZ. Dizygotic.

EEG (Electroencephalogram). "Brain waves"; recordings of fluctuations in the electrical potentials generated by the brain.

Effective allele. A term applied to those polygenes that produce an increase in a quantitative trait.

Electrophoresis. In this context, separation of proteins or their constituents by differential rate of migration of the particles when placed in an electrical field.

Elliptocytosis. A hereditary condition in which the red blood cells are elliptical instead of circular.

Enzyme. An organic catalyst; an organic compound, usually protein, that increases the rate at which chemical reactions occur in the body. Usually the reaction will not occur to an effective extent without the enzyme.

Equatorial plate. *see* Metaphase plate.

Equilibrium, Genetic. The state manifested by a population that remains the same, genotypically and phenotypically, generation after generation.

Erythroblastosis fetalis. A pathological condition in which red blood cells are destroyed in the fetus or newborn with resultant anemia and other severe symptoms, including jaundice.

Erythroblasts. Nucleated cells from which red blood cells are formed.

Erythrocytes. Red blood cells.

Escherichia coli. A common bacterium found in the intestines; extensively used for genetical research.

Eugenic. Adjective applied to any force or trend that contributes to genetic improvement of mankind.

Eugenics. "The study of agencies under social control that may improve or impair the racial [i.e., hereditary] qualities of future generations, either physically or mentally." (Francis Galton)

    (1) **Negative Eugenics.** Programs for decreasing the number of children produced by people with inferior genetic traits.

    (2) **Positive Eugenics.** Programs for increasing the production of children by people with superior genetic traits.

Eugenic sterilization. Surgical operation on the reproductive organs to prevent (1) ova from reaching the uterus in females, or (2) sperm cells from being included in the semen of males.

Eugenist. A person interested in the possibility of genetic improvement of mankind and prevention of genetic deterioration.

Expressivity, Variable. A situation in which individuals with the same genotype show different phenotypes.

F_1. First filial generation; offspring of homozygous dominants mated to homozygous recessives and therefore necessarily heterozygous.

F_2. Second filial generation; offspring of F_1 individuals mated together, or, more broadly, offspring of any heterozygotes mated to each other, as $Aa \times Aa$.

Fecund. Capable of producing offspring.

Fertilization. Union of sperm and ovum to form a zygote (fertilized ovum).

Fetus. Unborn young in the final six months before birth.

Fibrin. Elastic, fibrous material present in blood clots; formed from fibrinogen.

Fibrinogen. A blood plasma protein necessary for normal clotting of the blood; it is converted to fibrin.

Fixation. In this context, a condition within a population in which all the genes at a certain locus are the same (e.g., all A), the allele (e.g., a) having been lost from the gene pool.

Follicle (in the ovary). A "bubble-like" structure within the tissue of the ovary; it contains an ovum surrounded by fluid.

Founder principle. When a new colony is founded by emigration from a population, the emigrants may not possess a typical (random) sample of the genes present in the population. Thus by chance the colony may come to differ from the ancestral population.

Freemartin. A female calf, usually sterile, born twin to a male.

Gamete. A mature germ cell, sperm or ovum.

Gene. The unit of inheritance; a portion of a DNA molecule within a chromosome. *see* Cistron; Muton; Recon.

Gene mutation. Alteration of that portion of a DNA molecule comprising a gene.

Gene pool. The totality of genes possessed by a population. The term may be used to refer to a single pair of alleles, or to two or more pairs.

"Genetic death." Removal of a gene from the gene pool of a population or from a given line of descent.

Genetic drift. Chance fluctuations in gene frequencies; more characteristic of small populations than of large ones.

Genetic homeostasis. Self-regulating capacity of populations, enabling them to adapt to varied or changing environments and conditions of life.

Genetic isolate. *see* Isolate.

"Genetic load." The total of the mutations in an individual's germ plasm, consisting of new mutations plus old ones inherited from ancestors.

Genetic polymorphism. *see* Polymorphism.

Genotype. The assemblage of genes found in the chromosomes of an individual or a selected portion thereof; one's "genetic formula."

Geographic race. A population occupying a geographic territory and having certain traits that, on the average, distinguish its members from members of other populations. Differences usually reflect differences in gene *frequencies* in the gene pools of the various geographic races.

Germ cell. A reproductive cell, sperm, or ovum, or one of the precursor stages in meiosis of sperm or ovum.

Germ plasm. A general term for germ cells in all stages and the tissues from which they arise.

Germinal mutations. Genetic changes in germ cells.

Glucose-6-phosphate dehydrogenase (G6PD). An enzyme; a deficiency of this enzyme causes hemolysis if antimalarial drugs such as primaquine are taken or if the fava bean is eaten.

Glutamic acid. One of the amino acids entering into the structure of proteins, e.g., of hemoglobin.

Gonadal dysgenesis. *see* Turner's syndrome.

G6PD. *see* Glucose-6-phosphate dehydrogenase.

Guanine. One of the organic bases (purines) found in DNA and RNA.

H antigen. An antigen found in the red blood cells of most group O people (and in varying amounts in the cells of people in other blood groups).

Haploid number (n). The number of chromosomes in a germ cell, gamete, following meiosis.

Hardy-Weinberg formula. In a population characterized by random mating and Mendelian inheritance, the ratio of individuals homozygous for the dominant gene to heterozygous individuals to individuals homozygous for the recessive gene is as $p^2 : 2pq : q^2$, where p is the relative frequency of the dominant allele, q the frequency of the recessive allele.

Hellin's law. If $1/n$ represents the fraction of births giving rise to twins, $1/n^2$ represents the fraction of births giving rise to triplets, and $1/n^3$ the fraction of births giving rise to quadruplets.

Hematopoietic tissue. Embryonic tissue from which blood cells are formed.

Hemizygous. Adjective applied to an individual who has a single gene at a given locus instead of a pair of alleles. It is true of males for genes carried in the X chromosome and not homologous to genes in the Y chromosome.

Hemoglobin. The iron-containing compound in red blood cells, giving them their color. Important in the transportation of oxygen.

Hemolysis. Destruction of red blood cells.

Hemophilia. One of several diseases in which the blood does not clot normally.

Hemophilia A. The deficiency is lack of antihemophilic globulin in the serum.

Hemophilia B. The deficiency is lack of plasma thromboplastin component. Also called PTC deficiency or Christmas disease.

Heterosis. A condition in which hybrids are superior to both parents in some respect: hybrid vigor. In this context it refers to a situation in which heterozygotes (*Aa*, for example) are superior in some way to both homozygotes (*AA* and *aa*).

Heterozygote (Heterozygous). An individual in which the members of a pair of genes are unlike, e.g., *Aa*.

Holandric genes. *see* Y-linked genes.

Homeostasis. Self-regulating ability of the body, or of a population (*see* Genetic homeostasis).

Homologous chromosomes. Chromosomes that belong to the "same pair," as evidenced by the fact that they pair together in synapsis. They contain the same gene loci.

Homozygote (Homozygous). An individual in which the members of a pair of genes are alike, e.g., *AA*, or *aa*.

Hormones. "Chemical messengers"—substances secreted into the blood stream by the endocrine glands; they exert control over bodily development and metabolism.

Huntington's chorea. A nervous disorder characterized by spasmodic, involuntary movements of the face and limbs, with gradual loss of mental faculties and the development of dementia.

Hybrids. Individuals of mixed ancestry. The term is variously used: (1) to apply to heterozygotes, (2) to apply to offspring produced when members of one race (or species) mate with members of another one.

Hybrid vigor. *see* Heterosis.

Hypertrichosis. In this context, growth of hair on the surface of the pinna (auricle) of the ear and along the rim (see Fig. 12.6).

Ichthyosis congenita. A severe abnormality characterized by deeply fissured, leathery skin.

Idiogram. *see* Karyotype.

Incompletely sex-linked genes. Genes located in those portions of the X and Y chromosomes that pair together in synapsis.

Independent assortment. In the formation of gametes—the distribution of the members of one pair of genes does not influence the distribution of the members of other pairs (see Fig. 3.9). True when the different pairs of genes are in different chromosomes.

Individual differential fertility. Differences among individuals in number of children produced; as a result of it the gene pool of one generation is not necessarily a random sample of the gene pool of the preceding generation.

Infantile amaurotic idiocy. Severe mental abnormality characterized by accumulation of fatlike substances (lipids) in the brain cells and retina; progressive development of idiocy and blindness in early infancy.

Institutionalization. As employed in eugenics, prevention of reproduction by keeping males and females separated in institutions.

Interphase. The state of a cell not undergoing mitosis (see Fig. 3.2).

Inversion. Chromosomal aberration in which one portion of a chromosome becomes reversed in relation to the original sequence of contained genes (see Fig. 16.3).

  Paracentric inversion. The reversed portion is confined to one arm of the chromosome, i.e., it does not include the centromere.

  Pericentric inversion. The reversed portion includes the centromere.

IQ. Intelligence Quotient. Mental age divided by chronological age, multiplied by 100. (This is the traditional computation; another method of computation is being used increasingly.)

Isoagglutinogen. An antigen (agglutinogen) that occurs normally in an individual, i.e., without artificial stimulation.

Isoantibodies. Antibodies that people normally possess.

Isochromosome. A chromosome in which the centromere is in the middle and the two arms are alike in genic content, typically being the mirror images of each other (see Fig. 16.4).

Isolate, Genetic. The group of individuals among whom (random) mating may be considered to occur. Large populations are more or less completely subdivided into isolates by such factors as distance, geographic barriers, race, religion, social status, etc.

Karyotype. The chromosomes contained in a cell. The term is especially applied to diagrams made by lining up the chromosomes in homologous pairs (see Fig. 15.3; 16.6).

Kindred. Group of relatives in one or more generations.

Klinefelter's syndrome. Abnormality caused by possession of two X chromosomes and one Y chromosome (XXY). Characteristics are those of a male, but the testes are not functional; the individual may have feminine breast development.

Lethal gene. A gene that kills its possessor, usually before birth. The ones that can be studied are recessive in the sense that they are carried by heterozygotes and kill only homozygotes.

Leucocytes. White blood cells.

Leukemia. Malignancy of blood-forming tissues leading to production of excessive numbers of white blood cells.

Linkage. Location of genes in the same chromosome so that they do not assort independently in meiosis.

Lutheran gene. Gene determining the presence of the Lutheran antigen in the red blood cells of some people.

Lyon hypothesis. The hypothesis that in any given cell in a female one X chromosome is active, the other inactive. The inactive X chromosome is believed to form the Barr body.

Lysine. One of the amino acids entering into the structure of proteins, e.g., of hemoglobin.

Macromolecule. A structured aggregation of smaller molecules functioning as a unit, e.g., DNA.

Marital fertility.   Number of children relative to the number of wives in a population.

Marker gene.   A gene utilized in investigations to indicate the presence of a certain chromosome with its genetic contents.

Maximum-likelihood methods of detecting autosomal linkage.   Methods that depend on the probability that an observed relationship of traits in the parents to traits in the children would arise if there were linkage, compared to the probability that the relationship would arise if the traits were not linked.

Meiosis.   The process by which diploid precursor cells give rise to haploid gametes (ova or sperm) (see Fig. 3.5; 3.8).

Melanin.   Brown pigment, found, for example, in cells of skin, hair, and iris of the eye.

Melanocytes.   Cells containing pigment (melanin).

Mendelian laws.   First law: genes occur in pairs in the cells of individuals; when gametes are produced the members of a pair separate so that each gamete receives only one member of the pair (law of segregation). Second law: the manner in which the members of one pair of genes are distributed to gametes does not influence the manner in which other pairs of genes are distributed (law of independent assortment).

Mental defective.   *see* Mental deficiency.

Mental deficiency.   Intelligence below the normal level. Frequently the line is drawn at an IQ of 70, persons below that score being considered mentally deficient or retarded. Sometimes the term *mental retardation* is applied to persons with an IQ between 70 and 50, the term *mental defective* being applied to persons with an IQ below 50.

Mental retardation.   *see* Mental deficiency.

Messenger RNA.   RNA that is synthesized in the nucleus on a DNA template (pattern), then passes into the cytoplasm, attaching to one or more ribosomes and serving as a template on which amino acids are assembled to form a polypeptide chain (see Fig. 4.4).

Metabolism.   The total of the chemical processes carried on in the body, including digestion, respiration, secretion, excretion, release and utilization of energy, and so on.

Metacentric.   Referring to chromosomes that have the centromere in the middle or close to it.

Metaphase.   The stage in mitosis in which the chromosomes are lined up at the equator of the spindle (see Fig. 3.2).

Metaphase plate.   Arrangement of chromosomes in the metaphase of mitosis (see Fig. 3.2).

Microcephaly.   Type of mental deficiency in which the brain is abnormally small.

Microgeographic race.   A population occupying a small unit of territory and characterized by some, usually small, differences from other such populations.

Micron.   1/1000 of a millimeter.

Mitosis.   The process of nuclear division in which the chromosomes are duplicated and distributed equally to the daughter cells, so that each of the latter has exactly the same chromosomal content as the other.

Modifying gene.   A gene that alters the effect of another gene not its own allele.

Mongolism. Type of mental deficiency accompanied by a syndrome of physical traits, including short stature, stubby fingers, a large, fissured tongue, and a round head (see Fig. 16.7). Also called Down's syndrome or Trisomy-21.

Monosomic. Having one less chromosome than the normal number.

Monozygotic, MZ. Literally, one zygote; referring to twins, triplets, and so on, which develop from a single ovum; "identical" twins or triplets.

Moron. Person with an IQ between 70 and 50; "educable."

Mosaic. Composed of cells of two or more kinds with respect to antigens, genes, or chromosomes.
> (1) **Red blood cell mosaic.** An individual having red blood cells of two or more kinds with respect to the antigens they contain.
> (2) **Sex chromosome mosaic.** An individual in whose body some cells have a certain number or type of sex chromosomes, whereas other cells have a different number or type.

mrem. Millirem; unit employed in measuring the amount of radiation (see footnote on p. 282).

Multiple alleles. A series of genes, any one of which can occupy a given locus in a chromosome.

Multiple genes. *see* Polygenes.

Multiple neurofibromatosis. A hereditary trait characterized by the growth of benign tumors at nerve endings in the skin.

Muscular dystrophy. *see* Pseudohypertrophic muscular dystrophy.

Mutagenic agents. Chemicals or radiations that induce the formation of mutations.

Mutation. Alteration of the genetic material; it may involve microscopically visible changes in the chromosomes (chromosomal aberrations), or changes in the structure of the DNA molecule (gene or point mutations).

Mutation pressure. The tendency of genes to mutate at a rather constant, though low, rate.

Muton. "The smallest element [of a DNA molecule] that, when altered, can give rise to a mutant form of the organism." (Seymour Benzer)

MZ. Monozygotic.

Nail-patella syndrome. A hereditary anomaly in which the fingernails are abnormal, the patella (kneecap) is small or missing, and other skeletal abnormalities occur.

Natural selection. Literally, selection by Nature; determining which individuals or groups shall live and reproduce and which shall not. It results from the cumulative action of all forces that tend to cause individuals of one genetic constitution to leave larger numbers of offspring than do individuals of another genetic constitution. *see* Differential fertility.

Negative eugenics. *see* Eugenics.

Negative selection. Prevention of reproduction of persons having a certain genotype and/or phenotype.

Neurohormones. Hormones concerned with the interrelationships of the nervous system and the endocrine glands in regulating bodily functions.

Nonadaptive traits. Characteristics that are neutral: neither beneficial nor detrimental.

Nondisjunction. Failure of chromosomes to separate normally. Homologous chromosomes may fail to separate from each other following synapsis in meiosis (see Fig. 15.1; 15.2). Chromatids (daughter chromosomes) may fail to separate from each other in the anaphase of mitosis.

Nonsecretor. A person who has antigens A or B in red blood cells but not in such secretions as saliva.

Normal frequency curve. The bell-shaped curve usually approximated when large populations are measured with respect to some quantitative trait that varies continuously, e.g., stature, weight, IQ scores (see Fig. 22.2).

Norm of reaction. The limits within which an individual can adapt to living under different environmental conditions.

Nucleic acids. Organic compounds composed of a phosphoric acid radical, sugar, two purines, and two pyrimidines. *see* DNA; RNA.

Nucleolus. A conspicuous, deeply staining body often found within the nucleus of a cell.

Nucleoproteins. Organic compounds composed of proteins and nucleic acids.

Nucleotide. Organic compound composed of a molecule of sugar, a phosphoric acid radical, and an organic base (purine or pyrimidine) (see Fig. 4.1).

Nucleus. A relatively large body found inside a cell in the interphase stage; it contains the chromosomes (see Fig. 3.5).

Oöcytes, Primary and Secondary. Stages in gamete formation (meiosis) in the female (see Fig. 3.8).

Oögenesis. Production of gametes (meiosis) in the female (see Fig. 3.8).

Oögonium. Primordial germ cell in a female (see Fig. 3.8).

Overdominance. *see* Heterosis.

Ovum. The mature female germ cell or gamete; the egg.

p. Relative frequency of a dominant gene. *see* Hardy-Weinberg formula.

Panmictic population. One in which matings occur according to the laws of probability, insofar as the genetic trait being studied is concerned.

Panmixis. See Random mating.

Paracentric inversion. *see* Inversion.

Parental selection. *see* Preadoption.

Parsimony, Principle of. Do not formulate complicated explanations for phenomena for which simple explanations will suffice.

Parthenogenesis. Development of an individual from an unfertilized ovum.

Partial penetrance. *see* Penetrance.

Partially sex-linked genes. *see* Incompletely sex-linked genes.

Pattern baldness. The common type of baldness in which the sides and the lower portions of the back of the head retain hair.

Pedigree. A record of inheritance, frequently presented as a diagram, for two or more generations of a kindred.

Penetrance, Partial. When a dominant gene does not produce the expected phenotype in every possessor of the gene, or recessive genes do not produce the expected phenotype in every individual homozygous for them.

Peptide. A compound containing two or more amino acids. Peptides join to form polypeptides, which in turn join to form proteins.

Pericentric inversion. *see* Inversion.

Phenocopy. A characteristic or trait that is not hereditary nor the product of genetic change, but closely resembles a phenotype that in other individuals is produced as a result of genetic change (mutation).

Phenotype. The appearance or observable nature of an individual.

Phenylalanine. One of the amino acids; concerned in phenylketonuria.

Phenylketonuria, PKU. An "error of metabolism" characterized by inability to oxidize phenylalanine to tyrosine; it is accompanied by severe mental retardation unless remedial measures are taken.

Pituitary gland. A small gland of internal secretion attached to the brain.

Placenta. Structure formed in the uterus by a combination of tissue of the uterine wall with tissue from the embryonic membranes. Within it the blood vessels of the embryo come into close contact with the blood vessels of the mother (see Fig. 20.2; 20.3).

Plasma. The fluid portion of the blood.

Plasma thromboplastin component, PTC. A portion of the blood-clotting mechanism that is deficient in people who have hemophilia B.

Pleiotropic gene. Any gene that has more than one phenotypic effect.

Point mutation. *see* Gene mutation.

Polar bodies, First and Second. In meiosis in the female—tiny cells almost devoid of cytoplasm, homologous to secondary oöcyte and ovum, respectively (see Fig. 3.8).

Pollen. Spore containing the male gamete in flowering plants.

Polygenes. Genes that are independent in mode of inheritance but combine to produce a trait. Usually the genes are cumulative in their effect and the trait is a quantitative one, e.g., stature, weight, degree of pigmentation.

Polymorphism. Literally, having many forms; frequently applied to differences among individuals within one race.

Genetic polymorphism. "The occurrence together in the same locality of two or more discontinuous forms of a species in such proportions that the rarest of them cannot be maintained merely by recurrent mutation." (E. B. Ford)

Polyovular follicle. An ovarian follicle containing more than one ovum.

Polypeptide chain. A group of peptides linked together. *see* Peptide.

Polyploidy. Chromosomal aberration in which the number of chromosomes is increased by the full haploid number, or multiples thereof.

Polysomy. *see* Aneuploidy.

Polytypic. Literally, of many types; a term sometimes applied to the differences between races.

Population genetics. Genetical principles applied to groups of individuals. *see* Hardy-Weinberg formula.

Position effect. The fact that the functioning of a gene may be influenced by its position relative to other genes in the chromosome.

Positive eugenics. *see* Eugenics.

Potassium-40. Radioactive isotope of potassium.

Preadoption. The idea that in the future parents may elect to have germ cells other than their own, derived from individuals having known superior traits, used in production of their children.

Prenatal adoption. *see* Preadoption.

Primordial germ cells. Embryonic cells that, through meiosis, will give rise to gametes; spermatogonium and oögonium (see Fig. 3.5; 3.8).

Proband. *see* Propositus.

Prophase. Early stage of mitosis (see Fig. 3.2).

Propositus. Index case: the individual possessing a certain trait who attracted the attention of the investigator to the family.

Protanopia. A type of partial color blindness in which the eye is relatively insensitive to red, and has difficulty distinguishing red from dim yellow or green.

Proteins. Nitrogenous compounds of high molecular weight forming the most important structural and enzymatic constituents of the body. Composed of amino acids.

Pseudohypertrophic muscular dystrophy (Duchenne type). An X-linked pathological condition, generally occurring in males, in which the muscles degenerate progressively; the boy becomes more and more crippled and dies before reaching maturity.

PTC. (1) **Phenylthiocarbamide.** A chemical that has a taste (usually bitter) to some people but is tasted by other people only when the solution is very concentrated. People who are relatively insensitive to it are called nontasters.
   (2) **Plasma thromboplastin component.** *see* Hemophilia B.

Purine. One class of organic bases found in nucleic acids.

Pyrimidine. One class of organic bases found in nucleic acids.

q. Relative frequency of a recessive gene. *see* Hardy-Weinberg formula.

Races. Populations that differ in the frequencies of certain of the genes in their gene pools.

rad. Unit employed in measuring the amount of radiation (see footnote on p. 282).

Random mating. Mating determined by chance (i.e., by the laws of probability) insofar as the genetic trait being studied is concerned, as opposed to assortative mating.

Random sample. In this context, a sample of a population so selected that it has the same gene frequencies as does the entire population.

Recessive. (1) A gene that does not produce a phenotypic effect in a heterozygote. (2) A trait that is shown phenotypically only by homozygotes.

Recombination. When linked genes do not stay together in inheritance but are reassorted. It is observable when crossing over occurs in heterozygotes.

Recon. The smallest unit of a DNA molecule that can be exchanged in crossing over (recombination).

Red blood cell mosaic. *see* Mosaic.

rem. Unit employed in measuring amount of radiation (see footnote on p. 282).

Repeat. *see* Duplication.

Repeat frequency. In this context, the frequency with which mothers who have had one pair of twins subsequently have additional pairs.

Replacement level of a population. The number of births necessary to ensure that the number of adults of reproductive age shall remain constant from generation to generation.

Reproductive isolation. A situation in which the gene pools of two or more populations are kept separate because the members of the different populations do not interbreed even though they come into contact with each other.

Repulsion linkage. With reference to two pairs of genes, the dominant gene of one pair is located in the same chromosome as the recessive gene of the other pair, and vice versa; e.g., (*Ab*) (*aB*).

Retinoblastoma. Cancer of the retina of the eye.

Rh, "rhesus factor." A group of red blood cell antigens discovered by the finding that some human cells react with antibodies formed against rhesus monkey cells.

Rh incompatibility. A marriage in which the wife is Rh-negative and the husband Rh-positive.

Rh-negative. People whose red blood cells do not react with anti-Rh_o (anti-D) antibodies (see Table 10.1).

Rh-positive. People whose red blood cells react with anti-Rh_o (anti-D) antibodies (see Table 10.1).

Ribosomes. Small particles in the cytoplasm of a cell forming the sites of protein synthesis. The messenger RNA attaches to them (see Fig. 4.4).

RNA (ribonucleic acid). Nucleic acid found in both the nucleus and cytoplasm of cells; its sugar component is ribose.

roentgen, r. Unit commonly employed in measuring the amount of radiation, based on the amount of ionization produced (see footnote on p. 282).

Satellites. Tiny masses of chromatin found attached to the short arms of some chromosomes (see Fig. 16.6).

Schizophrenia. A form of mental disorder or psychosis in which there is a splitting of the personality and a withdrawal from normal human relationships.

Secondary nondisjunction. Production of gametes with abnormal chromosome numbers as a result of nondisjunction in individuals who already have an abnormal chromosomal constitution, e.g., production of XX gametes by an XXX female.

Secondary sex characteristics. Those bodily traits, other than the reproductive organs themselves, by which members of one sex differ from members of the other.

Secretor. A person possessing a water-soluble form of antigens A and/or B; these antigens are found in such secretions as saliva.

Seminiferous tubule dysgenesis. *see* Klinefelter's syndrome.

Serum. The fluid portion of the blood remaining after blood has clotted (with removal of the cells and of fibrin).

Sewall Wright effect. *see* Genetic drift.

Sex chromatin bodies. *see* Barr bodies.

Sex chromosome mosaic. *see* Mosaic.

Sex chromosomes. The X and Y chromosomes.

Sex-controlled genes. *see* Sex-influenced genes.

Sex hormones. Substances secreted into the blood by the ovary and testis; they control many phases of bodily development and functioning, including the development of the secondary sex characteristics.

Sex-influenced genes. Autosomal genes that in one sex produce a phenotypic effect in both homozygotes and heterozygotes, but in the other sex produce a phenotypic effect in homozygotes only.

Sex limitation. A term applied to traits that appear phenotypically in only one sex, although the genes for them may be carried by both sexes.

Sex linkage. Having the gene carried in the sex chromosomes, usually the X chromosome.

Siamese twins. Conjoined twins, connected by some portion of their bodies.

Siblings, Sibs. Brothers and sisters.

Sib-pair method of detecting autosomal linkage. The method involves comparing sibs taken two at a time as to agreement or lack of agreement in possession of two traits under investigation.

Sibship. A family of brothers and/or sisters.

Sickle-cell anemia. A severe disease in which the red blood cells become sickle- or crescent-shaped at low oxygen tensions and are destroyed in large numbers (see Fig. 4.5). Genotype: $Hb^S\,Hb^S$.

Sickle trait. Characteristic of people whose red blood cells assume bizarre shapes when deprived of oxygen, but in whom symptoms of anemia do not develop (see Fig. 4.5). Genotype: $Hb^S\,Hb^A$.

Similarity method of demonstrating monozygosity. A method whereby the similarities of twins are checked with respect to a large number of genetic traits.

Simple sib method of correcting pooled data. A means of correcting for the fact that when heterozygotes cannot be identified directly, only parents who have at least one child showing a presumed recessive trait can be included in an investigation. The sibs of the propositi, but not the propositi themselves, are counted in computing the normal-to-affected ratio.

Socioeconomic groups. Classifications of people on such bases as income, means of livelihood, education, and the like.

Somatic cell. A body cell, as opposed to a germ cell.

Somatic mutations. Genetic changes in somatic cells.

Sperm, Spermatozoan. The mature male germ cell or gamete.

Spermatid. A stage in the production of gametes, meiosis, in the male (see Fig. 3.5).

Spermatocytes, Primary and Secondary. Stages in gamete formation, meiosis, in the male (see Fig. 3.5).

Spermatogenesis. Production of gametes, meiosis, in the male (see Fig. 3.5).

Spermatogonium. Primordial germ cell in a male (see Fig. 3.5).

Sterilization. *see* Eugenic sterilization.

Stratification. In this context, a concurrence of traits because of uniformity of the gene pool of a population, rather than because of genetic linkage.

Sublethal gene. A gene that kills its possessor in infancy or childhood. *see* Lethal gene.

Submetacentric. Referring to chromosomes having the centromere somewhat nearer one end than the other but with both arms quite long.

Subspecies. *see* Geographic race.

Survival of the fittest. The idea that under conditions of competition for existence some individuals are superior to others and hence survive and reproduce, whereas the inferior individuals fail to do so, at least to as great an extent. *see* Natural selection.

Synapsis. Pairing of chromosomes in primary spermatocytes and primary oöcytes (see Fig. 3.5; 3.8).

Syndrome. A term for the group of symptoms characterizing a certain disease or abnormality.

Telophase. Final stage in mitosis (see Fig. 3.2).

Test cross. *see* Back cross.

Tetrad. Cluster of four chromatids formed when two chromosomes pair in synapsis in the metaphase stage of primary spermatocytes and primary oöcytes (see Fig. 3.5; 3.6; 3.8).

Tetraploid. Having twice the usual number of chromosomes, i.e., four haploid sets of chromosomes.

Tetrasomic. Having two more chromosomes than the normal number.

Thalassemia. An inherited abnormality of the blood. Homozygotes for the gene concerned have severe anemia, called *thalassemia major*. Heterozygotes have a much milder condition called *thalassemia minor*.

Thermal agitation. Heat-induced movement of molecules.

Thymine. One of the organic bases (pyrimidines) found in DNA.

Trait association. Occurrence together in an individual of two or more traits, for reasons other than genetic linkage.

Transfer RNA (Soluble RNA). RNA molecules attached to amino acids, one type of molecule for each of the 20 amino acids. Each molecule "recognizes" its corresponding code word in a messenger RNA molecule, and brings its amino acid into alignment so that it may enter into formation of a polypeptide chain (see Fig. 4.4).

Translocation. Chromosomal aberration in which a portion of one chromosome becomes attached to a nonhomologous chromosome (of a different pair) (see Fig. 16.2).

Reciprocal translocation. Mutual exchange of material between two nonhomologous chromosomes.

trans phase of linkage. *see* Repulsion linkage.

Triploid. Having three haploid sets of chromosomes, three of each kind of chromosome.

Trisomy. Having one more chromosome than the normal number; one kind of chromosome is present in triplicate.

Trisomy 21. see Mongolism.

Truncate distribution. An atypical sample of a population, certain types of individuals or matings being omitted.

Trypsin. A digestive enzyme that acts on proteins.

Turner's syndrome. Abnormal condition caused by presence of one X chromosome only, and no Y chromosome (XO). Characteristics are those of a juvenile female, but the ovaries are absent or vestigial.

Tyrosinase. An enzyme that acts on tyrosine; important in the synthesis of melanin.

Tyrosine. An amino acid; precursor of melanin.

Umbilical cord. An embryonic structure containing blood vessels and extending from the embryo to the placenta (see Fig. 20.1).

Uracil. One of the organic bases (pyrimidines) found in RNA.

Valine. One of the amino acids entering into the structure of proteins, e.g., of hemoglobin.

Variable expressivity. *see* Expressivity.

Variance, Mean intrapair. A statistic indicating the average amount of difference between members of pairs of twins.

von Dungern-Hirschfeld hypothesis. The hypothesis that red blood cell antigens A and B are inherited on the basis of two pairs of genes which undergo independent assortment.

X chromosome. The sexes differ in possession of this chromosome: females have two X chromosomes, males only one.

Xeroderma pigmentosum. A skin disease characterized by development of numerous pigmented spots which frequently become cancerous.

Xg^a blood groups. Blood groups based on the presence or absence of the antigen named Xg^a. Presence of the antigen is determined by a dominant, X-linked gene.

X-linked genes. Genes located in the X chromosome, especially those in the part of it that is not homologous to any portion of the Y chromosome.

XO. *see* Turner's syndrome.

XXY. *see* Klinefelter's syndrome.

Y chromosome. A sex chromosome normally possessed by males only.

Y-linked genes. Genes located in the Y chromosome, especially those in the part of it that is not homologous to any portion of the X chromosome.

Zygote. A fertilized ovum, formed by the union of two gametes (ovum and sperm).

INDEX

A blood group in races, 370
  See also ABO blood groups
A priori method, 66, 412
AB blood group in races, 370
ABO blood groups, 365
  defined, 411
  disease and, 156–57
  inheritance of, 127–44
    anthropological applications, 126–40
    medico-legal applications, 133–35
    multiple allele theory, 130–33
    secretors, 140–42
    Von Dungern-Hirschfeld hypothesis, 127–30, 401–2
ABO incompatibility, 152–54
  defined, 411
  Rh incompatibility combined with, 154–56
Abortion in Japan, 354
Abyssinians, B blood group in, 370
Acute radiation
  chronic radiation versus, 284–85
  defined, 411
Adenine
  in code triplets, 44–46
  defined, 411
  in DNA, 41
Afibrinogenemia
  defined, 117, 411
  diagnosis of, 2
  genetic counseling for, 380
  prospect of child with, 117–18
Africa
  ABO blood-group frequency in, 140
  family planning in, 354
  mean reflectance of skin in, 170
Age of parents and mongolism, 257, 259
Agglutinins, defined, 56, 411
Agglutinogen N, 56

Agglutinogens, defined, 56, 411
Alanine, code triplets for, 45–46
Albinism
  animal, 85
  defined, 63, 411
  human
    consanguinity, 111–13
    expectation and estimates, 63–67, 96–97, 99–101, 116–17
    genetic counseling, 3, 384–85
    Mendelian ratios, 20–22
    pedigree of inheritance, 82–84
  as Mendelian recessive, 20–22
  negative selection against, 331–32
  simple sib method for, 68–70
  tyrosine and, 84
Alkaptonuria
  defined, 118, 411
  inheritance of, 118–20
Alleles
  defined, 12, 411
  effective, 162
  multiple, *see* Multiple allele theory
Alternative traits and twin method, 301–3, 310
American Indians
  ABO blood-group frequency among, 138–40
  adaptations by, 373
  genetic drift among, 363
Amino acids
  defined, 44, 411
  genetic code triplets coding for, 44–46
  sequence in hemoglobin, 51
  See also specific amino acids
Amnion
  defined, 297, 411
  of twins, 298
Anaphase, defined, 29, 411

429

Anastomosis, defined, 306, 411
Andalusian fowls, blue, color inheritance
  of, 18–19
Anemia
  blood groups and, 157
  Cooley's, 386
  pernicious, 157
  Rh incompatibility and, 56, 150
  sickle-cell
    defined, 50, 426
    diagnosis, 386
    malaria and, 272, 278
Aneuploidy, defined, 247, 412
Animals
  albinism in, 85
  domestic
    progeny test, 6
    selective breeding, 324–27
  human families compared with, 54–55
  Mendelian inheritance in, 15–18
    dominance absent, 17
    dominance present, 15–17
  races of, 369–71
  wild populations of, heterozygosity,
    277
  See also names of specific animals
Anthocyanin, 85
  defined, 412
Anthropology, use of blood tests in,
  136–40
  See also Natural selection; Races,
    human
Antibiotic-dependent bacteria, 268–70
Antibodies
  defined, 56, 412
  in serum, 127–28
  See also Blood groups; and specific
    antibodies
Antigen M, 56
Antigens
  defined, 56, 412
  in red blood cells, 127–28
  See also Blood groups; and specific
    antigens
Antimutagenic agents, 285
  defined, 412
Arginine, code triplets for, 45–46
Armadillos
  multiple births by, 289
  sex determination in, 232
Artificial insemination defined, 5, 412
Artificial parthenogenesis, possibility of, 6
Artificial pollination, 13
Ascertainment
  defined, 412
  dominance and, 59–66
    a priori method, 66
    albinism, 63–67

application of binomial formula, 61–
  63
  populations and models, 66–67
Asia
  family planning in, 353–54
  multiple births in, 291
  See also specific Asian countries
Asparagine, code triplets for, 46
Aspartic acid, code triplets for, 46
Assortative mating, 106–8
  defined, 89, 412
  negative selection and, 332–34
Australia
  aborigines of
    ABO blood-group frequency, 138–40
    B blood-group frequency, 370
    environmental adaptations, 374
    individual differences of fertility in,
      356
Autosomal genes, sex-influenced, 188
Autosomal inheritance, features of, 76–77
Autosomal linkage, 219–31
  in Drosophila, 219–23
  in man, 223–28
    linkage groups, 227–28
    maximum-likelihood methods, 226–
      27
    sib-pair method, 223–26
  usefulness of studies in, 228–30
  trait association versus linkage, 229–
    30
Autosomes
  chromosomal aberrations of, 246–62
  defined, 182, 412
  in Drosophila, 237

B blood group in races, 370
  See also ABO blood groups
Back cross, defined, 17, 412
Background radiation, effects of, 282–83
Bacteria
  genetic engineering of, 4
  mutation rate in, 268
  See also: Escherichia coli
Balance hypothesis, 277–79
  defined, 412
Baldness, pattern
  defined, 422
  sex-influenced gene in, 188
Barbados, family planning in, 353
Barr, Murray L., 239
Barr bodies, 255
  defined, 239, 412
  Lyon hypothesis and, 240–42
  Turner's syndrome and, 241, 243, 252
Benzer, Seymour, 47
Bermuda, Negro-white crosses in, 165–69

Binomial formula, use in two-child family, 61–63
Biological engineering, possibilities of, 4
  See also Genetic counseling; Eugenics
Birth control
  advances in, 387–89
  importance of, 352
  limitations of, 353
  methods of, 354–55
  population growth and, 349–50
  world-wide use of, 353
Blackfoot Indians, genetic drift among, 363
Bleeder's disease, *see* Hemophilia
Blood cells
  red, 50–52
    antigens, 127
    defined, 49, 416–17
    genetic change, 49–52
    mosaics, 306–7, 421
    sickling, *see* Sickle-cell anemia
  white, "drumsticks" in, 240
Blood diseases
  afibrinogenemia
    defined, 117, 411
    diagnosis, 2
    genetic counseling, 380
    prospect of child with, 117–18
  anemia, *see* Anemia
  erythroblastosis fetalis, 56
    defined, 415
    Rh incompatibility and, 151
  hemophilia
    defined, 195, 418
    diagnosis, 2
    genetic counseling, 380
    inheritance, 195–98, 206–11
    replenishing of gene, 270
  hemophilia A, 195–98
    defined, 418
    gene loci, 212
    inheritance, 206–11
  hemophilia B, 206, 213
    defined, 418
  leukemia
    chromosomal basis, 261
    defined, 419
    mongolism and, 261
Blood groups, 9
  ABO, 365
    defined, 411
    disease and, 156–57
    inheritance, 127–44, 401–2
  ABO incompatibility, 152–54
    defined, 411
    Rh incompatibility combined with, 154–56

disease and, 156–57
  dominance and, 60
  MN, 158
    antiserum reactions, 57
    assortative mating, 107–8
    genetic drift, 363–65
    genetic study of, 56–59
    proportion of population, 92–95, 97
  mutations and, 59
  in races, 370
  in studies of twins, 299
  Xg^a, 190–95
Blood Indians, genetic drift among, 263
Blue Andalusian fowls, color inheritance among, 18–19
Brachydactyly, defined, 77, 412
Breast cancer and blood groups, 157
Bridges, Calvin B., 221
Brother-sister mating, 393
Buccal smear, defined, 412

Cancer
  blood groups and, 157
  leukemia
    chromosomal basis, 261
    defined, 419
    mongolism and, 261
    mutations and, 263–64
  retinoblastoma
    defined, 75, 425
    genetic counseling, 384, 390
    inheritance, 75–76
Canoe Indians, adaptation by, 373
Carriers
  of albinism, 82
  defined, 412
Castration, 387
  defined, 413
Cataract of the eyes
  defined, 413
  variability in, 80–82
Catholic Church and contraception, 387
Cattle, twins among, 305–6
Caucasians
  crosses with Negroes, *see* Mulattoes
  distal hyperextensibility among, 102
  mean reflectance of skin among, 170
  multiple births among, 291
Cell division, *see* Mitosis
Centriole, defined, 27, 413
Centromeres
  defined, 413
  in isochromosomes, 251
  in metacentric chromosomes, 254
  in pericentric inversions, 250
  in submetacentric chromosomes, 254

Ceylon, family planning in, 353
Chance, *see* Probability
Chemicals, mutagenic, 264–65, 421
Chiasma, defined, 33–34, 413
Chimeras, *see* Mosaics
Chin form of twins, 300
China, blood groups in, 136, 370
Chi-square test, 403–5
    defined, 142, 413
Chorion
    defined, 297, 413
    of twins, 298
Christmas disease, 198, 206
    defined, 413
Chromatid, defined, 25, 413
Chromatin, sex, *see* Barr bodies
Chromomeres, 25, 30–31, 413
Chromonema
    condensation of, 26
    defined, 413
Chromosomal aberrations, 246–62
    autosomal, 246–62
    defined, 49, 246, 413
    deletions, 249–50
    duplications, 250
    formation of isochromosomes, 251–52
    inversions, 250–51
    mongolism and, 255–62
    translocations, 250
Chromosomal mutations, *see* Chromo-
        somal aberrations
Chromosomes
    chromomeres in, 30–31
    classification of, 254–55
    defined, 26, 413
    deletions of, 249–50, 414
    mapping of, 211–15
    in meiosis, 31–37
    in mitosis, 27–31
    number of pairs of, 31
    nature of, 25–38
        finer structure, 26–27
        size and appearance, 25
    normal human, 253–55
    sex, *see* Sex chromosomes; X chromo-
        somes; Y chromosomes
    studies of, 27
    submetacentric, 254, 426
Chronic radiation
    acute radiation versus, 284–85
    defined, 413
Cistron, defined, 149, 413
Classical hypothesis, 276–77
    defined, 413
Coat color
    in birds, 18–19
    in guinea pigs, 15–17
        random mating, 89–91

in mice, 79
Code triplets, 44–46
Codominant genes, defined, 51, 413
Colchicine, 253
    defined, 414
Colon cancer and blood groups, 157
Color blindness
    defined, 414
    inheritance of
        recombination of X-linked genes,
            206–11
        X-linked, 184–87, 189
Committee on the Genetic Effects of
        Atomic Radiation of the Na-
        tional Academy of Sciences–
        National Research Council, 286
Complementary genes, defined, 85, 414
Concordant traits of twins, defined, 301,
        414
Congenital afibrinogenemia, *see* Afibrino-
        genemia
Congo, B blood group in, 370
Consanguinity, 111–13
    defined, 111, 414
    effects of inbreeding, 113–20
        first-cousin marriages, 393, 399–400
        increased consanguinity among par-
            ents of offspring showing rare
            recessive traits, 116–20
        new mutations, 115–16
        total risk, 120
    See also Inbreeding
Contraception
    advances in, 387–89
    use of, 354
Cooley's anemia, genetic counseling for,
        386
Coon, Carleton, 372
Corn, chromosome maps for, 213
Cosmic radiation
    defined, 414
    effects of, 282–83
    mutagenic effects of, 265
Counseling, genetic, *see* Genetic coun-
        seling
Coupling linkage, defined, 209, 414
Crick, F. H. C., 45
Crossing over
    defined, 33–34, 414
    of X-linked genes, 206–11
Cultural inheritance, defined, 414
"Culture-free" intelligence tests, 313
Cysteine, code triplets for, 46
Cytosine
    in code triplets, 44–46
    defined, 414
    in DNA, 41

Daltonism
  defined, 414
  X-linked inheritance and, 184–87
Darwin, Charles, 269, 366
Davenport, Charles B., 165, 168–69
DDT-resistant house flies, 268, 270
De George, Frances, V., 310, 312
Deafness, inherited, 85
Deletions, chromosomal, 249–50
  defined, 414
Denver system, 254
Deoxyribonucleic acid, *see* DNA
Deuteranopia
  defined, 206, 414
  gene loci for, 212
Diabetes mellitus
  blood groups and, 157
  defined, 414
Diet
  phenylketonuria and, 216
  stature and, 340
  weight and, 179
Differential fertility, defined, 270, 414
Differential survival, defined, 270
Diploid, defined, 35, 414
Discordant traits of twins, defined, 301,
    415
Disease
  blood groups and, 156–57
  environment and, 216
  heredity and, *see specific diseases*
Disjunction, defined, 233, 415
Distal hyperextensibility
  defined, 415
  estimating proportion of population
      with, 103–6
  measuring, 101, 103
Dizygotic (DZ) twins, 288–89
  alternative traits of, 301–3, 310
  defined, 289, 415
  embryonic development of, 297–99
  environment and, 304–5
  genetic basis for, 293–96
  mean intrapair variances between, 311–
      23
  proportion in twinning, 291–93
  schizophrenia and, 301–5
DNA (deoxyribonucleic acid), 265
  defined, 41, 415, 422
  gene mutations and, 246, 263
  genetic function of, 4
  possibility of altering, 4
  purines in, 41
  pyrimidines in, 41
  structure of, 27, 42–43
  See also Chromosomes; Genes
DNA code, 47
  code triplets and, 44–46

  in protein synthesis, 48
Domestic animals
  progeny test for, 6
  selective breeding of, 324–27
Dominance absent in Blue Andalusian
    fowls, 18–19
Dominance present in guinea pigs, 15–17
Dominant genes, 11
  blood types and, 60
  drift of, 362
  genetic counseling for, 381–84
  mutation from recessive, 271–73
  mutation to recessive, 273–74
  problem of ascertainment and, 59–66
    a priori method, 66
    albinism, 63–67
    application of binomial formula, 61–
        63
    populations and models, 66–67
  total negative selection and, 326–28
Dominant inheritance
  features of, 76–77
  in human pedigree studies, 72–87
    partial penetrance, 78–79
    variable expressivity, 80–82
Dominant traits
  defined, 11, 415
  genetic counseling for, 381–84
Dosage effect, defined, 18
Double crossing over, 213–15
  defined, 415
Double-jointedness of the thumbs, *see*
    Distal hyperextensibility
Down's syndrome, *see* Mongolism
Drosophila
  autosomal linkage in, 219–23
  autosomes in, 237
  chromomeres in, 30
  chromosome maps for, 213
  defined, 415
  eye color in, 329
  lethal genes in, 274, 277
  linkage groups in, 227
  mutation rate in, 265
  number of genes in, 267
  relationship of nondisjunction to age
      in, 257
  salivary gland cells of, 30
  sex chromosomes in, 237
  studies of, 249
  XXY-type chromosomes in, 237
"Drumsticks," 307
  defined, 415
Dunker community
  effects of consanguinity in, 123
  genetic drift in, 363–64

Duplications
of chromosomes, 250
defined, 415
of genes, 43
Dyad, defined, 34, 415
Dysgenic, defined, 337, 415
DZ, see Dizygotic (DZ) twins

Ears of twins, 300
Economic groups and differences in heredity, 337–40
Education
fertility and, 344–47
race and, 375–77
Effective alleles, defined, 162, 415
Embryos of twins, 297–99, 305–6
Embryonic deaths and ABO incompatibility, 154
England
blood groups in, 136, 370
twin studies in, 319–20
Environment
adaptation to, 364
disease and, 81, 216
genetic counseling and, 390
height and, 178
intelligence and, 316–22
mutations and, 268
racial adaptation to, 373–74, 376–77
twins and, 304–5
weight and, 179
Enzymes, 212
defined, 44, 415
interaction with genes, 79
Equatorial plate, defined, 29
Equilibrium, genetic, defined, 90, 415
Erlenmeyer-Kimling, L., 322
Erythroblastosis fetalis, 56
defined, 415
Rh incompatibility and, 151
Erythrocytes, defined, 415
See also Hemoglobin; Red blood cells
Escherichia coli
defined, 416
mutation rate in, 268
streptomycin-dependent, 268–70
Eskimos, B blood group in, 370
Eugenic sterilization, 387–89
defined, 416
Eugenics
choice of qualities in, 325
defined, 324, 416
founding of, 3
methods used in, 324–26
origin of, 324
Eugenics Survey of Vermont, 388

Evolution
genes and
balance hypothesis, 277–79
classical hypothesis, 276–77
mutations and, 269
See also Natural selection
Excess fertility and education, 344
Expressivity, variable, 80–82
defined, 416
Eye cataracts
defined, 413
variability in, 80–82
Eye color, 9
in Drosophila, 229
polygenic inheritance of, 171–75
of twins, 300

Fallout, mutagenic properties of, 283
Families, human, see Human families
Females, human, see Women
Fertility
defined, 414
excess, 344
group differences in, 336–48
education of parents, 344–47
income groups, 345–46
intelligence, 338, 340–43, 346
inverse ratio, 336–37
prevailing present-day trends, 343–
48
socioeconomic differences and differences in heredity, 337–40
individual differences in, 355–57
marital, defined, 420
Fertilization, defined, 416
Fetal deaths and ABO incompatibility,
154
First Mendelian law, 12, 420
First polar body, defined, 35
First-cousin marriages
genetic risk in, 393
homozygous for recessive gene (formula), 399–400
See also Consanguinity; Inbreeding
Fischer quintuplets, 292
Fishes, Y-linked inheritance in, 200
Founder principle, defined, 363, 416
Fraser, F. C., 390
Fraser, G. R., 278
Freeman, F. N., 317
Fruit flies, see: Drosophila

Galton, Sir Francis, 3, 324
Gametes
defined, 13, 416
formation of, 31–37
independent assortment and, 37–38
number of genes in, 267

Gamow, George, 44
Gardner, I. C., 317
Gastric ulcers and blood groups, 157
Gene frequencies, 223
Gene mutations, *see* Mutations
Gene pool
  defined, 91, 416
  variety of genes in, 359
Genes
  autosomal, sex-influenced, 188
  codominant, 51, 413
  complementary, 85, 414
  defined, 11, 149, 416
  diversity of, 359
    natural selection, 367–69
  dominant, *see* Dominant genes; Dominant inheritance
  double crossing-over, 213–15, 415
  duplication of, 43
  enzyme interaction and, 79
  evolution and, 276–79
  incompletely sex-linked, 184
  independent assortment of, 37–38, 418
  lethal
    balance hypothesis, 277–79
    classical hypothesis, 276–77
    defined, 271–72
  marker, 215–17
    defined, 215, 420
  modifying
    defined, 15, 420
    importance, 79
    polygenes and, 176–77
  multiple, *see* Polygenes; Polygenic inheritance
  mutations of, *see* Mutations
  natural selection of, 276–79
  nature of, 41–49
    chemical components, 41–43
    DNA molecule and, 47–49
    genetic code, 47–49
    roles of RNA, 46–47
  number in gamete, 267
  partially penetrant, 78–79
  partially sex-linked, 422
  pleiotropic, 229, 423
  possibility of altering, 4
  recessive, *see* Recessive genes
  sex-influenced, 184, 188, 422, 426, 428
  studies of, 43
  sublethal, 271–72, 426
  vestigial, 219
Genetic code, 44–46
  amino acid triplets and, 44–45
  nature of gene and, 47–49
  roles of RNA in, 46–47
Genetic counseling, 380–95
  for control of parenthood, 387–89

  for dominant traits, 381–84
  environment and, 390
  for recessive traits, 384–87
  problems in, 3, 389–94
  See also Eugenics
Genetic death, defined, 270, 417
Genetic drift, 139, 360–66
  defined, 417
  origin of races and, 369
Genetic engineering, possibilities of, 4–5
  See also Eugenics; Genetic counseling
Genetic equilibrium, defined, 90, 415
Genetic formula, defined, 11
Genetic isolates
  consanguinity and, 120–23
  defined, 121, 419
Genetic load
  defined, 279, 417
  mutant genes and, 279–81
  natural selection and, 280
Genetic polymorphism, 157, 360, 412, 423
Genetic surgery, possibility of, 5
Genotype, defined, 11, 417
Genotypic ratio, defined, 15
Geographic race, defined, 370, 417
Germ cells
  defined, 417
  primordial, 31, 424
Germ plasm, defined, 417
Germany, genetic drift in migrants from, 363
Germinal mutations, defined, 264, 417
Giantism, 178
Glass, Bentley, 6
Glucose-6-phosphate dehydrogenase
  defined, 417
  gene loci for deficiency of, 212
Glutamic acid
  code triplets for, 45–46
  defined, 417
Glutamine, code triplets for, 46
Glycine, code triplets for, 46
Gold Coast, individual differences of fertility in, 355
Gonadal, dysgenesis, genetic basis of, *see* Turner's syndrome
Groups, *see* Human families; Populations
Growth-controlling hormone, 178
Guanine
  in code triplets, 44–46
  defined, 417
  in DNA, 41
Guinea pigs
  coat color in, 15–17
  human families compared with, 54–55
  matings of, 89
  oögenesis in, 36
  Y-linked inheritance in, 200

Gypsies, ABO blood-group-frequency in, 137–38

H antigen, defined, 417
Hair color
  in guinea pigs, 15–17
  of twins, 300
Hair quantity
  of pinna of ear, 199–200
  of twins, 300
Half-castes, 378
  See also Mulattoes
Haploid, defined, 35, 417
Hardy-Weinberg formula, 120, 122–23, 129, 132, 193
  in estimating frequency of heterozygotes, 95–97
  stated, 91–95, 417
  X-linked inheritance and, 189–90
Hawaii, race mixture in, 378
Hb, see Hemoglobin
Height
  diet and, 178
  human, 177–79
  plant, 161–65, 175–76
Hellin's law, 291, 417
Hemoglobin
  amino acid sequence in, 51
  defined, 49–50, 52, 417
  genetic change in, 49–52
  sickle-cell, see Sickle-cell anemia
  types of, 50–52
  See also Red blood cells
Hemophilia
  defined, 195, 418
  diagnosis of, 2
  genetic counseling for, 380
  inheritance of, 195–98
    recombination of X-linked genes, 206–11
  replenishing of gene for, 270
Hemophilia A, 195–98
  defined, 418
  gene loci for, 212
  inheritance of, 206–11
Hemophilia B, 206, 213
  defined, 418
Heterosis, defined, 273, 418
Heterozygotes
  balance hypothesis on, 277–79
  defined, 12, 418
  estimating frequency of, 95–97
  genetic counseling and, 385
  normal value of, 378
Histidine, code triplets for, 46
Hitchhiker's thumb, see Distal hyperextensibility

Holland, incompatibility matings in, 155
Homozygotes
  classical hypothesis on, 276–77
  defined, 12, 418
Hong Kong, family planning in, 353
Hormones
  defined, 418
  human stature and, 178
  sex
    defined, 425
    female, 188
    sterilization and, 387
  skin color and, 373
House flies, DDT-resistant, 268, 270
Hughes, Byron O., 172
Human families
  animals compared with, 54–55
  changing size of, 349–50
  dominance and problem of ascertainment in, 59–66
    a priori method, 66
    albinism, 63–67
    application of binomial formula, 61–63
    populations and models, 66–67
  genetic counseling for, see Genetic counseling
  Intelligence Quotients and size of, 338, 340, 346
  pedigree studies of, 72–87
    dominant inheritance, 72–82
    partial penetrance, 78–79
    recessive inheritance, 82–85
    variable expressivity, 80–82
  planning of, see Birth control
  simple sib method for, 67–70
  two-child, 60–63
  See also Consanguinity; Population; Twins
Hungary, ABO blood-group-frequency in, 138
Huntington's chorea, 265
  complete penetrance of gene in, 78
  defined, 73, 418
  dominant gene in, 11
  genetic counseling for, 381–83
  inheritance of, 11, 73–75, 78–79, 228
  linkage studies and, 228
  modifying genes in, 79
  total negative selection and, 326
Huxley, Sir Julian, 5–6
Hybrid vigor, defined, 273
Hybridization, defined, 324
Hydrogen peroxide and radiation, 285
Hypertrichosis of pinna of ear
  defined, 418
  inheritance of, 199–200

Inbreeding
  criteria for, 111
  effects of, 113–20
    first cousin marriages, 393
    increased consanguinity among par-
      ents of offspring showing rare
      recessive traits, 116–20
    new mutations, 115–16
    total risk, 120
  genetic isolates and, 120–23
Income groups and differences in hered-
    ity, 345–46
Incompatibility, *see* ABO incompatibility;
    Rh incompatibility
Incompletely sex-linked genes, 200–3
  defined, 184, 418
Independent assortment of genes, 37–38
  defined, 418
India
  ABO blood-group-frequency in, 138
  family planning in, 353
  sterilizations in, 388
Individuals
  fertility of, 355–57
  mutations and fitness of, 271–72, 279
  Mendelian ratios and, 19–22
  variability of, 9, 359, 367–69
Institutionalization, 325–26
  defined, 419
Intelligence
  environment and, 316–22
  fertility and, 338, 340–43, 346
  genetic basis of, 179
  inbreeding and, 393
  metrical studies of, *see* Intelligence
    Quotient (IQ)
  study with twin method, 313–22
    environment varied and heredity
      constant, 316–22
  trends in population, 340–43
Intelligence Quotient (IQ)
  defined, 419
  family size and, 338, 340, 346
  socioeconomic groups and, 337–40
  trends in, 343
  of twins, 313–15, 317–22
Intelligence tests, *see* Intelligence Quo-
    tient
Interphase, defined, 29, 419
Inverse ratio and fertility, 336–37
Inversions, chromosomal, 250–51
  defined, 419
Ionizing radiations, *see* Radiations; *and*
    *specific forms of ionizing radia-
    tions*
IQ, *see* Intelligence Quotient

Isoagglutinogen, defined, 130, 419
Isochromosomes
  defined, 251, 419
  formation of, 251–53
Isolates, genetic
  consanguinity and, 120–23
  defined, 121, 419
Isoleucine, code triplets for, 46

Jamaica, Negro-white crosses in, 165–69
Japan, 130
  incompatibility studies in, 153–54, 156
  legalized abortion in, 354
Jarvik, Lissy F., 316, 322

Karyotypes, defined, 236, 419
Kindred, defined, 72, 419
Klinefelter's syndrome
  defined, 419
  genetic basis of, 236–38
Korea, family planning in, 353

Lapps, adaptations by, 374
Latin America, family planning in, 354
Law, use of blood tests in, 133–35
Le^a antigen, 158
Lethal gene
  balance hypothesis, 277–79
  classical hypothesis, 276–77
  defined, 271–72
Leucine, code triplets for, 46
Leucocytes
  "drumsticks" in, 240
  defined, 419
Leukemia
  chromosomal basis of, 261
  defined, 419
  mongolism and, 261
Liberia, individual differences of fertility
    in, 355
Linkage groups, 227–28
Linkages
  autosomal, 219–31
  coupling, 209, 414
  defined, 38, 419
  trait association versus, 229–30
  usefulness of studies in, 228–30
Lung cancer and blood groups, 157
Lutheran gene (Lu^a)
  defined, 419
  recombination frequency of, 227
Lyon, Mary, 240
Lyon hypothesis
  Barr bodies and, 240–42
  defined, 419
Lysenko, Trofim, 22

Lysine
  defined, 419
  code triplets for, 46

Macromolecule, defined, 47, 419
Malaria and sickle-cell hemoglobin, 272, 278
Malaysia, family planning in, 353
Males, human, see Men
Marker genes, 215–17
  defined, 215, 420
Marriage, see Consanguinity; Human families
Mating, assortative, 106–8
  defined, 89, 412
  negative selection and, 332–34
Maximum-likelihood methods, 226–27
  defined, 420
Mayr, Ernst, 363, 375
Mean intrapair variances, see Variances, mean intrapair
Measles in twins, 2, 301–2
Medicine
  applications of multiple allele theory in, 133–35
  blood groups and, 156–57
  genetic counseling in, 2, 380–81
  marker genes in, 215–16
  See also specific diseases
Meiosis
  abnormal, 233–39
  defined, 420
  phases of, 31–37
Melanin, 171, 372–73
  defined, 63, 420
Men (males)
  height of, 178
  meiosis in, 182–83
  porcupine, 198
  sex chromosomes in, see Sex chromosomes; Sex-linked inheritance; X chromosomes; Y chromosomes
  spermatogenesis in, 32–35
Mendel, Gregor, 1
  experiments of, 10–15, 88
  as father of genetics, 7
Mendelian laws of heredity
  first, 12, 420
  probability and, 21
  second, 37, 420
Mendelian ratios
  albinism and, 20–22
  fundamental, 15
  number of individuals and, 19–22
Mental deficiency
  defined, 420
  family size and, 340

genetic counseling for, 389
  See also Mongolism; Phenylketonuria
Messenger RNA, defined, 47, 420
Metacentric chromosomes, 254
  defined, 420
Metaphase, defined, 29
Metaphase plate, defined, 29, 420
Methionine, code triplets for, 46
Mice
  coat color in, 79
  mutation rate in, 265
  relationship of nondisjunction to age in, 259
  XO type, 235–36
  Y-linked inheritance in, 200
Microbes
  genetic engineering of, 4
  mutation rate among, 268
  See also: Escherichia coli
Microgeographic race, defined, 369, 420
Migration and population growth, 352
Milk production, genetic basis of, 187
Mitosis
  defined, 27, 420
  phases of, 27–31
MN blood types, 158
  antiserum reactions of, 57
  assortative mating and, 107–8
  estimating proportion of population with, 92–95, 97
  genetic drift in, 363–65
  study of, 56–59
Models and actual populations, 66–67
Modifying genes
  defined, 15, 420
  importance of, 79
  polygenes and, 176–77
Mongolism
  chromosomal basis of, 255–62
  defined, 421
  leukemia and, 261
  natural selection and, 270
Monosomic individuals, defined, 247, 421
Monozygotic (MZ) twins, 289
  alternative traits of, 301–3, 310
  defined, 289, 421
  embryonic development of, 297–99
  environment and, 304–5
  genetic basis for, 293–96
  mean intrapair variances between, 311–23
  proportion in twinning, 291–93
  schizophrenia in, 301–5
Morgan, Thomas Hunt, 221
Moron, defined, 340, 421
Mosaics
  defined, 421
  red blood cell, among twins, 306–7

Mulattoes
  eye color in, 174
  inheritance of skin color in, 165–71
Muller, H. J., 5, 270, 265, 277, 316
Multiple alleles
  anthropological applications of, 136–40
  medico-legal applications of, 133–35
  nature of, 130–33
    defined, 52, 421
  Rh inheritance and, 146–50
Multiple births, 288–96
  frequency of, 291–93
  inheritance and, 293–96
  use in human genetics, 301–8, 311–22
  See also Twins
Multiple neurofibromatosis
  defined, 421
  differential fertility in, 357
Multiple-gene inheritance, *see* Polygenic
    inheritance
Mustard gas, mutagenic properties of, 264
Mutagenic agents
  chemical, 264–65, 421
  defined, 421
  radiations as, *see* Radiations
Mutation pressure, defined, 281, 360
Mutations, 49–52
  blood types and, 59
  cancer and, 263–64
  chemically induced, 264–65, 421
  consanguinity and, 115–16
  from dominant to recessive, 273–74
  environment and, 268
  evolution and, 269
  genetic load and, 279–81
  human diversity and, 359–60
  individual fitness and, 271–72, 279
  natural selection and, 269–70
  radiation-induced, *see* Radiations
  rate of, 265–68, 281–85
  from recessive to dominant, 271–73
  significance of, 267–69
  types of, defined, 421
    chromosomal, *see* Chromosomal ab-
      errations
    gene (point), 246, 263, 416
    germinal, 264, 417
    somatic, 263, 426
MZ, *see* Monozygotic twins

Nail-patella syndrome
  defined, 421
  recombination frequency of gene in,
    227
Natural selection
  concept of fitness and, 266–67
  defined, 269, 421
  of genes

balance hypothesis, 277–79
classical hypothesis, 276–77
genetic load and, 280
human variety and, 366–78
  adaptations, 373–74, 376–77
  balanced polymorphism, 368
  blood groups, 370
  mutations, 367
  origin of races, 371–74
  mutations and, 269–70
Negative eugenics, defined, 325, 421
Negative selection, total
  defined, 421
  against dominant genes, 326–28
  against recessive genes, 328–35
Negroes
  adaptations by, 374
  crosses with whites, 165–71, 174
  distal hyperextensibility in, 102
  multiple births among, 291
"Neo-Hawaiians," 378
Neutrons, mutagenic properties of, 265
New York State Psychiatric Institute, 316
Newman, H. H., 317, 320
Nonadaptive traits, defined, 365, 421
Nondisjunction
  defined, 233, 421–22, 425
  Lyon hypothesis and, 240–42
Nonionizing radiations, mutagenic prop-
    erties of, 265
Nucleic acids, *see* DNA; RNA
Nucleoproteins, defined, 41, 422
Nucleotides, 41
  defined, 422
Nutrition
  phenylketonuria and, 216
  stature and, 340
  weight and, 179

O blood group in races, 370
  See also ABO blood groups
Ochoa, Sevro, 45
Old Order Dunker community
  effects of consanguinity in, 123
  genetic drift in, 363–64
Oneida Community, eugenics practiced
    by, 325
Oöcytes
  defined, 35, 422
  radiation-induced mutations in, 284
Oögenesis
  defined, 422
  in guinea pigs, 36
  in women, 35–37
Oögonium, defined, 35, 422
Orientals, *see* Asia; *and specific Asian
    countries*
Origin of Species, The (Darwin), 366

Osborne, Richard H., 310, 312
Overdominance, defined, 273
Ovum
    defined, 35, 422
    meiosis of, 31–37

Pakistan
    family planning in, 353
    individual differences of fertility in, 355
    sterilization in, 388
Panmictic population, 132
    consanguinity and, 115
    defined, 422
Panmixis, defined, 89, 422
Papuans, ABO blood-group frequency among, 138, 140
Paracentric inversions, 250–51
    defined, 419
Parental selection, defined, 5
Parenthood, control of, see Genetic counseling; Human families
Parsimony, principle of, defined, 14, 422
Parthenogenesis
    artificial, 6
    defined, 422
Partial color blindness, inheritance of, 206–11
Partial penetrance, 78–79
    defined, 78, 422
Partially sex-linked inheritance, 200–3
    defined, 184, 422
Paternity suits, use of blood tests in, 134–35
Pattern baldness
    defined, 422
    sex-influenced gene in, 188
Pearson, Karl, 142
Peas
    color of, 85
    Mendel's experiments with, 10–15, 88
Pedigrees
    defined, 422
    of human families
        dominant inheritance, 72–82
        partial penetrance, 78–79
        recessive inheritance, 82–85
        variable expressivity, 80–82
    of peas, 10–15, 88
Penetrance, partial, 78–79
    defined, 78, 422
Peptides, defined, 44, 422
Pericentric inversions, defined, 250, 419
Pernicious anemia and blood groups, 157
Phenocopies, defined, 390, 423
Phenotypes, defined, 11, 423
Phenotypic ratio, 15

Phenylalanine
    code triplets for, 46
    defined, 423
Phenylketonuria (PKU)
    defined, 423
    diet and, 216
    genetic counseling for, 382
    genetic load and, 280–81
    prevention of, 2
    test for, 386
    total negative selection and, 327
Phenylthiocarbamide (PTC)
    ability to taste, 9, 300
    defined, 424
Pineal gland and skin color, 373
Pinna of the ear, hypertrichosis of, see Hypertrichosis of pinna of ear
Pituitary gland
    defined, 423
    height and, 178
    skin color and, 373
PKU, see Phenylketonuria
Placenta
    defined, 423
    of twins, 298, 307
Plants
    height of, 161–65, 175–76
    pollination of
        artificial, 13
        defined, 423
    polyploid, 247, 249
    selective breeding of, 324–25
    See also Peas
Plasma thromboplastin component (PTC), see Hemophilia B
Pleiotropic genes, defined, 229, 423
Point mutations, defined, 246, 263, 416
Polar bodies, defined, 35, 423
Pollination
    artificial, 13
    defined, 423
Polygenes
    defined, 161, 423
    genetic counseling and, 389
    on X chromosome, 174
Polygenic inheritance
    in humans
        eye color, 171–75
        intelligence, 179
        skin color, 171–75
        stature, 177–79
        weight, 179
    modifying genes and, 176–77
    in plants, height, 161–65, 175–76
Polymorphism, 157, 360, 412, 423
Polypeptide chains, defined, 44, 423
Polyploidy, defined, 247, 423
Polysomy, defined, 247

Pooled data, method of correcting, 69
Population, 423
  assortative mating in, 106–8
  differences from models, 66–67
  estimating frequency of heterozygotes
      in, 95–97
  fertility of, *see* Fertility
  growth of, 348–51
    control methods, *see* Birth control
    foreign trends, 351–55
    future prospects, 351
    post-World War II, 349
  Hardy-Weinberg formula and, 91–95
  migration and, 352
  random mating in, 88–91
  single allele inheritance in, 97–106
  trends in intelligence, 340–43
Porcupine men, 198
Portugal, B blood group in, 370
Position effect, defined, 251, 423
Positive eugenics, defined, 325, 416
Pre-adoption, defined, 5, 423
Prenatal adoption, defined, 5–6
Preventive medicine, marker genes in,
    215–16
Primary Mental Abilities Test (PMA),
    315, 322
Primary oöcytes, defined, 35, 422
Primary spermatocytes, defined, 33, 426
Primordial germ cells, defined, 31, 424
Principle of parsimony, defined, 14, 422
Probability
  in arrangement of matings, 88
  formulas, derivation of, 399–400
  Mendelian laws and, 21
  role in heredity, 13–15, 21
Proband, defined, 68
Progeny test for domestic animals, 6
Proline, code triplets for, 46
Prophase, defined, 27, 424
Propositus
  defined, 68, 424
  sibs of, 67–70
Protanopia, defined, 206, 213, 424
Proteins
  defined, 44, 424
  synthesis of, 47–48
Pseudohypertrophic muscular dystrophy
    (Duchenne type), 268, 390
  defined, 424
Psychometric Laboratory (University of
    North Carolina), 315
Psychoses, 331
  genetic counseling for, 3, 389
  in twins, 301–5
Puerto Rico, family planning in, 353
Purine
  defined, 424

  in DNA, 41
Pygmies, B blood group in, 370
Pyrimidines
  defined, 424
  in DNA, 41

Quadruplets, frequency of, 291
Quintuplets, 292

Rabbits
  antibodies produced by, 127
  artificial parthenogenesis in, 6
  blood-type studies in, 56
Races
  animal, 369–71
  defined, 424
  geographic, 370, 417
  human
    adaptations, 373–74, 376–77
    blood groups, 370
    intelligence and educability, 373–77
    intermediate, 371
    intermixture, 377–78
    origins, 371–74
  microgeographic, 369, 420
  See also specific racial groups and nations
Radiations
  acute
    chronic radiation versus, 284–85
    defined, 411
  background, 282–83
  chronic
    acute radiation versus, 284–85
    defined, 413
  mutagenic properties of, 265, 281–86
    antimutagenic agents and, 281–85
    mutation rate, 281–85
    tentative conclusions, 285–86
  units of, 282n
  See also Cosmic radiation; Fallout;
      Radioactive isotopes; X-rays
Radioactive isotopes, mutagenic proper-
    ties of, 265, 271, 282–83
Random mating, 88–91
  defined, 89, 424
Recessive genes
  albinism, 20–22
  drift of, 362
  genetic counseling for, 381–84
  mutation from dominant, 273–74
  mutation to dominant, 271–73
  total negative selection against, 328–35
  See also Dominant genes; Dominant
      inheritance
Recessive inheritance in human pedigree-
    studies, 72–87

Recessive traits
  defined, 11, 424
  genetic counseling for, 384–87
Recon, defined, 47, 424
Rectal cancer and blood groups, 157
Red blood cells, 50–52
  antigens in, 127
  defined, 49, 416–17
  genetic change in, 49–52
  mosaics of
    defined, 421
    twins and, 306–7
  sickling of, see Sickle-cell anemia
Reed, Sheldon, 393
Reflectance spectrophotometer, 170
Repeat frequency, defined, 293, 424
Reproduction, see Birth control; Fertility;
    Human families; Population
Repulsion linkage, defined, 209, 425
Retinoblastoma
  defined, 75, 425
  genetic counseling for, 384, 390
  inheritance of, 75–76
Rh incompatibility, 150–52
  ABO incompatibility combined with,
    154–56
  defined, 425
  erythroblastosis from, 56, 150
Rh inheritance
  defined, 425
  gene recombination-frequency in, 227
  multiple-allele theory and, 146–50
  nature of, 145–50
  phenotypes in, 146
Rh-negative, defined, 145, 425
Rh-positive, defined, 145, 425
Rhesus factor (Rh factor), see Rh incom-
    patibility; Rh inheritance
Ribonucleic acid, see RNA
Ribosome, defined, 47
RNA (ribonucleic acid)
  defined, 41, 422, 425
  messenger, defined, 47, 420
  roles of, 46–47
  transfer, defined, 47, 427
Roman Catholic Church and contracep-
    tion, 387
Royalty and hemophilia, 197
Russell, W. L., 284

Salivary gland cells of Drosophila, 30
Schizophrenia, 331
  defined, 425
  genetic counseling for, 3, 389
  in twins, 301–5
Science, scope of, 2
Second Mendelian law, 37
Second polar body, defined, 35

Secondary oöcytes, defined, 35, 422
Secondary spermatocytes, defined, 34,
    426
Secretors
  defined, 425
  inheritance of, 140–42
Segregation, law of, 12
Selection, see Eugenics; Natural selection;
    Negative selection
Seminiferous tubule dysgenesis, see Kline-
    felter's syndrome
Serine, code triplets for, 46
Serum
  antibodies in, 127
  defined, 425
Sex chromatin, see Barr bodies
Sex chromosomes
  abnormal, 233–44
    Barr bodies, 239–42
    nondisjunction, 233–39
  defined, 182, 425
  in Drosophila, 237
  role in determining sex, 232–33
  mosaics of, defined, 242, 421
  See also X chromosomes; Y chromo-
    somes
Sex hormones
  defined, 425
  female, 188
  sterilization and, 387
Sex-linked inheritance, 182–205
  autosomal, 188
  baldness and, 188
  chromosomal basis of, 182–84
  defined, 207, 426
  hemophilia and, 195–98
  partial, 200–3
  X-linked, see X-linked inheritance
  Xg^a blood groups and, 190–95
  Y-linked, see Y-linked inheritance
Shields, James, 316, 319–20
Siamese twins, defined, 290, 426
Sib-pair method, 223–26
  defined, 225, 426
Sibs, defined, 21, 426
Sibs of propositi, 67–70
Sickle-cell anemia
  defined, 50, 426
  diagnosis of, 386
  malaria and, 272, 278
Similarity method, 299–301
  defined, 426
Simple sib method, 67–70
  defined, 426
Simple allele inheritance, estimating pro-
    portion of population with, 97–
    106
Skin cells, Barr bodies in, 240

Skin color
  mean reflectance in, 169–70
  polygenic inheritance of, 165–71
  problem of differences in, 372–73
Smallpox and blood groups, 157
Snyder's formulas, 99n
Socioeconomic groups
  defined, 337, 426
  differences in heredity and, 337–40
Somatic mutations, defined, 263, 426
Sperm cells
  defined, 32, 34–35, 426
  formation of, 32–35, 182–83, 426
  preservation of, 5
  radiation-induced mutations in, 284
Spermatids, defined, 35, 426
Spermatocytes, 426
  primary, defined, 34
  secondary, defined, 33
Spermatogenesis, 182–83
  defined, 32, 426
  in man, 32–35
Spermatogonia
  defined, 32, 426
  radiation-induced mutations in, 284
Spermatozoa, *see* Sperm cells
Stanford-Binet test, 314, 319
  criticism of, 338
Stature, *see* Height
Sterilization, 354
  defined, 416
  eugenic, 387–89, 416
Stomach cancer and blood groups, 157
Stratification, defined, 230, 426
Streptomycin-dependent bacteria, 268–70
Sublethal genes, defined, 271–72, 426
Submetacentric chromosomes, 254
  defined, 426
Subspecies, defined, 370
Survival of the fittest, *see* Natural selection
Synapsis, defined, 33

Taiwan, family planning in, 353
Telophase, defined, 29, 427
Temperature, mutagenic effect of, 277
Test cross, 220
  defined, 17
Tetrad, defined, 33, 427
Tetraploid cells, defined, 247, 427
Thalassemia
  defined, 427
  genetic counseling for, 386
Thermal agitation, 264
Threonine, code triplets for, 46
Thurstone's Primary Mental Abilities Test (PMA), 315, 322

Thymine
  in code triplets, 44–46
  defined, 427
  in DNA, 41
Tongue of twins, 300
Total negative selection, *see* Negative selection, total
Total risk of abnormality in first-cousin marriages, 120–21
Trait association
  defined, 427
  linkage versus, 229–30
Transfer RNA, defined, 47, 427
Translocations, chromosomal, 250
  defined, 427
Triplets, frequency of, 291
Trisomy, defined, 247, 427
Trisomy 21, *see* Mongolism
Tryptophan, code triplets for, 46
Tunisia, family planning in, 353
Turkey, family planning in, 353
Turner's syndrome
  Barr bodies and, 241, 243, 252
  defined, 427
  genetic basis of, 233
  isochromosomes and, 252–53
Twin method
  determination of zygosity and, 297–301
  uses of, 301–2
    alternative traits, 301–3
    heredity constant and environment varied, 316–22
    intelligence, 313–22
    pitfalls to be avoided, 303–8
    stature, 311–12
    weight, 312–13
Twins
  birth of
    frequency, 291–93
    hereditary factors in twinning, 293–96
    proportion of monozygotic and dizygotic twinning, 291–93
  connected embryonic membranes in animals, 305–6
  dizygotic (DZ), *see* Dizygotic twins
  formation and determination of, 297–301
    determination of zygosity, 297
    embryonic membranes, 297–99
    similarity method, 299–301, 426
  measles and, 2
  monozygotic (MZ), *see* Monozygotic twins
  red blood cell mosaics among, 306–7
  Siamese, 290, 426

Tyrosine
    albinism and, 84
    code triplets for, 46
    defined, 427

Ultraviolet light, mutagenic properties of, 265
Umbilical cord
    defined, 428
    twinning and, 298
"Unforked eyelashes" model, 224–26
United Arab Republic, family planning in, 353
United Nations Scientific Committee on the Effects of Atomic Radiation, 265, 282–83
United States
    genetic drift in, 363
    individual differences of fertility in, 355
    Negro-white crosses in, 169
    population explosion in, 349
    See also American Indians
Uracil
    in code triplets, 45–46
    defined, 428

Valine
    code triplets for, 46
    defined, 428
Variable expressivity, 80–82
Variance, mean intrapair
    between monozygotic and dizygotic twins, 311–23
    defined, 428
Vestigial genes, 219
Victoria (Queen of England), hemophilia carried by, 197
Von Dungern-Hirschfeld hypothesis of ABO inheritance, 127–30, 401–2, 428

Watson-Crick model of DNA structure, 43–44
Weight
    polygenes and, 179
    study with twin method, 312–13
West Germany, genetic drift in, 363
White blood cells, Barr bodies in, 240
White race, *see* Caucasians
Women
    fertility of, *see* Fertility

    height of, 178
    hemophilia and, 195–98
    ideals of family size, 349–50
    meiosis in, 183
    oögenesis in, 35–37
    sex chromosomes of, *see* Sex chromosomes; X chromosomes
    sex hormones in, 188
    See also Sex linkage

X chromosomes
    attenuated, 233, 421–22, 425
        Lyon hypothesis, 240–42
    defined, 182, 428
    in *Drosophila*, 237
    mapping of, 211–15
    polygenes on, 174
Xg^a blood groups, 190–95
    defined, 428
X-linked inheritance
    in color blindness, 184–87, 189
    defined
        chromosomes, 184
        genes, 428
    Hardy-Weinberg formula and, 189–90
    recombination of genes in, 206–11
    types of inheritance confused with, 187–89
XO type, 233–37
X-ray diffraction studies
    of chromosomes, 27
    of genes, 43
X-rays
    acute radiation from, 284
    exposure to, 283
    mutagenic effect of, 4, 265, 271, 283
XXX type, 237
XXY type, 236–37
XYY type, 237–38

Y chromosomes
    defined, 182, 428
    in *Drosophila*, 237
Y-linked inheritance, 198–200
    defined, 184, 428

Zygotes, defined, 428
Zygosity of twins, determination of, 297–301
    See also Dizygotic twins; Monozygotic twins